ELECTRICAL
TRANSMISSION AND DISTRIBUTION

ENGINEERING SCIENCE MONOGRAPHS

General Editors
Professor HUMPHREY DAVIES and
Dr H. TROPPER
both of Queen Mary College, University of London

ELECTRIC POWER TRANSMISSION AND DISTRIBUTION

SECOND EDITION

by

P. J. FREEMAN, M.Sc., C.Eng., M.I.E.E., M.Inst.M.C.

Senior Lecturer in Electrical Engineering
City of Birmingham Polytechnic

HARRAP LONDON

First published in Great Britain 1968
by GEORGE G. HARRAP & CO. LTD
182 High Holborn, London WC1V 7AX

Second Edition, with S.I. units 1974
Reprinted 1976; 1977; 1979

© *P. J. Freeman* 1968, 1974

ISBN 0 245 52449 5

PRINTED IN GREAT BRITAIN BY OFFSET LITHOGRAPHY BY
BILLING AND SONS LTD, GUILDFORD AND LONDON

Preface to the Second Edition

The seven years since the appearance of the first edition of this book have seen two important changes: the introduction of S.I. units and decimal currency. These changes have necessitated a complete revision of the book.

During the past six years the book has become established as a standard work on Transmission and Distribution at the undergraduate level and is now widely used by students and engineers in the supply industry. Although the education and training of Electrical Technicians and Technician Engineers is under review at the present time, it is hoped that the book will continue to be of help to this level of student. At the other end of the spectrum, the book has been recently recommended by Professor E. Openshaw Taylor as one of the references suitable for candidates preparing for the Council of Engineering Institutions Part II Examination No. 343—Electrical Power Engineering.

The subject matter dealt with is essentially the same as in the first edition but the opportunity has been taken to update the text where necessary. The book deals with the essential elements of power supply systems such as overhead lines, underground cables, circuit breakers, insulators and protection. The interconnection of these elements to form a complete supply system and its behaviour under normal, short circuit and surge conditions are described. There is also a section on the economic factors which influence the design of supply systems. The text contains appropriate explanatory illustrations and worked examples and a selection of typical examination questions with answers is given at the end of each section.

ACKNOWLEDGEMENTS

The author is again greatly indebted to his wife, not only for her help in checking the revised manuscript, but also for her continued interest and encouragement throughout its preparation.

To My Wife

Contents

The short line—Variation of regulation with load power factor—Approximate regulation formulae—The single-phase distributor—Distributor fed from both ends—Distribution networks—Three-phase distributors—Three-phase feeders.

Use and construction of reactors—Effect of armature reaction—System resistance—Exponential transients—Short circuit calculations—Conversion to a common base—Location of reactors—Variation of total p.u. X with number of alternators and reactors—Use of network analyser for simulating short circuit conditions.

High voltage transmission—High voltage direct current transmission—Typical a.c. transmission system—Power station layout—Simple single bus-bar system—Sectionalized bus-bar system—Duplicate bus-bar system—Duplicate bus-bar system with tie-bar reactors—Back-to-back duplicate bus-bar system with tie-bar reactors—Grid substation layout—Consumer substation layout.

Principles of arc extinction—Circuit breaker ratings—Small circuit breakers—Air-break breakers—Self-blast oil circuit breakers—Impulse oil circuit breaker—Air-blast circuit breakers—Sulphur hexafluoride gas-blast circuit breakers—Growth of current when a purely inductive circuit is connected to a sinusoidal supply—Growth of current when a circuit having resistance and inductance is connected to a sinusoidal supply—Interpretation of circuit breaker

1

Short Lines, Distributors, and Feeders

The Short Line

In order to transmit electrical energy economically over large distances it is essential to use a high voltage. The most economical voltage is roughly proportional to the length of the transmission line. The capacitance of the line is also proportional to its length. Therefore the capacitance current ($= 2\pi f C V$) is roughly proportional to the square of the length.

For a short line, say under about 16 km in length, the capacitance current is so small that its effect may be neglected when calculating voltage drops, regulation, and efficiency. Therefore only the effects of line resistance and inductive reactance need be considered.

Example 1-1. A two-conductor, single-phase, short line has a total resistance of 0·4 Ω and a total inductive reactance of 0·15 Ω. The line supplies a load of 100 A at 400 V and 0·8 p.f. lagging.

Calculate: (a) the sending end voltage,
(b) the per unit regulation,
(c) the transmission efficiency.

(a) Taking the load current as the phasor of reference, the phasor diagram is as in figure 1.1.

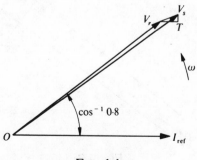

FIG. 1.1

13

In this diagram V_r represents the receive end voltage of 400 V and V_s the sending end voltage.

$$\overline{V}_r = 400(0.8 + j0.6) = 320 + j240 \text{ V},$$

Line voltage drop $= 100(0.4 + j0.15) = 40 + j15 \text{ V},$

$$\overline{V}_s = 360 + j255 \text{ V and } V_s = 441.2 \text{ V, say } \mathbf{441 \text{ V}}.$$

(b) The per unit regulation of a transmission line is defined as the rise in voltage at the receive end after the load is switched off, expressed as a fraction of the on-load receive end voltage.

Thus p.u. regulation $= \dfrac{V_s - V_r}{V_r} = \dfrac{441 - 400}{400} = \mathbf{0.103}.$

(c) Power loss in line $= I^2 \times R \text{ W} = 100^2 \times 0.4 \times 10^{-3} \text{ kW} = 4 \text{ kW}.$
Power output of line $= 400 \times 100 \times 0.8 \times 10^{-3} \text{ kW} = 32 \text{ kW}.$

Transmission efficiency $= 1 - \dfrac{\text{losses}}{\text{output} + \text{losses}} = 1 - \dfrac{4}{36} = \mathbf{0.889}.$

An alternative method of finding the regulation is as follows:

Figure 1.2 is an enlargement of part of figure 1.1. $V_s N$ is an arc of radius OV_s so that the regulation is represented by the line $V_r N$. This is approximately equal to $V_r P = V_r Q + QP = V_r Q + U V_s = V_r T . \cos \phi + T V_s . \sin \phi.$

But $V_r T$ is the IR drop and $T V_s$ is the IX drop.

Therefore $\qquad$ **regulation $\simeq IR . \cos \phi + IX . \sin \phi.$**

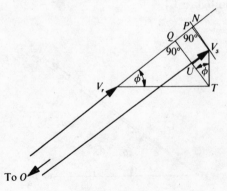

FIG. 1.2

Applying this to example 1-1:

$$\text{Regulation} \simeq (100 \times 0.4 \times 0.8) + (100 \times 0.15 \times 0.6)$$

$$= 32 + 9 = \mathbf{41\ V}.$$

This compares favourably with the previous value of 41·2 volts, indicating that the inaccuracy caused by neglecting *PN* is in the order of 0·5 per cent.

Variation of Regulation with Load Power Factor

Even if the receive end voltage and load current remain constant, the regulation varies greatly with load power factor. Under these conditions the line voltage drop remains constant in magnitude and

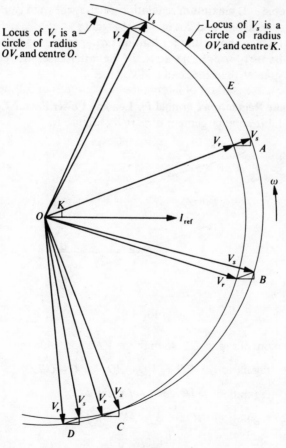

Locus of V_r is a circle of radius OV_r and centre O.

Locus of V_s is a circle of radius OV_r and centre K.

Fig. 1.3

phase but the phasor relationship between it and the receive end and send end voltages alters as shown in figure 1.3.

The condition for maximum regulation is obtained as follows:

$$\text{Regulation} \simeq IR \cdot \cos \phi + IX \cdot \sin \phi.$$

This will be a maximum when $\dfrac{d(\text{regulation})}{d\phi} = 0,$

i.e. when $IR(-\sin \phi) + IX \cdot \cos \phi = 0,$

or when $\dfrac{X}{R} = \tan \phi.$

This condition occurs at A in figure 1.3.

In example 1-1, maximum regulation occurs when $\tan \phi = 0.15/0.4$, i.e. when $\phi = 20° 33'$ and $\cos \phi = 0.94$ lagging.

Figure 1.3 also shows that for leading power factor loads the regulation may be zero or even negative. In the latter case, the receive end voltage is greater than the send end voltage.

Approximate Regulation Formula for Leading Power Factor Loads

Figure 1.4 is an enlargement of part B of figure 1.3.

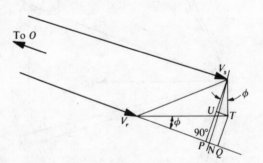

Fig. 1.4

V_sN is an arc of radius OV_s so that line V_rN represents the regulation.

Hence $\text{regulation} \simeq V_rP = V_rQ - PQ = V_rQ - UT.$

$\text{regulation} \simeq IR \cdot \cos \phi - IX \cdot \sin \phi.$

For zero regulation, $IR \cdot \cos \phi = IX \cdot \sin \phi,$

or $\dfrac{R}{X} = \tan \phi.$

This condition occurs at C in figure 1.3.

In example 1-1, zero regulation occurs when $\tan \phi = 0.4/0.15$, i.e. when $\phi = 69° \ 27'$ and $\cos \phi = 0.35$ leading.

Example 1-2. Calculate the per unit regulation of the short line in example 1-1 when the load is 100 A at 400 V and 0.1 p.f. leading.

This condition occurs at D in figure 1.3.

$$\bar{V_r} = 400(0.1 - j0.995) = 40 - j398 \text{ V}.$$

Line voltage drop $= 40 + j15$ V, as before.

$$\bar{V_s} = 80 - j383 \text{ V and } V_s = 391.3 \text{ V}.$$

$$\text{p.u. regulation} = \frac{391.3 - 400}{400} = \mathbf{-0.0218.}$$

Alternatively, regulation $\simeq IR . \cos \phi - IX . \sin \phi$

$$= (100 \times 0.4 \times 0.1) - (100 \times 0.15 \times 0.995) \text{ V}$$

$$= 4 - 14.9 = -10.9 \text{ V}.$$

Therefore p.u. regulation $= \dfrac{-10.9}{400} = \mathbf{-0.0273}.$

The error caused by using the approximate method is much greater in this region than in region E of figure 1.3.

The Single-phase Distributor

Example 1-3. A two-core, single-phase distributor, *ABCD*, is 640 m long, is fed at end *A* only, and supplies loads at *B*, *C*, and *D*. The distance from *A* to *B* is 274.3 m, that from *B* to *C* is 274.3 m, and that from *C* to *D* is 91.4 m. The distributor has a resistance of 0.2 Ω and an inductive reactance of 0.075 Ω, each per 914.4 m of single core.

Calculate the voltage required at *A* so that the voltage at *D* shall be 220 V when the loads are as follows:

60 A at 0.8 p.f. lagging, at *B*;

50 A at 0.9 p.f. lagging, at *C*;

30 A at unity p.f., at *D*.

The distributor is represented by a single-line diagram in figure 1.5.

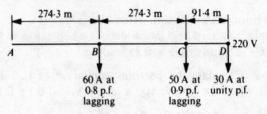

Fig. 1.5

Impedance of section $CD = 0.2(0.2 + j0.075) = 0.04 + j0.015\,\Omega$.
Volt drop $C \rightarrow D = 30(0.04 + j0.015) = 1.2 + j0.45$ V.

$$\bar{V}_c = 221.2 + j0.45 \text{ V.}$$

$$\text{Tan } \phi_c = \frac{0.45}{221.2} = 0.002. \qquad \phi_c = 7 \text{ minutes.}$$

This very small angle is ignored.
Impedance of section $BC = 0.6(0.2 + j0.075) = 0.12 + j0.045\,\Omega$.
Load Current at $C = 50(0.9 - j0.436) = 45 - j21.8$ A.
Total current in section $BC = 75 - j21.8$ A.
Volt drop $B \rightarrow C = (75 - j21.8)(0.12 + j0.45) = 9.98 + j0.75$ V.

$$\bar{V}_b = 231.2 + j1.2 \text{ V.}$$

$$\text{Tan } \phi_b = \frac{1.2}{231.2} = 0.0052. \qquad \phi_b = 18 \text{ minutes.}$$

This angle is also ignored.
Impedance of section $AB = 0.12 + j0.045\,\Omega$.
Load current at $B = 60(0.8 - j0.6) = 48 - j36$ A.
Total current in section $AB = 123 - j57.8$ A.
Volt drop $A \rightarrow B = (123 - j57.8)(0.12 + j0.045) = 17.4 - j1.4$ V.

$$\bar{V}_a = 248.6 - j0.2 \text{ V and } V_a = \textbf{249 V.}$$

The above solution is useful because it shows the phasor relationships between the various voltages and currents. However, it is more usual to use a less rigorous method based on the approximate regulation formula for a short line.

This method, like the one above, ignores the very small phase angles between the load voltages.

The values of $IR.\cos\phi$ and $IX.\sin\phi$ are obtained for each load separately and added thus:

For load at D, $(30 \times 0.28 \times 1) + (30 \times 0.105 \times 0) = 8.4$ V.
For load at C, $(50 \times 0.24 \times 0.9) + (50 \times 0.09 \times 0.436) = 12.8$ V.
For load at B, $(60 \times 0.12 \times 0.8) + (60 \times 0.045 \times 0.6) = 7.4$ V.

$$\text{Regulation} = 8.4 + 12.8 + 7.4 = 28.6 \text{ V},$$

hence $V_a = 220 + 28.6 = \textbf{249 V}$, as before.

Distributor fed from both ends

Example 1-4. Calculate the current distribution and the voltage at points B and C when the distributor in example 1-3 is fed at both ends at 250 V, the loads being unaltered.

In figure 1.6, the current fed in from end A is assumed to be x A and the currents in the other sections have been obtained using Kirchhoff's first law.

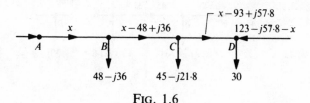

Fɪɢ. 1.6

Applying Kirchhoff's second law we obtain

$$x(0.12 + j0.045) + (x - 48 + j36)(0.12 + j0.045) + (x - 93 + j57.8)(0.04 + j0.015) = 0.$$

$$0.12x + j0.045x + 0.12x - 5.76 + j4.32 + j0.45x - j2.16 - 1.62 + 0.04x - 3.72 + j2.31 + j0.015x - j1.4 - 0.87 = 0.$$

$$0.28x + j0.105x - 11.97 + j3.07 = 0.$$

$$x = \frac{11.97 - j3.07}{0.28 + j0.105} = \frac{(11.97 - j3.07)(0.28 - j0.105)}{0.28^2 + 0.105^2}$$

$$= \frac{3.03 - j2.12}{0.0894} = 33.9 - j23.7 \text{ A}.$$

Hence the current distribution is as in figure 1.7.

Obviously, these currents are alternating, but the arrows are useful in that they indicate the direction of energy flow. Also they show that B is the point of minimum potential.

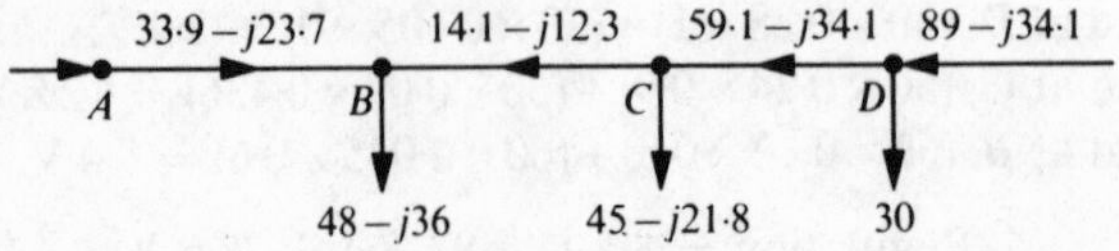

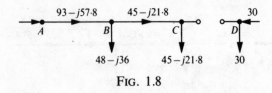

$$33 \cdot 9 - j23 \cdot 7 \quad 14 \cdot 1 - j12 \cdot 3 \quad 59 \cdot 1 - j34 \cdot 1 \quad 89 - j34 \cdot 1$$

A   B   C   D

$$48 - j36 \qquad 45 - j21 \cdot 8 \qquad 30$$

FIG. 1.7

A shorter solution than that above can be obtained using Thevenin's Theorem thus:

Open circuit section CD, then figure 1.8 represents the distributor. Volt drop $A \rightarrow C$

$$= (93 - j57 \cdot 8)(0 \cdot 12 + j0 \cdot 045) + (45 - j21 \cdot 8)(0 \cdot 12 + j0 \cdot 045)$$

$$= (138 - j79 \cdot 6)(0 \cdot 12 + j0 \cdot 045) = 20 \cdot 14 - j3 \cdot 34 = V_{D \rightarrow C}.$$

$\bar{Z}_{\text{rem}}$ = impedance of remainder of distributor = $0 \cdot 24 + j0 \cdot 09\,\Omega$.

$$93 - j57 \cdot 8 \qquad 45 - j21 \cdot 8 \qquad \qquad 30$$

A   B   C   D

$$48 - j36 \qquad 45 - j21 \cdot 8 \qquad 30$$

FIG. 1.8

Now, by Thevenin, $\quad I_{D \rightarrow C} = \dfrac{V_{D \rightarrow C}}{\bar{Z}_{\text{rem}} + \bar{Z}_{DC}}$

$$= \frac{(20 \cdot 14 - j3 \cdot 34)(0 \cdot 28 - j0 \cdot 105)}{0 \cdot 28^2 + 0 \cdot 105^2}$$

$$= \frac{5 \cdot 289 - j3 \cdot 05}{0 \cdot 0894}$$

$$= 59 \cdot 1 - j34 \cdot 1 \text{ A, as in figure 1.7.}$$

Volt drop $A \rightarrow B = (33 \cdot 9 - j23 \cdot 7)(0 \cdot 12 + j0 \cdot 045) = 5 \cdot 14 - j1 \cdot 31,$

giving the voltage at point B as

$$250 - 5 \cdot 14 + j1 \cdot 31 = 244 \cdot 86 + j1 \cdot 31, \text{ say } \mathbf{245}\ \mathbf{V}.$$

Volt drop $D \rightarrow C = (59 \cdot 1 - j34 \cdot 1)(0 \cdot 04 + j0 \cdot 015) = 2 \cdot 87 - j0 \cdot 47,$

giving the voltage at point C as

$$250 - 2 \cdot 87 + j0 \cdot 47 = 247 \cdot 13 + j0 \cdot 47, \text{ say } \mathbf{247}\ \mathbf{V}.$$

Check $\therefore$ Volt drop $C \rightarrow B = (14 \cdot 1 - j12 \cdot 3)(0 \cdot 12 + j0 \cdot 045) = 2 \cdot 24 - j0 \cdot 85$, giving the voltage at point B as $247 \cdot 13 + j0 \cdot 47 - 2 \cdot 24 + j0 \cdot 85 = 244 \cdot 89 + j1 \cdot 33$ V, as before.

Example 1-5. Calculate the current distribution when the distributor in example 1-4 is fed at end A at 250 V and at end B at 245 V, the loads being unaltered.

The equation obtained using Kirchhoff's laws now becomes

$$0 \cdot 28x + j0 \cdot 105x - 11 \cdot 97 + j3 \cdot 07 = 5$$

and
$$x = \frac{16 \cdot 97 - j3 \cdot 07}{0 \cdot 28 + j0 \cdot 105} = 49 \cdot 6 - j29 \cdot 5 \, \text{A}.$$

Hence the current distribution is as in figure 1.9.

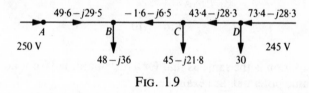

FIG. 1.9

Alternatively, the 'Superimposed Current Method' may be used thus:

Current flowing from $A \rightarrow D$ due to the 5 V difference in potential between ends = 'superimposed current'

$$= \frac{5}{\text{total } \overline{Z} \text{ of distributor}} = \frac{5}{0 \cdot 28 + j0 \cdot 105}$$

$$= 15 \cdot 7 - j5 \cdot 8 \, \text{A}.$$

Superimposing this current on the distribution obtained when both ends were at the same potential (see figure 1.7), the same values are obtained as in figure 1.9 thus:

Current $A \rightarrow B = 33 \cdot 9 - j23 \cdot 7 + 15 \cdot 7 - j5 \cdot 8 = 49 \cdot 6 - j29 \cdot 5 \, \text{A}.$

Current $C \rightarrow B = 14 \cdot 1 - j12 \cdot 3 - 15 \cdot 7 + j5 \cdot 8 = -1 \cdot 6 - j6 \cdot 5 \, \text{A}.$

Current $D \rightarrow C = 59 \cdot 1 - j34 \cdot 1 - 15 \cdot 7 + j5 \cdot 8 = 43 \cdot 4 - j28 \cdot 3 \, \text{A}.$

Current input at $D = 89 \cdot 1 - j34 \cdot 1 - 15 \cdot 7 + j5 \cdot 8 = 73 \cdot 4 - j28 \cdot 3 \, \text{A}.$

Distribution Networks

Example 1-6. Calculate the current distribution when the two-core ring main represented by the single-line diagram, figure 1.10, is fed at point *A*.

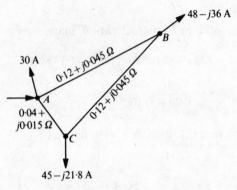

Fig. 1.10

The solution is the same as that for a distributor fed from both ends at the same potential. See example 1-4.

Hence the current distribution is as shown in figure 1.11.

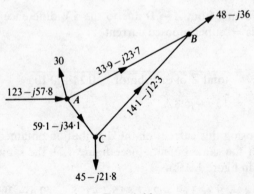

Fig. 1.11

Example 1-7. Calculate the current distribution when the two-core ring main represented by the single-line diagram, figure 1.12, is fed at point *A* at 250 V. Hence calculate the voltage at each load point.

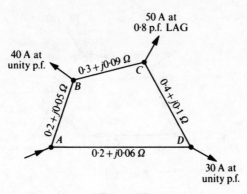

FIG. 1.12

Using Thevenin's Theorem, open-circuit *CD* as shown in figure 1.13.

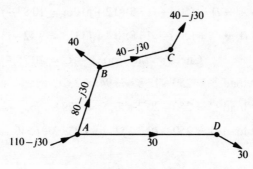

FIG. 1.13

Volt drop $A \to D = 30(0\cdot2 + j0\cdot06) = 6 + j1\cdot8$ V.

Volt drop $A \to C = (80 - j30)(0\cdot2 + j0\cdot05) + (40 - j30)(0\cdot3 + j0\cdot09)$

$$= 32\cdot2 - j7\cdot4 \text{ V.}$$

Volt drop $D \to C = 32\cdot2 - j7\cdot4 - 6 - j1\cdot8 = 26\cdot2 - j9\cdot2$ V.

$$\overline{Z}_{rem} = 0\cdot7 + j0\cdot2 \ \Omega.$$

Current $D \to C = \dfrac{V_{D \to C}}{\overline{Z}_{rem} + \overline{Z}_{DC}} = \dfrac{26\cdot2 - j9\cdot2}{0\cdot7 + j0\cdot2 + 0\cdot4 + j0\cdot1}$

$$= 20\cdot1 - j13\cdot8 \text{ A.}$$

Hence the current distribution is as shown in figure 1.14.

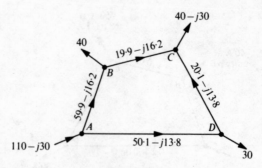

FIG. 1.14

Volt drop $A \rightarrow B = (59 \cdot 9 - j16 \cdot 2)(0 \cdot 2 + j0 \cdot 05) = 12 \cdot 8 - j2 \cdot 94$ V.

Volt drop $B \rightarrow C = (19 \cdot 9 - j16 \cdot 2)(0 \cdot 3 + j0 \cdot 09) = 7 \cdot 43 - j3 \cdot 05$ V.

Volt drop $A \rightarrow C = 20 \cdot 23 - j5 \cdot 99$ V.

Volt drop $A \rightarrow D = (50 \cdot 1 - j13 \cdot 8)(0 \cdot 2 + j0 \cdot 06) = 10 \cdot 83 - j2 \cdot 46$ V.

Volt drop $D \rightarrow C = (20 \cdot 1 - j13 \cdot 8)(0 \cdot 4 + j0 \cdot 1) = 9 \cdot 42 - j3 \cdot 5$ V.

Check: Volt drop $A \rightarrow C = 20 \cdot 25 - j5 \cdot 96$ V.

Voltage at load $B = 250 - 12 \cdot 8 + j2 \cdot 94 = 237 \cdot 2 + j2 \cdot 94$, say **237 V**.

Voltage at load $C = 250 - 20 \cdot 2 + j6 = 229 \cdot 8 + j6$, say **230 V**.

Voltage at load $D = 250 - 10 \cdot 8 + j2 \cdot 46 = 239 \cdot 2 + j2 \cdot 46$, say **239 V**.

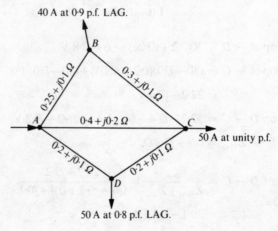

FIG. 1.15

Example 1-8. Calculate the currents in branches *AB* and *BC* of the distribution network shown in figure 1.15.

Converting mesh *ACD* to an equivalent star, as shown in figure 1.16:

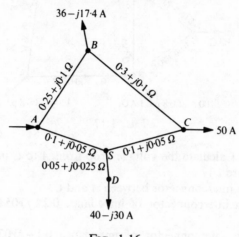

36 − j17·4 A

40 − j30 A

50 A

FIG. 1.16

$$SD = \frac{(0{\cdot}2+j0{\cdot}1)^2}{0{\cdot}8+j0{\cdot}4} = 0{\cdot}05+j0{\cdot}025 \ \Omega.$$

Using Thevenin's Theorem, open-circuit *BC*, then:

$$AS = SC = \frac{(0{\cdot}4+j0{\cdot}2)(0{\cdot}2+j0{\cdot}1)}{0{\cdot}8+j0{\cdot}4} = 0{\cdot}1+j0{\cdot}05 \ \Omega.$$

Volt drop $A \rightarrow S = (90-j30)(0{\cdot}1+j0{\cdot}05) \quad = 10{\cdot}5 \ +j1{\cdot}5$ V.

Volt drop $S \rightarrow C = 50(0{\cdot}1+j0{\cdot}05) \qquad\qquad = 5 \quad +j2{\cdot}5$ V.

Volt drop $A \rightarrow C = 15{\cdot}5 \ +j4$ V.

Volt drop $A \rightarrow B = (36-j17{\cdot}4)(0{\cdot}25+j0{\cdot}1) = 10{\cdot}75-j0{\cdot}75$ V.

Volt drop $B \rightarrow C = 4{\cdot}75+j4{\cdot}75$ V.

$$\overline{Z}_{\text{rem}} = 0{\cdot}45+j0{\cdot}2 \ \Omega.$$

$$\text{Current } B \rightarrow C = \frac{V_{B \rightarrow C}}{\overline{Z}_{\text{rem}}+\overline{Z}_{BC}} = \frac{4{\cdot}75+j4{\cdot}75}{0{\cdot}45+j0{\cdot}2+0{\cdot}3+j0{\cdot}1}$$

$$= \mathbf{7{\cdot}7+j3{\cdot}28} \ \textbf{A}.$$

Current $A \rightarrow B = 36-j17{\cdot}4+7{\cdot}7+j3{\cdot}28 = \mathbf{43{\cdot}7-j14{\cdot}1}$ **A**.

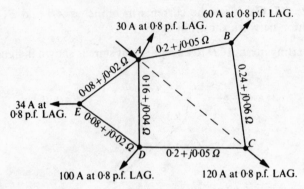

FIG. 1.17

Example 1-9. Calculate the voltage drop from A to C in the network shown in figure 1.17.

(a) with no interconnector between A and C,

(b) with an interconnector of impedance $0.2 + j0.05\,\Omega$ between A and C,

(c) with an interconnector of impedance $0.1 + j0.025\,\Omega$ between A and C.

(a) Since all the load power factors are the same and all the sections have the same ratio of R to X_L, the network may be represented by the d.c. network shown in figure 1.18.

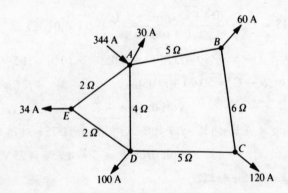

FIG. 1.18

Converting mesh ADE to an equivalent star, as shown in figure 1.19:

$$AS = SD = \frac{2 \times 4}{8} = 1\,\Omega. \qquad SE = \frac{2 \times 2}{8} = 0.5\,\Omega.$$

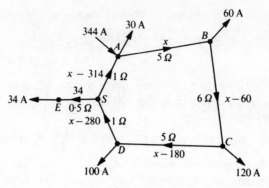

FIG. 1.19

Using Kirchhoff's laws:

$$5x + 6x - 360 + 5x - 900 + x - 280 + x - 314 = 0$$
$$18x = 1854$$
$$x = 103 \text{ A.}$$

Hence the current distribution is as shown in figure 1.20.

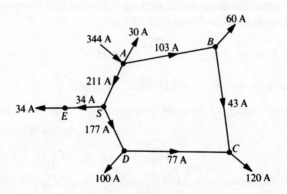

FIG. 1.20

Voltage drop $A \rightarrow C = (103 \times 5) + (43 \times 6) = 773$ V.

Now 1 A in the equivalent d.c. network corresponds to $0.8 - j0.6$ ampere in the original a.c. network. Also 1 Ω in the d.c. network corresponds to $0.04 + j0.01$ Ω in the a.c. network. Therefore 1 V voltage drop in the d.c. network corresponds to $(0.8 - j0.6)(0.04 + j0.01)$

$= 0{\cdot}038 - j0{\cdot}016$ V in the a.c. network. Hence

a.c. voltage drop $A \to C = 773\,(0{\cdot}038 - j0{\cdot}016)$

$$= 29{\cdot}4 - j12{\cdot}4 \text{ V, or } \mathbf{31{\cdot}9 \text{ V}}.$$

(b) Using Thevenin's Theorem, open-circuit AC, then the current distribution is as shown in figure 1.20 and the voltage drop $A \to C$ is 773 V as before.

$$R_{\text{rem}} = 11\,\Omega \text{ in parallel with } 7\,\Omega = \frac{11 \times 7}{18} = 4{\cdot}28\,\Omega.$$

An interconnector of impedance $0{\cdot}2 + j0{\cdot}05\,\Omega$ is represented by $5\,\Omega$ in the equivalent d.c. circuit. Therefore

$$\text{current } A \to C = \frac{773}{4{\cdot}28 + 5} = 83{\cdot}3 \text{ A},$$

voltage drop $A \to C = 83{\cdot}3 \times 5 = 417$ V,

corresponding a.c. voltage drop $A \to C = 417(0{\cdot}038 - j0{\cdot}016)$

$$= 15{\cdot}8 - j6{\cdot}66 \text{ V}$$

or $\mathbf{17{\cdot}1 \text{ V}}$.

(c) An interconnector of impedance $0{\cdot}1 + j0{\cdot}025\,\Omega$ is represented by $2{\cdot}5\,\Omega$ in the equivalent d.c. circuit. Hence

$$\text{current } A \to C = \frac{773}{4{\cdot}28 + 2{\cdot}5} = 114 \text{ A},$$

voltage drop $A \to C = 114 \times 2{\cdot}5 = 285$ V,

corresponding a.c. voltage drop $A \to C = 285(0{\cdot}038 - j0{\cdot}016)$

$$= 10{\cdot}8 - j4{\cdot}56 \text{ V}$$

or $\mathbf{11{\cdot}7 \text{ V}}$.

Which of the above alternatives would be adopted in practice depends on the system declared voltage. The voltage at each consumer's terminals must be within ± 6 per cent of the declared value. Hence the voltage drop from the point of maximum potential (A) to the point of minimum potential (C) must not exceed 12 per cent of the declared value.

Suppose that the declared value is 240 V, then the percentage voltage drop $A \to C$ for (a) = 13·3 per cent, that for (b) = 7·1 per cent, and that for (c) = 4·9 per cent.

Thus it can be seen that an interconnector is necessary. (b) would be adequate, unless future increases in load are likely, in which case (c) would be justified.

Three-phase Distributors

The methods used in the foregoing single-phase examples can be applied also to three-phase distributors supplying balanced loads.

Example 1-10. A three-phase, three-wire distributor supplies three-phase, star-connected, balanced loads at B, C, and D, and is represented by the single-line diagram in figure 1.21.

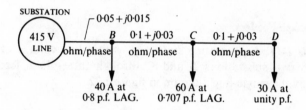

FIG. 1.21

Use an approximate method to find the total voltage regulation in one conductor of the distributor.

Ignoring all losses in the distributor, estimate the kVA output and load power factor of the substation transformer.

Calculating the values of $IR.\cos\phi + IX.\sin\phi$ for each load:

Load B: $(40 \times 0.05 \times 0.8) + (40 \times 0.015 \times 0.6)$ $= 1.96$ V.

Load C: $(60 \times 0.15 \times 0.707) + (60 \times 0.045 \times 0.707) = 8.27$ V.

Load D: $(30 \times 0.25 \times 1) + (30 \times 0.075 \times 0)$ $= 7.5$ V.

total voltage regulation in one conductor = **17·7 V.**

Calculating the values of phase watts for each load:

Load B: $240 \times 40 \times 0.8$ $= 7,680$ W.

Load C: $240 \times 60 \times 0.707 = 10,181$ W.

Load D: $240 \times 30 \times 1$ $= 7,200$ W.

total phase watts = 25,060 W.

Calculating the values of phase VAr for each load:

Load B: $240 \times 40 \times 0.6 \quad = 5{,}760 \text{ VAr}$.

Load C: $240 \times 60 \times 0.707 = 10{,}181 \text{ VAr}$.

Load D: $240 \times 30 \times 0 \quad\quad = 0 \text{ VAr}$.

total phase VAr $= 15{,}940 \text{ VAr}$.

kVA per phase $= \sqrt{(25.06^2 + 15.94^2)} = 29.7 \text{ kVA}$.

Total kVA $= 3 \times 29.7 = \textbf{89·1 kVA} \simeq \textbf{output of substation transformer}$.

Power factor of substation transformer $= \dfrac{25.06}{29.7} = \textbf{0·84 lagging}$.

Three-phase Feeders

Example 1-11. A generating station A, with a line voltage of 33 kV, supplies two substations B and C through three-phase feeders, as shown by the single-line diagram in figure 1.22.

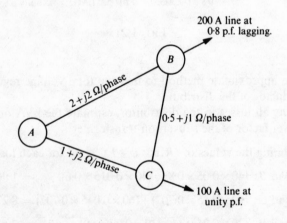

200 A line at
0·8 p.f. lagging.

B

$2 + j2\ \Omega/\text{phase}$

$0.5 + j1\ \Omega/\text{phase}$

A

$1 + j2\ \Omega/\text{phase}$

C

100 A line at
unity p.f.

FIG. 1.22

Calculate: (a) the voltage difference between B and C when feeder BC is open-circuited,

(b) the current distribution when all three feeders are connected,

(c) the total power wasted for conditions (a) and (b).

(a) With BC open-circuited:

Current $A \rightarrow B = 160 - j120 \text{ A}$.

Voltage drop $A \rightarrow B = (160 - j120)(2 + j2) = 560 + j80$ V.

Current $A \rightarrow C = 100 + j0$ A.

Voltage drop $A \rightarrow C = 100(1 + j2) = 100 + j200$ V.

Voltage drop $C \rightarrow B = 560 + j80 - 100 - j200 = 460 - j120$,

or 476 V.

(b) Using Thevenin's Theorem:

$$\overline{Z}_{rem} = 3 + j4 \ \Omega.$$

Current $C \rightarrow B = \dfrac{460 - j120}{3 + j4 + 0.5 + j1} = \mathbf{27 - j73, or\ 78\ A\ line}.$

Current $A \rightarrow C = 100 + 27 - j73 = \mathbf{127 - j73, or\ 147\ A\ line}.$

Current $A \rightarrow B = 160 - j120 - 27 + j73 = \mathbf{133 - j47, or\ 141\ A\ line}.$

(c) Total power wasted for condition (a)

$$= 3[(100^2 \times 1) + (200^2 \times 2)] \text{ W}$$

$$= \mathbf{270\ kW}.$$

Total power wasted for condition (b)

$$= 3[(147^2 \times 1) + (141^2 \times 2) + (78^2 \times 0.5)] \text{ W} = \mathbf{193\ kW}.$$

(This is about 1·3 per cent of the total power supplied.)

Example 1-12. Calculate the sending end line voltage in the system represented by the single-line diagram in figure 1.23.

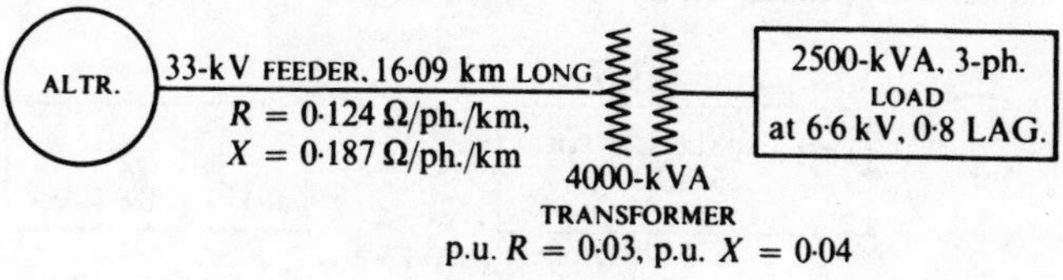

FIG. 1.23

Referring transformer values to the primary side:

$$\text{Full load primary current} = \frac{4,000}{\sqrt{3} \times 33} = 70 \text{ A}.$$

$$\text{Primary rated phase voltage} = \frac{33,000}{\sqrt{3}} = 19,100 \text{ V}.$$

Now p.u. $R = \dfrac{\text{full load primary current} \times R \text{ referred to primary}}{\text{primary rated phase V}}$,

and $\quad R$ referred to primary $= \dfrac{191 \times 3}{70} = 8 \cdot 2 \, \Omega/\text{phase}.$

Similarly,

$$X \text{ referred to primary} = \frac{191 \times 4}{70} = 10 \cdot 9 \, \Omega/\text{phase}.$$

Therefore $\quad$ total system $R = 2 + 8 \cdot 2 = 10 \cdot 2 \, \Omega/\text{phase},$

and $\quad\quad\quad$ total system $X = 3 + 10 \cdot 9 = 13 \cdot 9 \, \Omega/\text{phase}.$

$$\text{Line current} = \frac{2{,}500}{\sqrt{3} \times 33} = 43 \cdot 8 \text{ A}.$$

Taking this current as reference,

receiving end kV $= 19 \cdot 1(0 \cdot 8 + j0 \cdot 6) = 15 \cdot 28 + j11 \cdot 46.$

The total voltage drop $= 0 \cdot 0438(10 \cdot 2 + j13 \cdot 9) = 0 \cdot 447 + j0 \cdot 609 \text{ kV}.$
Therefore sending end kV $= 15 \cdot 73 + j12 \cdot 07,$ or $19 \cdot 8 \text{ kV}$ phase, or
34·3 kV line.

(The above solution conforms to the usual practice of assuming star connections throughout and a balanced three-phase load.)

Example 1-13. Calculate:
(a) the alternator terminal voltage, and
(b) the current in each feeder
in the system prepresented by the single-line diagram in figure 1.24.

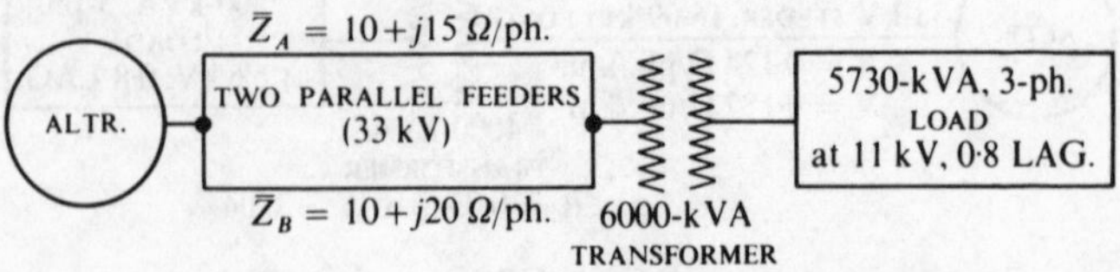

Fig. 1.24

(a) Transformer full load primary current $= \dfrac{6{,}000}{\sqrt{3} \times 33} = 105 \text{ A}.$

Transformer primary rated phase voltage $= \dfrac{33{,}000}{\sqrt{3}} = 19{,}100 \text{ V}.$

$$R \text{ referred to primary} = \frac{191 \times 1 \cdot 05}{105} = 1 \cdot 91 \ \Omega/\text{phase.}$$

$$X \text{ referred to primary} = \frac{191 \times 7 \cdot 9}{105} = 14 \cdot 4 \ \Omega/\text{phase.}$$

$$\text{Total impedance of feeders} = \frac{(10 + j15)(10 + j20)}{20 + j35}$$

$$= 5 \cdot 08 + j8 \cdot 61 \ \Omega/\text{phase.}$$

Total system impedance $= 7 + j23 \ \Omega/\text{phase.}$

$$\text{Line current} = \frac{5{,}730}{\sqrt{3} \times 33} = 100 \ \text{A.}$$

Taking this current as reference,

$$\text{receiving end kV} = 19 \cdot 1(0 \cdot 8 + j0 \cdot 6) = 15 \cdot 28 + j11 \cdot 46.$$

The total voltage drop $= 0 \cdot 1(7 + j23) = 0 \cdot 7 + j2 \cdot 3$ kV. Therefore sending end kV $= 15 \cdot 98 + j13 \cdot 76$, or $21 \cdot 1$ kV phase, or **36·5 kV line**.

(b) $I_A = 100\left[\dfrac{10 + j20}{20 + j35}\right] = 55 \cdot 5 + j3 \cdot 08$, or **55·6 A**.

$I_B = 100 - 55 \cdot 5 - j3 \cdot 08 = 44 \cdot 5 - j3 \cdot 08$, or **44·6 A**.

EXAMPLES 1

1. Derive an approximate expression for the voltage regn. in a short line, having resistance and reactance, supplying a single load. State the conditions which permit this formula to be applied to a distributor with several loads.

A 415-V, three-phase distributor AD of resistance $0 \cdot 2 \ \Omega$ and reactance $0 \cdot 05 \ \Omega$ each per 914 metres of single conductor supplies the following loads when fed at end A only:

Load point	Distance in metres	Load current	Load power factor
A	0	50 A	1·0
B	$AB = 366$	50 A	0·8 lag
C	$BC = 366$	60 A	1·0
D	$CD = 732$	x A	0·8 lag

If the supply voltage at A is the maximum permissible, find the greatest possible value of x and hence the maximum loading in kW at the point D, such that the voltage at the point D is at the lowest permissible value. (See page 28.)

If the loads at C and D are switched off, calculate the rise of voltage at the point B.

(Answers **50·6 A, 27 kW, 8·6 V**.)

2. Explain why the effect of capacitance may be ignored in a short a.c. distributor calculation.

A 415-V, three-phase distributor AD of resistance 0·1 Ω and reactance 0·05 Ω each per 914 metres of single core supplies a load at A and the following loads when fed at end A only:

Load point	Distance in metres	Load current	Load power factor
B	$AB = 914$	40 A	1·0
C	$AC = 1,828$	40 A	0·8 lag
D	$AD = 3,656$	x A	0·8 lag

If the supply voltage at A is the maximum permissible, find the greatest possible value of x and hence the maximum loading in kW at the point D, such that the voltage at the point D is at the lowest permissible value.

If the loads at C and D are switched off, calculate the rise of voltage at the point B.

(Answers **36·4 A, 19·8 kW, 8·4 V**.)

3. Calculate the current distribution in the a.c. network fed at A and loaded as shown in figure 1.25.

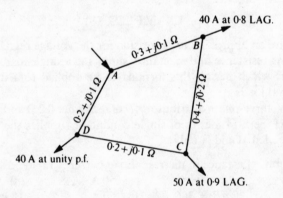

FIG. 1.25

Also determine the maximum voltage drop in the network.

(Answers $A \rightarrow B = 48\cdot8 - j24$, $B \rightarrow C = 16\cdot8$, $A \rightarrow D = 68\cdot2 - j21\cdot8$, $D \rightarrow C = 28\cdot2 - j21\cdot8$, max. volt drop $A \rightarrow C = 23\cdot7 + j0\cdot9$ or 23·7 V.)

4. Calculate the maximum voltage drop in the a.c. network fed at A and loaded as shown in figure 1.26.

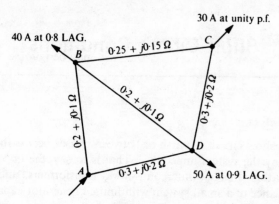

FIG. 1.26

(Answers **20·3 + j4·7 or 21 V from A to C.**)

5. Calculate the sending end line voltage, the sending end power factor and the efficiency of the system represented by the single-line diagram in figure 1.27.

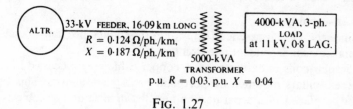

FIG. 1.27

(Answers **34·8 kV, 0·79 lag, 0·96 overall.**)

2

Short Circuit Conditions

Use of Reactors

When a short circuit to earth or between phases occurs the current is limited by the system impedance. That is to say, the impedance of the alternators, bus-bar interconnectors, transformers, and feeders. The impedance of a small system with limited generator capacity may be sufficient to limit the short circuit kVA at any point to a value which the circuit breakers are capable of interrupting. In large systems, however, additional impedance will be required. This is provided by reactors which limit the short circuit current to a value which can be interrupted by the breakers before damage to plant occurs.

Construction of Reactors

(a) Air-cored type

Since there is no magnetic saturation the inductance (and therefore reactance) is independent of current.

Circular coils of bare, stranded, copper cable are embedded in cast concrete pillars mounted on porcelain pedestal insulators. This type must be placed in a separate non-metallic cubicle as the cable is at phase voltage to earth.

Alternatively, insulated cable may be used in which case the reactor is suitable for outdoor operation up to about 25 kV line.

In any case air-cored reactors are not usually used above 33 kV line.

Air-cored reactors are cheap and robust but physically large due to the relatively low operating flux. They are suitable for smaller reactance values only.

If situated near metal objects, magnetic shielding must be used to prevent the reactor flux inducing eddy currents in the objects. Without shielding, the proximity of metal objects would increase the power lost in the reactor and alter its inductance.

The shield consists of a few short-circuited, circular, copper turns externally mounted with their magnetic axes in line with that of the reactor. These turns are of a sufficiently large diameter so as not to reduce the inductance of the reactor unduly. The flux set up by the reactor is restricted to the region within the short-circuited turns because any flux beyond their diameter would link the short-circuited turns and be opposed by the m.m.f. due to the currents induced in them.

(b) Iron-cored type

Due to magnetic saturation the reactance is not constant at all currents. To limit the change of reactance the cross-sectional area of the cores is made as large as possible so that the working flux density varies within the more linear portion of the B/H curve.

The turns of the reactor pass through the centres of six or eight laminated iron cores symmetrically spaced to form a circle. Each core forms a closed magnetic circuit and the magnetic shielding thus provided is usually good enough to obviate the need for additional shielding by short-circuited copper turns.

This type of reactor can be immersed in an oil-filled steel tank which facilitates high voltage operation, cooling, and outdoor use.

The turns of the reactor must have exceptionally strong bracing to withstand the very great mechanical stresses which occur under short circuit conditions.

The inductance to resistance ratio is much greater than for the air-cored type. So also is the ratio of inductance to physical size. Iron-cored reactors may be designed for any system voltage. They are more expensive than air-cored reactors.

Effect of Armature Reaction

The short circuit current delivered into a fault by an alternator is limited by its armature reaction as well as by the reactance of its stator windings.

However, due to the time taken by the demagnetising flux, associated with the short circuit current, to penetrate the already highly inductive main field system, armature reaction does not help to limit the short circuit current during the first few cycles after the fault occurs. In a 50-MW alternator, for example, armature reaction may take up to 50 cycles to become effective in reducing the short circuit current.

Since the time taken by protective relays to trip the breakers added to the time taken by the breakers to clear the fault may be as little as three or four cycles, the effect of armature reaction is ignored when calculating short circuit currents.

System Resistance

The reactance of a system is usually much greater than its resistance. It is therefore general practice to ignore the limiting effect of resistance when calculating short circuit currents.

This greatly simplifies the calculations, particularly if the system is a complex one. Also it enables a complex a.c. system to be simulated by a d.c. model in which the reactances of the a.c. system are represented by resistors. The short circuit current at any point can then be measured and scaled up.

Exponential Transients

If a purely inductive system is short circuited when the voltage waveform is passing through zero, then the exponential component of the short circuit current is greatest. If, on the other hand, the short circuit occurs when the voltage waveform is passing through a peak value, then the exponential component is zero. (These conditions are dealt with more fully in Section 4.)

Thus the amount of asymmetry in the short circuit current waveform depends on the instant in the voltage cycle at which the short circuit occurs.

Since asymmetrical conditions often last for at least five cycles, circuit breakers must be designed so as to be capable of interrupting asymmetrical currents.

In short circuit calculations, however, asymmetry is usually ignored.

Short Circuit Calculations

As has been previously explained, the effects of armature reaction, resistance, and asymmetry will be ignored.

Example 2-1. A 25-kVA, 400/100-V, single-phase transformer has a per unit reactance of 0·05.

Calculate the primary current and the short circuit kVA when a zero impedance short circuit occurs on the secondary whilst rated voltage is applied to the primary.

$$\text{Primary full load } I = \frac{25,000}{400} = 62{\cdot}5 \text{ A.}$$

$$\text{p.u. } X = 0{\cdot}05 = \frac{(\text{ohmic } X \text{ referred to primary}) \times 62{\cdot}5}{400}.$$

$$\text{Therefore, ohmic } X \text{ referred to primary} = \frac{0{\cdot}05 \times 400}{62{\cdot}5} = 0{\cdot}32\ \Omega.$$

$$\text{Primary short circuit } I = \frac{400}{0{\cdot}32} = \textbf{1,250 A.}$$

Alternatively   primary S/C I = primary F/L $I \times \dfrac{1}{\text{p.u. } X} = 62 \cdot 5 \times 20$

$$= \textbf{1,250 A.}$$

$$\text{S/C kVA} = 400 \times 1{,}250 \times 10^{-3} = \textbf{500.}$$

Alternatively   S/C kVA = F/L kVA $\times \dfrac{1}{\text{p.u. } X} = 25 \times 20 = \textbf{500.}$

Conversion to a Common Base

In a system comprising several components, their full load kVA or MVA ratings are usually different. It is then necessary to convert to a common kVA or MVA base before calculating the S/C current and S/C kVA or MVA.

In example 2-1 a 25-kVA base was used, that is the same base as the full load rating of the transformer. The same result is obtained, however, if any other base is used, as in example 2-2.

Example 2-2. Repeat example 2-1 using a 30-kVA base.

Base current corresponding to 30 kVA $= \dfrac{30{,}000}{400} = 75 \text{ A.}$

Ohmic X referred to primary is unchanged and $= 0 \cdot 32\ \Omega$.

$$\text{p.u. } X = \frac{75 \times 0 \cdot 32}{400} = 0 \cdot 06.$$

Thus   S/C I = base current $\times \dfrac{1}{\text{p.u. } X} = 75 \times \dfrac{1}{0 \cdot 06} = \textbf{1,250 A}$, as before.

Also   S/C kVA = kVA base $\times \dfrac{1}{\text{p.u. } X} = 30 \times \dfrac{1}{0 \cdot 06} = \textbf{500}$, as before.

Note that the base chosen above is $1 \cdot 2 \times$ the transformer full load kVA. Also that the p.u. X on a 30-kVA base is $1 \cdot 2 \times$ that on a 25-kVA base. Therefore, in order to convert p.u. X values to a new base, direct proportion must be used.

Example 2-3. A three-phase, 11-kV alternator having p.u. X of 0·25 at 30 MVA is connected to the primary of a three-phase transformer having p.u. X equal to 0·1 at 40 MVA. Calculate the primary current and S/C MVA when a three-phase, symmetrical short circuit occurs on the secondary of the transformer, (a) using a 30-MVA base, (b) using a 40-MVA base.

(a) Assuming star-connection.

$$\text{Base current corresponding to 30 MVA} = \frac{30,000,000}{\sqrt{3} \times 11,000}$$

$$= 1,575 \text{ A line and phase.}$$

p.u. X of transformer converted to a 30-MVA base $= \dfrac{30}{40} \times 0{\cdot}1 = {\cdot}075.$

Since the alternator and transformer are in series, total p.u. $X = 0{\cdot}25 + 0{\cdot}075 = 0{\cdot}325.$

$$\text{S/C } I = \text{base } I \times \frac{1}{\text{p.u. } X} = 1{,}575 \times \frac{1}{0{\cdot}325} = \mathbf{4{,}845 \text{ A}}.$$

$$\text{S/C MVA} = \text{MVA base} \times \frac{1}{\text{p.u. } X} = 30 \times \frac{1}{0{\cdot}325} = \mathbf{92{\cdot}3}.$$

(b) Base current corresponding to 40 MVA

$$= \frac{40,000,000}{\sqrt{3} \times 11,000} = 2{,}100 \text{ A}.$$

p.u. X of alternator converted to a 40-MVA base $= \dfrac{40}{30} \times {\cdot}25 = {\cdot}3333.$

$$\text{Total p.u. } X = 0{\cdot}3333 + 0{\cdot}1 = 0{\cdot}4333$$

$$\text{S/C } I = 2{,}100 \times \frac{1}{0{\cdot}4333} = \mathbf{4{,}845 \text{ A}} \text{ as before}$$

$$\text{S/C MVA} = 40 \times \frac{1}{0{\cdot}4333} = \mathbf{92{\cdot}3}, \text{ as before.}$$

Example 2-4. Calculate the short circuit fault current and S/C MVA when a three-phase symmetrical short circuit occurs at F in the three-phase system represented by the single-line diagram in figure 2.1, (a) using a 50-MVA base, (b) using a 100-MVA base.

(a) Secondary current corresponding to 50 MVA

$$= \frac{50,000,000}{\sqrt{3} \times 132,000} = 219 \text{ A}.$$

The two alternators are in parallel with respect to the fault so that their reactance is half what it would be if there were only one alternator. Thus the effective p.u. X of the two alternators equals 0·1.

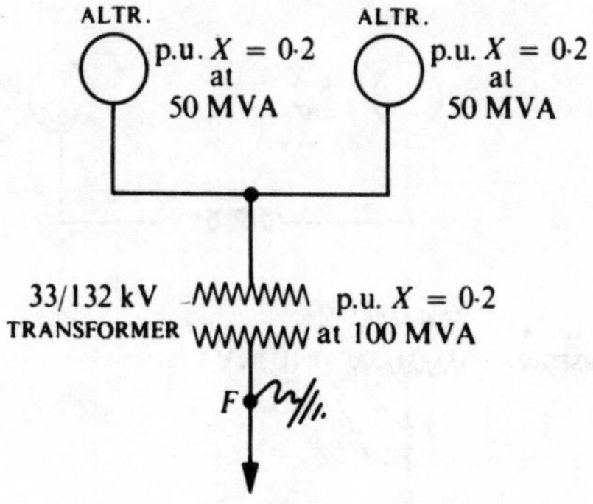

FIG. 2.1

p.u. X of transformer converted to a 50-MVA base = 0·1.

$$\text{Total p.u. } X = 0\cdot1 + 0\cdot1 = 0\cdot2.$$

$$\text{S/C secondary } I = 219 \times \frac{1}{0\cdot2} = \textbf{1,095 A.}$$

$$\text{S/C MVA} = 50 \times \frac{1}{0\cdot2} = \textbf{250.}$$

(b) Secondary current corresponding to 100 MVA = $2 \times 219 = 438$ A.
p.u. X of each alternator converted to a 100-MVA base = 0·4.
Effective p.u. X of the two alternators = 0·2.

$$\text{Total p.u. } X = 0\cdot2 + 0\cdot2 = 0\cdot4.$$

$$\text{S/C secondary } I = 438 \times \frac{1}{0\cdot4} = \textbf{1,095 A.}$$

$$\text{S/C MVA} = 100 \times \frac{1}{0\cdot4} = \textbf{250.}$$

Example 2-5. Using a 50-MVA base, calculate the p.u. X and inductance of reactor 'x' required to limit the S/C MVA to 100 when a three-phase symmetrical short circuit occurs at F in the three-phase, 50-Hz system represented by the single-line diagram in figure 2.2.

p.u. X of alternator A = 0·2.
p.u. X of transformer = 0·4.

$$\text{p.u. } X \text{ of alternators and reactor} = \frac{0\cdot2(0\cdot15 + x)}{0\cdot2 + 0\cdot15 + x}.$$

$$\textbf{Total p.u. } X = 0\cdot4 + \frac{0\cdot03 + 0\cdot2x}{0\cdot35 + x}.$$

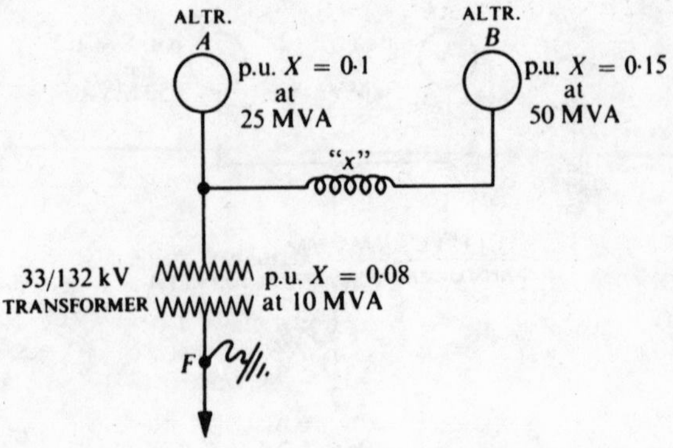

FIG. 2.2

Now
$$\text{S/C MVA} = \text{MVA base} \times \frac{1}{\text{total p.u. } X}.$$

Therefore
$$\text{Total p.u. } X = \frac{\text{MVA base}}{\text{S/C MVA}}.$$

$$0 \cdot 4 + \frac{0 \cdot 03 + 0 \cdot 2x}{0 \cdot 35 + x} = \frac{50}{100}.$$

Hence
$$x = 0 \cdot 05.$$

$$\text{Base } I = \frac{50,000,000}{\sqrt{3} \times 33,000} = 875 \text{ A}.$$

Now
$$\text{p.u. } X = \frac{\text{base } I \times X_L}{\text{rated phase } V}.$$

$$X_L = \frac{0 \cdot 05 \times 19,100}{875} = 1 \cdot 09 \ \Omega/\text{phase}.$$

$$L = \frac{1 \cdot 09}{314} = 0 \cdot 00347 \text{ H or } \textbf{3·47 mH/phase}.$$

Location of Reactors

In an extensive system there are three possible locations for reactors:
(a) In series with the alternators as in figure 2.3,
(b) In series with the feeders as in figure 2.4,
(c) Between the bus-bar sections as in figures 2.5 and 2.6.

(a) Reactors in series with alternators

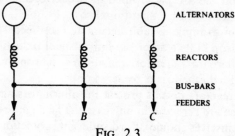

FIG. 2.3

These are not commonly used because:

(i) Modern power station alternators have sufficient leakage react-ance to enable them to withstand a symmetrical short circuit across their terminals.

(ii) Under normal healthy conditions there is a relatively large voltage drop and power loss in each reactor due to the load current.

(iii) When a short circuit occurs on the bus-bars or near the bus-bar end of a feeder, the high fault current causes large voltage drops in the reactors which reduce the bus-bar voltage to such a low value that the alternators are likely to fall out of synchronism. A large part of the system would then be interrupted whilst the alternators were being re-synchronized after isolation of the fault.

For these reasons alternator reactors are now only used to protect old alternators of low reactance.

(b) Reactors in series with feeders

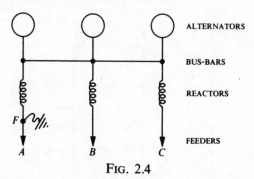

FIG. 2.4

These are more commonly used than alternator reactors for the following reasons:

(i) In an extensive system there are usually hundreds of feeder circuit breakers but only a few alternator circuit breakers. It is therefore essential to limit the S/C kVA which the feeder breakers will have to interrupt in order to reduce their initial cost.

(ii) When, for example, a fault occurs at F on feeder A, there is a large voltage drop in its reactor but only a small reduction in bus-bar voltage. The alternators therefore remain in synchronism and the fault can be isolated with the loss of feeder A only.

(iii) Feeder reactors do not protect the alternators against bus-bar faults, but these are rare and in any case the leakage reactance of the alternators themselves should afford sufficient protection.

Disadvantages of using feeder reactors are:

(i) As with alternator reactors, there is a relatively large voltage drop and power loss in each reactor during normal healthy conditions.

(ii) If the number of alternators is increased, the p.u. X of the feeder reactors must be increased in order to keep the S/C kVA within the rupturing capacities of the existing feeder breakers.

(c) Reactors between bus-bar sections

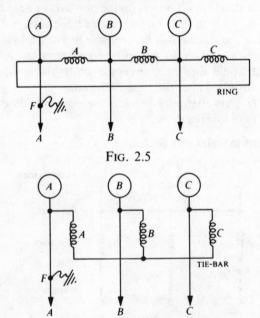

FIG. 2.5

FIG. 2.6

These are more commonly used than feeder reactors because reactors between bus-bar sections give all the advantages of feeder reactors without their disadvantages.

During normal healthy conditions, each alternator supplies its own feeder and there is little or no current in the reactors.

But when, for example, a fault occurs at F on feeder A, the S/C kVA delivered into the fault by alternator A is limited only by its leakage reactance whilst that delivered by the other alternators is limited by their reactance and that of the reactors.

In the RING SYSTEM shown in figure 2.5, alternator B would feed into the fault through reactor A and alternator C through reactor C (see figure 2.11).

In the TIE-BAR SYSTEM shown in figure 2.6, alternator B would feed into the fault through reactors B and A in series and alternator C through reactors C and A in series.

In these ways, the reactors tend to localize the majority of the fault current to one alternator only.

For the foregoing three-section system it can be shown that tie-bar reactors would need only one third of the reactance of ring reactors (see example 2-6). On the other hand the tie-bar reactors would have to carry twice as much current as the ring reactors.

Since L is directly proportional to N^2, the number of turns on each ring reactor would be $\sqrt{3}$ times that on each tie-bar reactor. But the cross-sectional area of conductor used and the mechanical bracing required would be less for the ring reactor than for the tie-bar reactor.

The cost and size of the reactors for either system are therefore similar; if anything, the ring reactors would be slightly cheaper.

There is the additional advantage that, if each reactor is to have its own isolating circuit breakers, those for the ring system require only half the rupturing capacity of those for the tie-bar system. Also, the tie-bar system requires an additional three-phase bus-bar (see Power Station Layout).

Example 2-6. A three-phase, 33-kV generating station is laid out as in figure 2.6. On a 60-MVA base the p.u. X of each alternator is 0.2 and that of each reactor 0.1.

Calculate: (a) the S/C MVA and the S/C current distribution when a symmetrical three-phase short circuit occurs at F,

(b) the required p.u. X of each reactor in an equivalent ring system so that the S/C MVA is as in (a),

(c) the S/C current distribution for this ring system.

(a) The equivalent reactance diagram for the tie-bar system is shown in figure 2.7.

$$\text{Total p.u. } X = \frac{0.2 \times 0.25}{0.45} = 0.111.$$

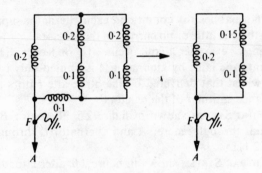

Fig. 2.7

$$\text{S/C MVA} = 60 \times \frac{1}{0.111} = \mathbf{540}.$$

$$\text{Base } I \text{ corresponding to 60 MVA} = \frac{60,000,000}{\sqrt{3} \times 33,000} = 1,050\,\text{A}.$$

$$\text{S/C } I \text{ at fault} = 1,050 \times \frac{1}{0.111} = 9,450\,\text{A}.$$

Let alternator A supply x amperes of this, then from figure 2.7:

$$0.2x = 0.25(9,450 - x). \qquad \text{Hence } x = 5,250\,A.$$

Therefore the S/C current distribution is as shown in figure 2.8.

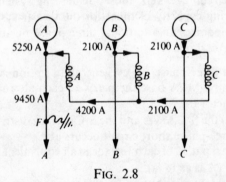

Fig. 2.8

(b) The equivalent reactance diagram for the ring system is shown in figure 2.9, where y is the required p.u. X of each reactor.

The delta is transformed to an equivalent star as shown in figure 2.10.

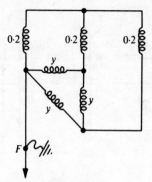

Fig. 2.9

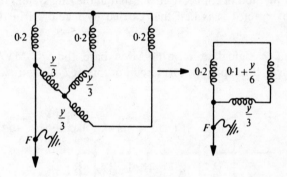

Fig. 2.10

Total p.u. $X = (0.1 + 0.5y)$ in parallel with 0.2, therefore

$$\text{total p.u. } X = \frac{0.2(0.1 + 0.5y)}{0.3 + 0.5y}.$$

$$\text{S/C MVA} = 540 = 60 \times \frac{0.3 + 0.5y}{0.02 + 0.1y}.$$

Hence $\qquad\qquad y = \mathbf{0.3}.$

Thus the reactance of each ring reactor is three times that of each tie-bar reactor.

(c) S/C I at fault $= 9{,}450$ A. Let alternator A supply z amperes of this, then from figure 2.10:

$$0.2z = (9{,}450 - z)(0.1 + 0.5y). \qquad \text{Hence } z = 5{,}250 \text{ A}.$$

By symmetry, there will be no current in reactor B. Therefore the S/C current distribution is as shown in figure 2.11.

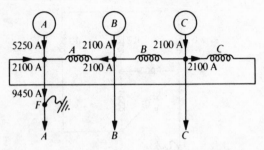

FIG. 2.11

Note that the S/C current delivered by each alternator is the same for either method of connection, but that in the ring system the current carried by reactor A is half that carried by reactor A in the tie-bar system.

Example 2-7. Calculate, on a 60-MVA base, the S/C MVA when a symmetrical, three-phase short circuit occurs at F in figure 2.12.

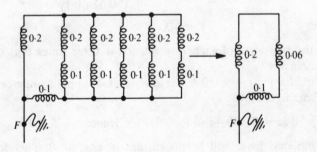

FIG. 2.12

The equivalent reactance diagram is as shown in figure 2.13.

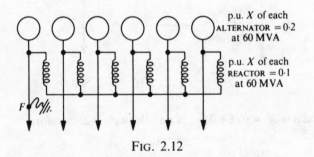

FIG. 2.13

$$\text{Total p.u. } X = \frac{0.16 \times 0.2}{0.16 + 0.2} = 0.0889.$$

$$\text{S/C MVA} = 60 \times \frac{1}{0.0889} = \textbf{675}.$$

It is obvious from figure 2.13 that, even with an infinite number of alternators and reactors, the total p.u. X cannot be less than 0·1 in parallel with 0·2 = 0·0667. Hence the greatest short circuit MVA which can occur in this system is 60/0·0667 = 900.

Therefore, provided that the feeder circuit breakers are capable of rupturing 900 MVA, any number of alternators may be added.

Example 2-8. Calculate, on a 60-MVA base, the S/C MVA when a symmetrical, three-phase short circuit occurs at F in figure 2.14.

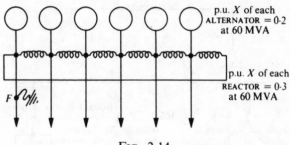

Fig. 2.14

The equivalent reactance diagram is as shown in figure 2.15.

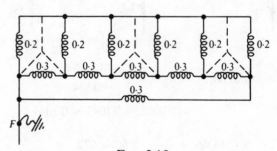

Fig. 2.15

This system may be simplified by repeatedly using delta-star transformation as shown in figure 2.16.

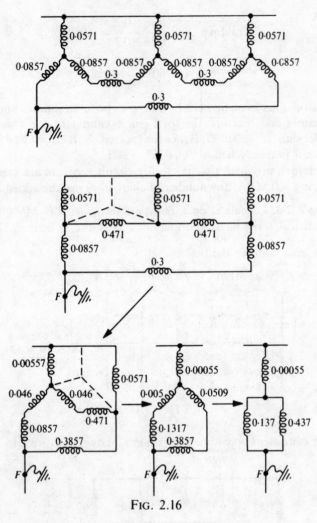

Fig. 2.16

Hence   total p.u. $X = 0.00055 + \dfrac{0.137 \times 0.437}{0.574}$

$$= 0.00055 + 0.1043 = 0.1049$$

and   S/C MVA $= \dfrac{1}{0.1049} \times 60 = \mathbf{572}.$

Variation of Total p.u. X with Number of Alternators and Reactors

Using alternators having p.u. $X = 0.2$, tie-bar reactors having p.u. $X = 0.1$ and ring reactors having p.u. $X = 0.3$, and working on a

60-MVA base, a comparison of the two methods of connection can be obtained:

No. of alternators and reactors	Total p.u. X for tie-bar system	Total p.u. X for ring system
2	0·133	0·127
3	0·111	0·111
4	0·100	0·1066
6	0·0889	0·1049
∞	0·0667	—

It can be seen that for the figure quoted, the total p.u. X varies less for the ring than for the tie-bar system.

Example 2-9. The ratings of the components of the three-phase system represented by the single-line diagram in figure 2.17 are as follows:
Each alternator has p.u. $X = 0.3$ at 30 MVA.
Each alternator transformer has p.u. $X = 0.0667$ at 20 MVA.
Each tie-bar reactor has p.u. $X = x$ at 30 MVA.
11/132-kV, step-up feeder transformer has p.u. $X = 0.1$ at 20 MVA.
132/11-kV, step-down feeder transformer has p.u. $X = 0.1$ at 20 MVA.
Reactance of feeder = 29 Ω per conductor.

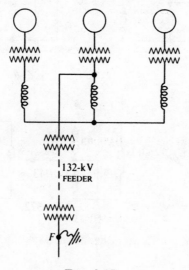

Fig. 2.17

Working on a 30-MVA base, calculate the value of x required so that the current in a three-phase symmetrical short circuit at F shall not exceed 3,000 amperes.

$$\text{Base } I \text{ corresponding to 30 MVA and 132 kV} = \frac{30,000,000}{\sqrt{3} \times 132,000}$$

$$= 131 \text{ A.}$$

$$\text{Feeder phase } V = \frac{132,000}{\sqrt{3}} = 76,200 \text{ V.}$$

$$\text{p.u. } X \text{ per phase of feeder} = \frac{I \times X_L}{V} = \frac{131 \times 29}{76,200} = 0.05.$$

For a 30-MVA base, the equivalent reactance diagram is shown in figure 2.18.

Hence $$\text{total p.u. } X = \frac{(0.2 + 1.5x)0.4}{0.6 + 1.5x} + 0.35.$$

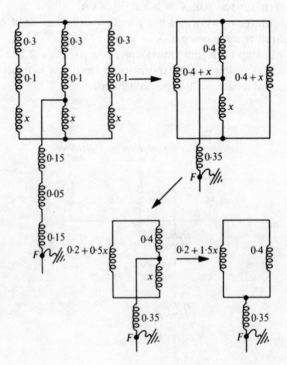

FIG. 2.18

Base I corresponding to 30 MVA and 11 kV $= \dfrac{30{,}000{,}000}{\sqrt{3} \times 11{,}000}$

$$= 1{,}575 \text{ A}.$$

Total p.u. X required $= \dfrac{\text{base } I}{\text{S/C } I} = \dfrac{1{,}575}{3{,}000} = 0{\cdot}525.$

But $\qquad 0{\cdot}525 = \dfrac{0{\cdot}08 + 0{\cdot}6x}{0{\cdot}6 + 1{\cdot}5x} + 0{\cdot}35$

thus $\qquad 0{\cdot}105 + 0{\cdot}2625x = 0{\cdot}08 + 0{\cdot}6x$

Hence $\qquad x = \dfrac{0{\cdot}025}{0{\cdot}3375} = \mathbf{0{\cdot}0741 \text{ p.u.}}$

Example 2-10. A three-phase, 50-Hz system in which 33-kV bus-bars are supplied by four 11-kV alternators through two parallel overhead 132-kV transmission lines is represented by the single-line diagram in figure 2.19.

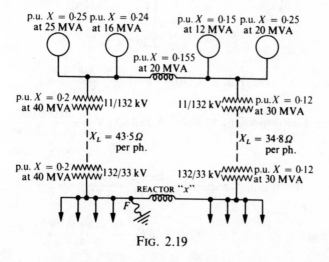

Fig. 2.19

Using a 20-MVA base, calculate the per unit reactance and inductance per phase of reactor 'x' so that the current in a three-phase symmetrical short circuit at F does not exceed 1,750 A.

Base I corresponding to 20 MVA and 132 kV $= \dfrac{20{,}000{,}000}{\sqrt{3} \times 132{,}000}$

$$= 87{\cdot}5 \text{ A}.$$

$$\text{Transmission line phase } V = \frac{132,000}{\sqrt{3}} = 76,200 \text{ V.}$$

$$\text{Left-hand line p.u. } X = \frac{87 \cdot 5 \times 43 \cdot 5}{76,200} = 0 \cdot 05.$$

$$\text{Right-hand line p.u. } X = \frac{87 \cdot 5 \times 34 \cdot 8}{76,200} = 0 \cdot 04.$$

For a 20-MVA base, the equivalent reactance diagram is shown in figure 2.20.

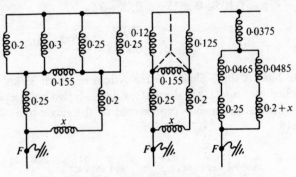

Fɪɢ. 2.20

$$\text{Total p.u. } X = 0 \cdot 0375 + \frac{0 \cdot 2965(0 \cdot 2485 + x)}{0 \cdot 545 + x}$$

$$\text{Base } I \text{ corresponding to 20 MVA and 33 kV} = \frac{20,000,000}{\sqrt{3} \times 33,000}$$

$$= 350 \text{ A.}$$

$$\text{Total p.u. } X \text{ required} = \frac{\text{base } I}{\text{S/C } I} = \frac{350}{1,750} = 0 \cdot 2.$$

Therefore
$$0 \cdot 2 = 0 \cdot 0375 + \frac{0 \cdot 0736 + 0 \cdot 2965x}{0 \cdot 545 + x},$$

and
$$0 \cdot 0736 + 0 \cdot 2965x = 0 \cdot 1625(0 \cdot 545 + x),$$

so that
$$x = \frac{0 \cdot 0149}{0 \cdot 134} = \textbf{0·111 p.u.}$$

Now
$$\text{p.u. } X = \frac{\text{base } I \times X_L}{\text{phase } V},$$

from which
$$X_L = \frac{0 \cdot 111 \times 19{,}100}{350} = 6 \cdot 06 \ \Omega/\text{phase},$$

and
$$L = \frac{6 \cdot 06}{314} = 0 \cdot 0193 \ \text{H or } \mathbf{19 \cdot 3 \ mH/phase}.$$

Use of Network Analyser for Simulating Short Circuit Conditions

The system in example 2-10 can be represented by the simple d.c. network shown in figure 2.21.

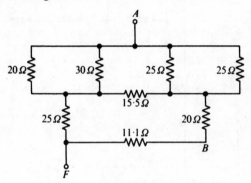

Fig. 2.21

Each 0·01 of p.u. X in the original system is represented by 1 Ω in the d.c. network. Hence the total resistance of this network measured between A and F is 20 Ω and represents the total p.u. $X = 0 \cdot 2$ of the actual system.

The conditions in the actual system when there is a short circuit at F can be simulated by connecting a 35-V, d.c. supply across AF in the network. The current at F in the d.c. network is then $35/20 = 1 \cdot 75$ A representing the S/C current $= 1{,}750$ A in the actual system.

The currents in any branch of the d.c. network can be measured with an ammeter. Currents in the 33-kV sections of the actual system are obtained by multiplying the ammeter readings by 10^3, those in the 132-kV sections by multiplying by $10^3/4$, and those in the 11-kV sections by multiplying by 3×10^3.

The S/C MVA at **any** point is obtained by multiplying the ammeter reading by $\sqrt{3} \times 33$.

Faults in other parts of the system can also be analysed. For example, a S/C fault at B can be simulated by connecting the 35-V, d.c. supply across AB instead of AF.

By using this type of analyser the S/C fault current and S/C MVA in any part of an extensive system can be quickly ascertained.

EXAMPLES 2

1. The ratings of the components of the three-phase system represented by the single-line diagram in figure 2.22 are as follows:

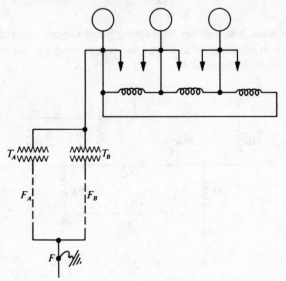

FIG. 2.22

Each alternator has p.u. $X = 0.3$ at 30 MVA.

Each ring reactor has p.u. $X = 0.15$ at 30 MVA.

Transformer T_A has p.u. $X = 0.1$ at 20 MVA.

Transformer T_B has p.u. $X = 0.1$ at 10 MVA.

The 66-kV feeders, F_A and F_B, each have a reactance of 21·8 Ω per conductor.

Working on a 20-MVA base, calculate the total p.u. X, the S/C MVA and current fed into a symmetrical three-phase short circuit at F.

(Answers **0·206 p.u., 97·3 MVA, 850 A.**)

2. The ratings of the components of the three-phase system represented by the single-line diagram in figure 2.23 are as follows:

Alternator A has p.u. $X = 0.15$ at 15 MVA.

Transformer A has p.u. $X = 0.1$ at 20 MVA.

Alternator B has p.u. $X = 0.2$ at 30 MVA.

Transformer B has p.u. $X = 0.1$ at 15 MVA.

Feeders CC and DD each have a reactance of 7·3 Ω per phase.

The 33-kV feeder E is connected to the mid-point of DD and has p.u. $X = 0.03$ at 10 MVA.

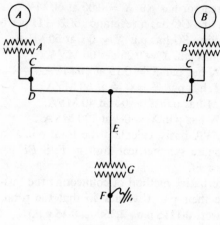

FIG. 2.23

The 33/11-kV, step-down transformer G has p.u. $X = 0.08$ at 15 MVA.

Using a 15-MVA base, calculate the p.u. X of the reactor to be connected in series with feeder E so that the current fed into a three-phase symmetrical short circuit at F does not exceed 1,500 amperes. (Answer **0.269 p.u.**)

3. The generating stations A and B are interconnected by two 132-kV transmission lines as in figure 2.24.

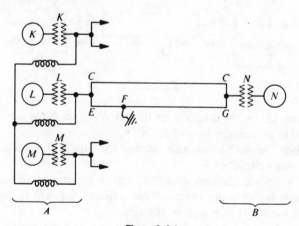

FIG. 2.24

Alternator K has p.u. $X = 0.2$ at 60 MVA.
Alternator L has p.u. $X = 0.2$ at 60 MVA.
Alternator M has p.u. $X = 0.1$ at 30 MVA.

Each tie-bar reactor has p.u. $X = 0.05$ at 60 MVA.

Transmission line CC has a reactance of 26.1 Ω per phase.

Transmission line EG has p.u. $X = 0.1$ at 60 MVA.

Alternator N has p.u. $X = 0.25$ at 100 MVA.

Transformer K has p.u. $X = 0.15$ at 60 MVA.

Transformer L has p.u. $X = 0.15$ at 60 MVA.

Transformer M has p.u. $X = 0.1$ at 40 MVA.

Transformer N has p.u. $X = 0.2$ at 120 MVA.

Using a 60-MVA basis, calculate the total p.u. X and current fed into the three-phase symmetrical fault at F, if EF is one quarter of the total distance EG.

Sketch an alternative method of connecting the bus-bar reactors at A and calculate their p.u. X values so that the total p.u. X to F is unaltered. (Answers **0.1115 p.u., 2,350 A, 0.15 p.u.**)

4. (a) Explain why reactors are necessary in large power systems.

(b) Describe the construction of both air-cored and iron-cored reactors. State why the magnetic shielding of reactors is necessary and explain how it is achieved.

(c) Draw single-line diagrams to show three possible locations of reactors in power systems and comment on each.

5. Two 11-kV generating stations are interconnected by two 132-kV transmission lines as in figure 2.25.

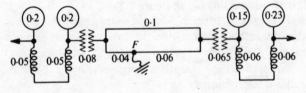

Fig. 2.25

The numbers on the diagram are the p.u. X values of the components expressed to a common base of 60 MVA.

Calculate the S/C MVA and current fed into a three-phase symmetrical short circuit at F.

Draw a circuit diagram of a d.c. network suitable for analysing this system. Indicate the values of the resistors required using 1 Ω to represent each 0.01 of p.u. X in the system.

Indicate the points in the d.c. network to which a d.c. supply should be connected in order to simulate a short circuit fault at F. Calculate the value of d.c. voltage required in order that the fault current at F in the analyser is 10^{-3} times the fault current in the system.

(Answers **514 MVA, 2,240 A, 26.3 V.**)

3

Supply System Layout

High Voltage Transmission

Power stations are often situated at considerable distances from centres of power consumption. Coal-fired stations are built near coal-fields whenever possible in order to reduce transport costs. Nuclear stations are usually situated in remote areas and the location of hydro-electric stations is dependent on the availability of an adequate head of water.

Thus the distance between a power station and the nearest load centre may in some cases be in the order of 160 km.

In most developing countries, the demand for electrical energy to supply domestic, commercial and industrial loads is increasing. Ever increasing amounts of electrical energy are therefore having to be transmitted over considerable distances. In order to do this econom-ically, transmission voltages have to be increased every few years.

A mainly overhead, three-phase grid network is used to interconnect the power stations and load centres. In this country, where distances are comparatively short, the present supergrid network is at 400 kV between lines. In larger countries 600, 800, and 1,000-kV lines are either under construction or already in operation.

Example 3-1. 150 MVA at 0·8 power factor lagging is to be transmitted over a distance of 360 km by means of a three-phase overhead line. Assuming the same current density and conductor material, compare line voltages of 100 kV and 200 kV on the scores of:

    (a) volume of conductor material,
    (b) resistance voltage drop,
    (c) per unit resistance drop,
    (d) $I^2 R$ loss.

(a) For the same current density, the conductor cross-sectional area for 100 kV is twice that for 200 kV. Thus the volume of conductor material is inversely proportional to line voltage.

(b) For the 100-kV line, $I = \dfrac{150 \times 10^6}{\sqrt{3} \times 100 \times 10^3} = 866\,\text{A}$. For the

200-kV line, $I = 433\,\text{A}$. Let the resistance per phase of the 100-kV line $= R\,\Omega$, then the resistance per phase of the 200-kV line $= 2R\,\Omega$. Therefore resistance voltage drop for the 100-kV line $= 866 \times R\,\text{V}$, and that for the 200-kV line $= 433 \times 2R\,\text{V}$. Thus the resistance voltage drop is constant.

(c) Phase voltage for the 100-kV line $= \dfrac{100 \times 10^3}{\sqrt{3}} = 57{,}700\,\text{V}$, and

that for the 200-kV line, 115,400 V. Therefore p.u. R drop for the 100-kV line $= \dfrac{866R}{57{,}700}$, and that for the 200-kV line $= \dfrac{866R}{115{,}400}$. Thus the p.u. R drop is inversely proportional to the line voltage.

(d) $I^2 R$ loss per phase of the 100-kV line is $866^2 \cdot R\,\text{W}$ and that per phase of the 200-kV line is $433^2 \cdot 2R\,\text{W}$. Thus the $I^2 R$ loss is also inversely proportional to the line voltage.

From the above example it is obvious that the higher voltage gives the most economical transmission. It must be remembered, however, that the initial cost of the 200-kV line will be considerably greater due to larger towers, more insulators and more expensive transformers at either end. (See page 210.)

High Voltage Direct Current Transmission

The use of direct rather than alternating current has the following advantages:

(a) A smaller volume of conductor material is required to transmit a given power load.

(b) There is no continuous capacitance charging current.

(c) There is no line inductive reactance and therefore no line reactive voltage drop.

(d) Insulation difficulties are not as great as on alternating current.

(e) There are no dielectric hysteresis losses in the insulation of underground and undersea d.c. cables.

The main disadvantage is that it is necessary to convert a.c. to d.c. at the sending end and d.c. to a.c. at the receiving end. Although this can be done efficiently and at reasonable cost, the use of d.c. transmission is obviously limited to those applications where this disadvantage is outweighed by the advantages above. This is further discussed in Section 5.

One example of the present use of d.c. transmission is the undersea d.c. cable link between the French and British a.c. grid networks.

Typical a.c. Transmission System

Figure 3.1 is a single-line diagram representing a three-phase system.

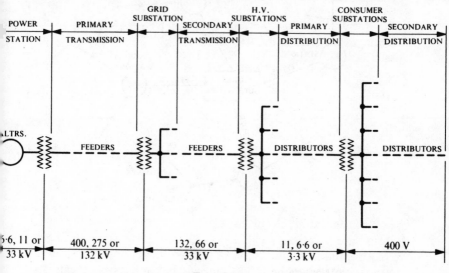

FIG. 3.1

Not all the stages shown are necessarily present in every system. During the last few years, load densities in the centres of cities and in some urban districts have risen so much that the case for intermediate voltages between 132 kV and 11 kV is considerably weakened. Where loads of the order of 60 MVA exist within areas of one or two km radius it is more economical in capital, land and transformation losses to provide bulk supply points at which the voltage is stepped down direct from 132 kV to 11 kV.

Systems like the one shown usually radiate in more than one direction from each power station. The primary feeders from different power stations are interconnected at the grid substations to form the National Grid Network.

The secondary feeders from each grid substation may be arranged radially as in figure 3.2, or to form a ring as in figure 3.3.

In the radial system, failure of a feeder interrupts the supply to a substation. Therefore duplicate feeders would be necessary for important consumers such as hospitals. Ideally the grid substation should be at the 'hub' of the feeders and in built up areas this is rarely possible.

In the ring system, failure of one interconnecting feeder does not interrupt the supply to any of the substations. The grid substation need not be at the 'hub' of the feeders.

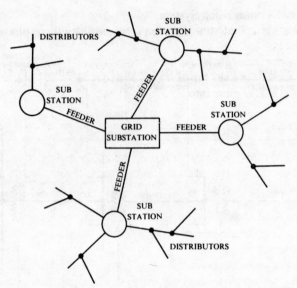

FIG. 3.2

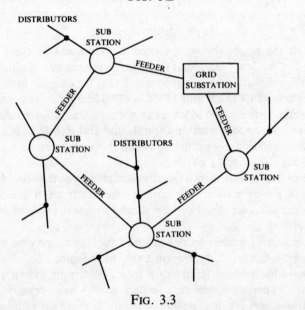

FIG. 3.3

The ring system has the higher initial cost but lower power losses and is the more popular of the two methods.

In designing feeders, the cross-sectional area of conductor is kept as small as possible. Thus current densities and voltage drops are relatively high. Variations in voltage drop caused by changes in load can be offset by altering the tappings on power station and grid substation transformers.

The smaller transformers in H.V. and consumer substations will not have automatic on-load tap-changers fitted. Thus the voltage drop in distributors is a far more important criterion than their current carrying capacity.

The variation of voltage at each consumer's terminals is limited by a Government Regulation to ±6 per cent of the declared system voltage. Because of the above considerations, supply systems are so designed that most of this voltage variation takes place in the secondary distribution networks.

Power Station Layout

In each case, single-line diagrams will be used to represent three-phase systems.

It must always be possible to isolate circuit breakers, reactors, alternators, transformers and bus-bars so that inspection, cleaning and maintenance can be carried out. In many cases special earthing switches are used to earth high voltage equipment during maintenance. These switches are not shown in the earlier diagrams.

Simple Single Bus-bar System

A typical example is shown in figure 3.4.

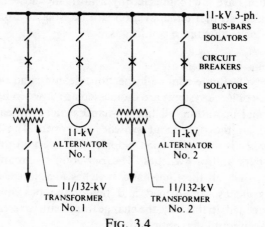

FIG. 3.4

Isolators are switches which are operated under conditions of no current and are therefore much simpler and cheaper than circuit breakers which must be capable of breaking maximum S/C currents.

The feeders and alternators are connected alternately to the bus-bars as shown in order to reduce the bus-bar cross-sectional area.

Sectionalized Bus-bar System
Larger systems are divided into sections as shown in figure 3.5.

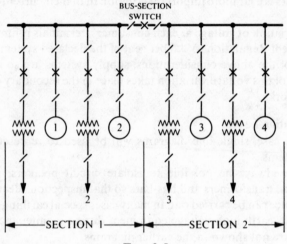

FIG. 3.5

The sections are interconnected by a normally-closed, bus-section circuit breaker so that either section can be isolated from the other under fault or maintenance conditions.

Duplicate Bus-bar System
In order to facilitate routine inspection, cleaning and maintenance, the bus-bars of large systems are duplicated as shown in figure 3.6.

For normal operation, all the left-hand switches of each pair are closed and all the right-hand switches are open. The bus-coupler circuit breaker is normally open. Suppose it is desired to inspect the main bus-bars and/or switches. The bus-coupler circuit breaker is first closed, then all the right-hand switches are closed, then all the left-hand switches are opened and finally the bus-coupler circuit breaker is opened. In this way, the change from main to reserve bus-bars is achieved without interrupting the supply.

Duplicate Bus-bar System with Tie-bar Reactors
In the example shown in figure 3.7, two sections only are drawn, with provision for further sections on the right of the diagram.

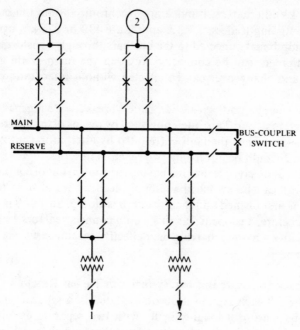

FIG. 3.6

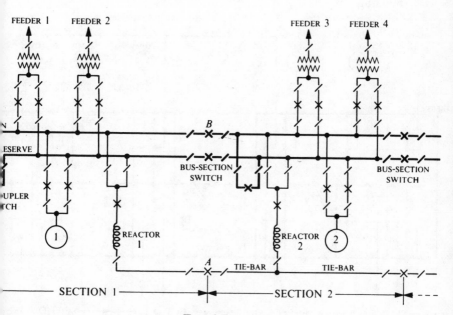

FIG. 3.7

The 11-kV alternators, 1 and 2, are synchronized onto the bus-bars and the outgoing feeders, 1, 2, 3, and 4, are 132 or 275-kV overhead transmission lines connected to the bus-bars through transformers.

All equipment can be connected to either the main or the reserve bus-bars and changeover can be effected without interruption of the supply.

The bus-coupler and bus-section circuit breakers are normally open so that sections 1 and 2 are interconnected by means of the two reactors and the tie-bar. Thus the fault current fed by alternator 1 into a fault on section 2 would be limited by two reactors in series.

In the event of, say, alternator 2 having to be taken out of commission, alternator 1 can be switched to supply feeders 3 and 4 as follows. Switch A is first opened and then switch B is closed. Switch B must not be closed before A is opened as this would connect reactors 1 and 2 in parallel with each other, halving their effective reactance with reference to section 3.

Back-to-back Duplicate Bus-bar System with Tie-bar Reactors

In figure 3.8 each section is accommodated in a separate building. The bus-bars are run longitudinally with two separate circuits connected back-to-back in order to reduce the overall length of each building.

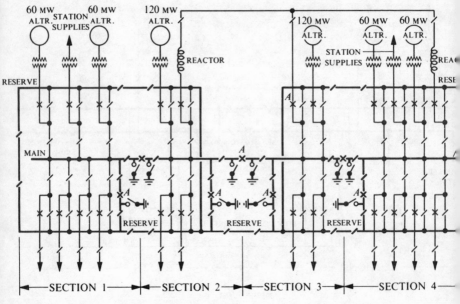

FIG. 3.8

The 11-kV alternators are connected through step-up transformers to the 132-kV bus-bars. The 3·3-kV station supplies are taken from the bus-bars through step-down transformers. Capacitor type voltage transformers are used for instrumentation and synchronization.

The circuit breakers marked *A* and all the isolators connected to the reserve bus-bars are normally open. Earthing isolators are provided for earthing high voltage sections during maintenance. These isolators are interlocked so that they cannot be closed whilst the section to which they are connected is alive. Also, once the earthing isolators are closed, the appropriate interlock keys remain in the possession of the maintenance men so that the section cannot be re-energized until work has been completed.

Grid Substation Layout

275-kV and 132-kV grid substations are laid out in a similar way to power stations. For example, if the alternators in figure 3.7 were replaced by incoming feeders, then the diagram would represent the layout of a large grid substation.

The switchgear may be outside or indoors. Indoor substations have less trouble with pollution flashovers on insulators but are more expensive than outdoor substations.

Consumer Substation Layout

Smaller substations vary in complexity but usually form part of a distribution ring which must not be opened under normal conditions.

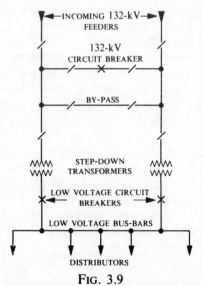

FIG. 3.9

The number of high voltage circuit breakers required to achieve this varies from one to four. Figure 3.9 shows a single high voltage circuit breaker substation.

Maintenance on the high voltage circuit breaker can be carried out by closing the by-pass isolators, opening the breaker and then opening the isolators on either side of the breaker. Maintenance on the transformers and low voltage circuit breakers is made possible by their duplication. Again, safety interlock keys are provided.

EXAMPLES 3

1. A medium voltage and a high voltage three-phase transmission line are to be used to transmit identical loads at the same current densities over the same distance.

Compare the two lines on the scores of:

(a) volume of conductor material required,
(b) resistance voltage drop,
(c) per unit resistance drop,
(d) I^2R loss,
(e) initial cost.

2. Discuss the advantages and disadvantages of high voltage direct current transmission compared with high voltage three-phase transmission.

3. Give a single-line diagram of connections showing the general layout of an extensive supply system.

Briefly explain why different line voltages are used in the various parts of the system and indicate typical values.

4. Draw single-line diagrams to show the difference between radial and ring distribution networks and compare the two systems.

5. Give a single-line diagram of connections showing the layout of the bus-bar sections in a power station. Include the tie-bar, the reserve bar and the necessary reactors, isolators and circuit breakers for at least two alternators and two feeders. Briefly indicate why these items are necessary.

State, with reasons, the switching sequence for transferring the supply of a feeder from its own alternator to another one.

6. Draw single-line diagrams showing the layouts of:

(a) a large grid substation,
(b) a single high voltage circuit breaker substation.

State how and why earthing isolators and interlocks are used.

4

Circuit Breakers

Principles of Arc Extinction

When a circuit breaker is used to interrupt a direct current, only a small voltage is developed between the contacts as they begin to separate. The current continues to flow in the form of an arc between the contacts. The heat generated by the I^2R losses in the arc ionizes the insulating medium in which the arc is struck. Thus the voltage required to maintain the arc is fairly small and the contacts have to be moved a considerable distance apart before the voltage available is insufficient to maintain the arc.

On high voltage, heavy current breakers, therefore, means have to be provided for (i) making the length of the arc path greater than the distance between the contacts and (ii) replacing the hot ionized gas between the contacts with a cool un-ionized medium.

The process of arc extinction is less difficult in a.c. breakers because the current and voltage each pass through zero 100 times a second on a 50-Hz system. The extinction of a.c. arcs is dealt with more fully later in this section.

Circuit Breaker Ratings

It is usual to express the breaking capacity of circuit breakers in kVA or MVA. The breaking capacity is obtained from the product of the greatest r.m.s. current which can be interrupted and the r.m.s. voltage across the contacts immediately after final arc extinction. Although this gives some guide to the breaking capacity of a breaker, more detailed test performance data are also required. These are dealt with later in this section.

Small Circuit Breakers, 400 V → 3·3 kV line, up to 30 kA, up to 25 MVA

These may be air-break breakers or contactors in which there is little or no attempt at arc control apart from the fitting of insulated arcing chutes. Convection air currents in each chute are generated by the heat of the arc. In this way, the arc is bent upwards so that its length rapidly becomes very much greater than the straight-line distance between the contacts.

Small oil-break breakers are also used. In these, the fixed and moving contacts are submerged in a tank containing insulating oil. Some assistance to arc extinction is then derived from the gas bubble generated around the arc. This causes turbulence in the oil which helps to remove ionized arc products from the arc path.

Both the above types have relatively long and inconsistent arcing times and are therefore only suitable for the lower ratings indicated.

In air breakers the contact arcing tips have to be replaced more frequently than in oil breakers. In oil breakers some oil is carbonized during each arc extinction and a sludge is eventually formed. The tanks therefore have to be drained, cleaned and refilled with clean oil at intervals dependent on the frequency of operation. There is less fire and explosion risk with air breakers than with oil, provided that the air breakers are not situated near sources of inflammable vapour.

3·3 → 6·6 → 11 kV, 25 → 150 → 500 → 750 MVA, Air-break Breakers

The arc chutes now have internal insulated arc splitters. Coils carrying the current to be interrupted can be arranged to create a magnetic field in the arc chute which assists the air convection currents in moving the arc upwards through the splitters. Such coils are called 'blow-out' coils since the arc is magnetically 'blown out'.

On the larger sizes, the 'blow-outs' consist of steel inserts in the arcing chutes. These are so arranged that the magnetic field induced in them by the current in the arc moves it upwards.

This type of breaker becomes more bulky, the arc chutes more complex and the initial cost higher as the voltage and MVA increase. Generally, less maintenance is required than with the equivalent oil breaker and also there is less fire and explosion risk.

Self-blast Oil Circuit Breakers

The pressure of the gas bubble set up by the arc in the oil is utilized to force cool, un-ionized oil into the arc path. This increases the rate of rise of insulation resistance between the contacts and is achieved by using the cross-jet explosion pot shown in figure 4.1.

In a three-phase, double-break breaker, six explosion pots would be fitted. When the contacts part, the arc creates gas at high pressure which is guided round the right-hand throat plate to blow the arc across and through the splitter plates. These have large cooling surfaces and cool, clean oil follows the gas, thus replacing the dielectric in the arc path.

For heavy currents, the gas pressure is high and the number of splitter plates needed varies from two to five. For lower currents, more

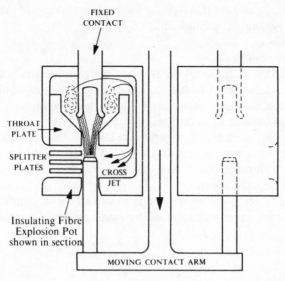

FIXED
CONTACT

THROAT
PLATE

SPLITTER
PLATES

CROSS
JET

Insulating Fibre
Explosion Pot
shown in section

MOVING CONTACT ARM

FIG. 4.1

plates are needed. The arc can also be magnetically controlled in an explosion pot by inserting insulated steel plates in the arc splitters.

Self-blast oil circuit breakers are made in single break units up to 66 kV, 2,500 MVA. For higher voltages and breaking capacities, multi-break units are made in which two or more sets of series connected contacts per phase are opened simultaneously. Difficulty may then be experienced in maintaining equal voltages across the contact gaps. This is dealt with later in this section.

The main disadvantage of the self-blast oil breaker is that, when interrupting currents considerably less than rated current, much less gas pressure is generated. This causes the arcing time to be long and inconsistent and is overcome in the following breaker.

Impulse Oil Circuit Breaker

In this type, oil is forced across the arc path by pressure produced in a mechanical pump connected to the circuit breaker operating linkage. This has three advantages:

(i) The pressure no longer depends on the magnitude of the current being broken.

(ii) The pump can be so arranged that the oil attains a high velocity before the contacts separate.

(iii) The volume of oil required and the overall size of the breaker are considerably reduced.

Multi-break units of this type are used at line voltages of over 250 kV and have breaking capacities of 2,500 MVA.

Air-blast Circuit Breakers

Up to 66 kV line, the oil breaker is simpler and initially costs less than the equivalent air-blast breaker. Oil breakers require more maintenance, however, particularly oil changes, the number of which depends on the frequency and severity of operation.

Air-blast breakers are more expensive initially, but above 66 kV line, high speed operation is very important. The air-blast breaker has a shorter arc duration time than oil, requires less maintenance and greatly reduces the fire risk.

In the air-blast breaker the arc is blown out with compressed air obtained from a reservoir supplied by a compressor. Thus this type of

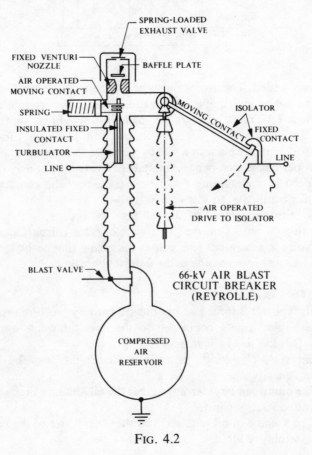

FIG. 4.2

breaker is similar to the oil impulse breaker in that the pressure and velocity of the insulating medium are independent of the magnitude of the current being broken.

The direction of the compressed air stream may be perpendicular, axial or radial with respect to the arc path.

66-kV Air-blast Circuit Breaker

A breaker employing firstly perpendicular and then axial air blasts is shown in figure 4.2.

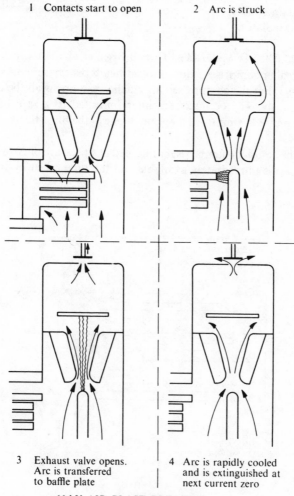

66-kV AIR BLAST BREAKER

FIG. 4.3

When the breaker is electromagnetically tripped, the blast valve opens and compressed air rushes through the turbulator. Some of the air is diverted to open the laterally-moving, spring-loaded contact. The exhaust valve then opens and the arc is driven through the venturi nozzle into an axial position between the baffle plate and the fixed arcing contact. Thus the arc is rapidly cooled in an un-ionized medium and is extinguished at the next current zero. This sequence is shown in more detail in figure 4.3.

Immediately after arc extinction, the air-operated isolator opens and the main contacts then reclose. The external circuit is reclosed by closing the isolator.

400-kV, 25,000-MVA, Air-blast Circuit Breaker

This breaker comprises 3 double blast-heads per phase symmetrically arranged so that the compressed air reaches and opens all the contacts simultaneously. The contacts are interconnected to give 6 breaks in series per phase. A simplified diagram of one of the blast-heads is shown in figure 4.4.

Air in the contact chamber is maintained at a pressure of 2070 kN/m^2. Thus the air is immediately available and the time taken by the air to

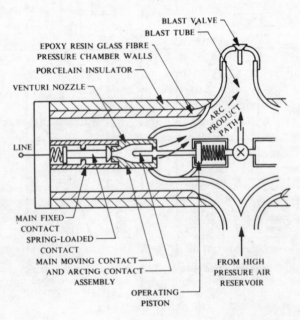

FIG. 4.4

traverse the tubes connecting the contact chambers to the air reservoir is eliminated.

When the breaker is tripped, the compressed air behind the operating piston is released through valve X to atmosphere. The arcing contact and the main moving contact to which it is attached move to the right. The main fixed and moving contacts part immediately, but the spring-loaded contact remains in contact with the main moving contact for the first part of the travel. By the time the spring-loaded contact stops, the main moving contact has acquired a high velocity giving a fast break. The arc is blown through the venturi nozzle onto the central arcing contact and is rapidly cooled. The arc products are blown up the blast-tube and out through the blast-valve which opens when the contacts first begin to move. After arc extinction, the contacts remain open so that an air-operated isolator is not required. The total operating time is about two and a half cycles on 400 kV, of which the arc extinction time is between a half and one cycle.

A 650-kV breaker similar to that above is being developed.

Sulphur Hexafluoride Gas-blast Circuit Breakers

Sulphur hexafluoride (SF_6) is an electronegative gas, that is the molecules of the gas attract free electrons. It is therefore a particularly good arc-quenching medium because it rapidly absorbs the free electrons produced in an arc. Thus at a current zero, the arc path is very quickly converted from a relatively good conductor to a very good insulator. The arc duration time is therefore very much shorter than that in air at the same pressure. Also the dielectric strength of SF_6 increases rapidly with increasing pressure making it a much better insulator when compressed than insulating oil or compressed air.

The following advantages are gained from using SF_6 rather than air:

(i) A reduced number of breaks in series per phase can be used for a given voltage rating.

(ii) Due to the short arc duration time, contact burning is very limited even for very high short circuit currents.

(iii) The arc products, consisting mostly of powder having good insulating properties, can be removed easily during maintenance inspection.

(iv) The gas blast is not discharged to the atmosphere so that operation is much quieter than that of an air blast breaker.

(v) SF_6 is chemically inert and stable, non-toxic and non-inflammable.

(vi) The SF_6 breaker is less bulky than the equivalent air blast breaker.

SF_6 has the following disadvantages:

(i) It is an expensive gas and therefore has to be filtered and re-used.

(ii) A small amount of make-up gas is required over long periods.

(iii) The gas must be pumped into a storage vessel whilst inspection and maintenance are carried out.

(iv) The gas liquefies at $1,520 \text{ kN/m}^2$ and $10°C$. Therefore small thermostatically controlled heaters are required on outdoor breakers to maintain the temperature of the high pressure reservoirs above $10°C$.

The smaller SF_6 breakers up to 500 MVA at 33 or 46 kV use the same principle as the impulse oil breaker. That is, a mechanical pump is used to force the gas through the arc path. The contact chamber is kept full of gas at 310 kN/m^2 gauge.

For voltages of 66 kV and above, and breaking capacities of 5,000 MVA and over, the contact chamber is kept full of gas at 276 kN/m^2 gauge and the arc is quenched by means of a gas-blast obtained from a reservoir maintained at $1,520 \text{ kN/m}^2$ gauge.

SF_6 breakers with breaking capacities up to 15,000 MVA at 230 kV have been in service in the USA since 1961. SF_6 breakers are being developed in the USA and in this country with breaking capacities of 35,000 MVA at 500 kV and 4,000 A.

The general arrangement of a 230-kV, 15,000 MVA, three-phase SF_6 breaker is shown in figure 4.5.

The approximate overall dimensions are 7·3 m long and 4 m wide by 5·5 m high.

Growth of Current when a Purely Inductive Circuit is Connected to a Sinusoidal Supply

In figure 4.6, Ψ indicates the instant in the voltage cycle at which the switch is closed.

At any instant, applied v is equal and opposite to induced voltage.

Hence
$$v = +L \cdot \frac{di}{dt} = V_m \cdot \sin(\omega t + \Psi),$$

or
$$\frac{di}{dt} = \frac{V_m}{L} \cdot \sin(\omega t + \Psi).$$

The solution of this differential equation is

$$i = -\frac{V_m}{\omega L} \cdot \cos(\omega t + \Psi) + A,$$

or
$$i = -I_m \cdot \cos(\omega t + \Psi) + A.$$

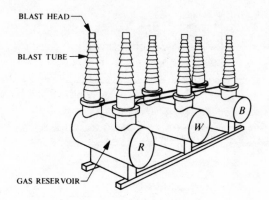

FIG. 4.5

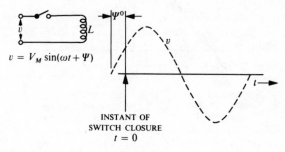

$v = V_M \sin(\omega t + \Psi)$

FIG. 4.6

At the instant of switch closure, $t = 0$, and $i = 0$,

therefore $0 = -I_m . \cos \Psi + A$, so that $A = I_m . \cos \Psi$.

If the switch is closed when $\Psi = 90°$, that is when $\dot{v} = V_m$, then

$A = I_m . \cos 90° = 0$.

Therefore

$i = -I_m . \cos(\omega t + 90°) + 0 = -I_m . \sin(\omega t + 180°) = I_m . \sin \omega t$.

Thus for this instant of switch closure, the current is sinusoidal as shown in figure 4.7.

If the switch is closed when $\Psi = 0°$, that is when $v = 0$, then

$A = I_m . \cos 0° = I_m$,

$i = -I_m . \cos(\omega t + 0°) + I_m = I_m + I_m . \sin(\omega t + 270°)$.

Thus for this instant of switch closure, the current has a steady d.c. component, I_m, and a sinusoidal component as shown in figure 4.8.

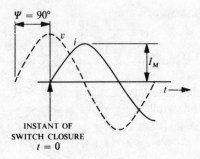

FIG. 4.7

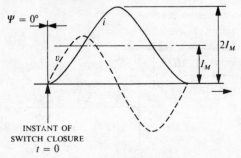

FIG. 4.8

If the switch is closed when $\Psi = 30°$, then $A = I_m \cdot \cos 30° = 0.866 \cdot I_m$, and we have

$$i = -I_m \cdot \cos(\omega t + 30°) + 0.866 \cdot I_m = 0.866 \cdot I_m + I_m \cdot \sin(\omega t + 300°).$$

Again, the current has d.c. and sinusoidal components, as shown in figure 4.9.

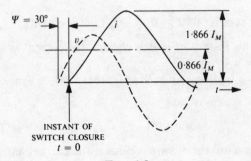

FIG. 4.9

Thus for any instant of switch closure, the current has two components:

(i) A steady d.c. component having a value between $+I_m$ and $-I_m$, depending on the instant in the voltage cycle at which the switch is closed.

(ii) A sinusoidal component of constant amplitude, I_m.

The closure of the switch in figure 4.6 is analogous to the occurrence of a short circuit in a supply system in which the resistance of the conductors is negligible. Therefore, the above theory can also be used to determine the S/C current waveform in such a system.

Growth of Current when a Circuit having Resistance and Inductance is Connected to a Sinusoidal Supply

Again, the current waveform depends on the instant in the voltage cycle at which the switch is closed.

The current now has an exponential d.c. component and a sinusoidal a.c. component.

In general, $i = I_m . \sin(\omega t + \Psi - \phi) + B\,e^{-Rt/L}$,

where
$$I_m = \frac{V_m}{\sqrt{[R^2 + (\omega L)^2]}},$$

Ψ = instant of switch closure in voltage cycle,

$$\cos\phi = \frac{R}{\sqrt{[R^2 + (\omega L)^2]}}.$$

At the instant of switch closure, $i = 0$ and $t = 0$, so that

$$0 = I_m . \sin(\Psi - \phi) + B \quad \text{and} \quad B = -I_m . \sin(\Psi - \phi).$$

Thus the exponential d.c. component is a maximu̇
$\Psi - \phi = 270°$, zero when $\Psi - \phi = 0°$ or $180°$, and a mini
$\Psi - \phi = 90°$.

The closure of the switch in figure 4.10 is analogous to t
of a short circuit in a supply system in which the res
conductors cannot be neglected.

Thus the degree of asymmetry of the S/C current wave
on the instant in the voltage cycle at which the short cir

In a high voltage supply system, the resistance of the
usually small compared with their inductive reactance
nearly $90°$. In such cases, the worst S/C current transien
Ψ is near $0°$, $180°$ or $360°$.

Example 4-1. A 50-Hz sinusoidal voltage of peak value 576 V is applied to a series circuit having a resistance of 0·1 Ω and an inductive reactance of 0·567 Ω.

Calculate the exponential and sinusoidal components of current for the following instants of switch closure in the voltage cycle and sketch the voltage and current waveforms for each case.

(a) $\Psi = 350°$. (b) $\Psi = 80°$. (c) $\Psi = 170°$. (d) $\Psi = 140°$.

$$Z = \sqrt{(0·1^2 + 0·567^2)} = 0·5757 \ \Omega.$$

$$\cos\phi = \frac{R}{Z} = \frac{0·1}{0·5757} = 0·1737 \text{ lagging.}$$

Hence $\phi = 80°$.

$$L = \frac{0·567}{314} = 0·001805 \text{ H}. \qquad I_m = \frac{V_m}{Z} = \frac{576}{0·5757} = 1{,}000 \text{ A}.$$

Let the sinusoidal component of the current be x amperes and the exponential component, y amperes.

(a) $x = I_m . \sin(\omega t + \Psi - \phi) = 1{,}000 . \sin(\omega t + 270°).$

$\quad B = -I_m . \sin(\Psi - \phi) = -1{,}000 . \sin 270° = +1{,}000 \text{ A}.$

$\quad y = B \, e^{-Rt/L} = 1{,}000 \, e^{-(0·1t)/(0·001085)} = 1{,}000 \, e^{-55·41t}.$

Calculating instantaneous values at quarter-cycle intervals:

t	0	0·005	0·01	0·015	0·02	0·025	0·03
x	$-1{,}000$	0	$+1{,}000$	0	$-1{,}000$	0	$+1{,}000$
y	$+1{,}000$	$+758$	$+575$	$+436$	$+330$	$+250$	$+190$
$x+y$	0	$+758$	$+1{,}575$	$+436$	-670	$+250$	$+1{,}190$

The voltage and current waveforms are shown in figure 4.10.

(b) $x = I_m . \sin(\omega t + \Psi - \phi) = 1{,}000 . \sin \omega t.$

$\quad B = -I_m . \sin(\Psi - \phi) = 0.$

$\quad y = B \, e^{-Rt/L} = 0.$

herefore the voltage and current waveforms are as shown in e 4.11.

$x = I_m . \sin(\omega t + \Psi - \phi) = 1{,}000 . \sin(\omega t + 90°).$

$B = -I_m . \sin(\Psi - \phi) = -1{,}000 . \sin 90° = -1{,}000 \text{ A}.$

$= B \, e^{-Rt/L} = -1{,}000 \, e^{-55·41t}.$

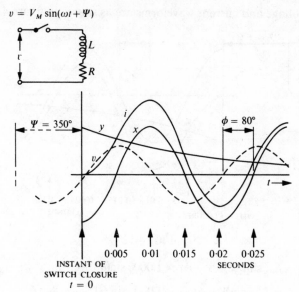

Fig. 4.10

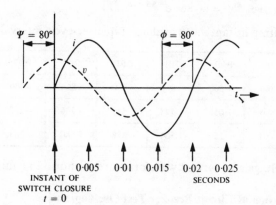

Fig. 4.11

Calculating instantaneous values at quarter-cycle intervals:

t	0	0·005	0·01	0·015	0·02	0·025	0·03
x	+1,000	0	−1,000	0	+1,000	0	−1,000
y	−1,000	−758	−575	−436	−330	−250	−190
$x+y$	0	−758	−1,575	−436	+670	−250	−1,190

The voltage and current waveforms are as shown in figure 4.12.

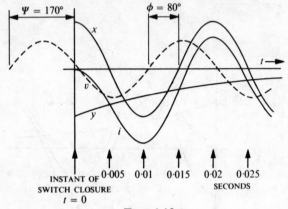

FIG. 4.12

(d) $x = I_m \cdot \sin(\omega t + \Psi - \phi) = 1{,}000 \cdot \sin(\omega t + 60°)$.

$B = -I_m \cdot \sin(\Psi - \phi) = -1{,}000 \cdot \sin 60° = -866\,\text{A}$.

$y = B\,e^{-Rt/L} = -866\,e^{-55 \cdot 41t}$.

Calculating instantaneous values at quarter-cycle intervals:

t	0	0·005	0·01	0·015	0·02	0·025	0·03
x	+866	+500	−866	−500	+866	+500	−866
y	−866	−656	−498	−378	−286	−217	−165
$x+y$	0	−156	−1,364	−878	+580	+283	−1,031

The voltage and current waveforms are as shown in figure 4.13.

Interpretation of Circuit Breaker Test Oscillograms

In figure 4.14, breaker B is the one being tested. If a BREAK test only is required, the contacts of breaker B are closed before the short circuit is connected by means of breaker A. The tripping of A is delayed in order to give B time to interrupt the fault. The resulting test oscillogram for one phase only is as shown in figure 4.15.

Graph 1 shows the variation of alternator phase voltage during the test. The effect of armature reaction has been greatly exaggerated. In practice, a significant reduction in alternator voltage is not usually noticeable until several cycles have elapsed. Therefore breakers must be designed to interrupt S/C currents at normal system voltage.

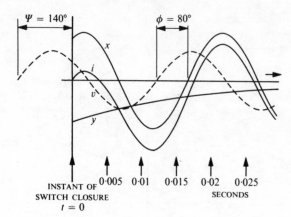

F<small>IG</small>. 4.13

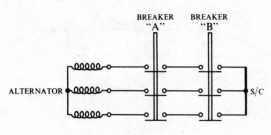

F<small>IG</small>. 4.14

If the phase angle of the circuit is 80°, then maximum asymmetry of the S/C current will result if the S/C is connected when $\Psi = 350°$, as in example 4-1(a). The S/C current waveform is then as shown in graph 2.

The time delay, t, between the instant of short circuit and that at which the breaker contacts separate depends on:

(i) the time taken for the relay to operate,

(ii) the time constant of the circuit breaker tripping solenoid,

(iii) the time taken to move the breaker contacts to a position where a gap is created between them.

t is usually between two and three cycles as in figure 4.15. On very high voltage systems every effort is being made to reduce this delay by improvement in both breaker and relay design. In breaker design, methods of reducing the time taken to move the contacts are being evolved. Also fully transistorized relays are being developed so as to eliminate the time taken in moving the mechanical parts of conventional relays.

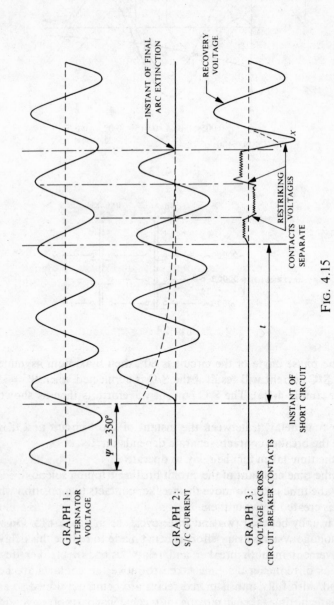

FIG. 4.15

Graph 3 shows the voltage between the breaker contacts which is zero until the instant of contact separation. In oil break, air blast, and gas blast breakers, the arc which is drawn out as the contacts separate burns with a fairly low voltage across it until the next current zero when the arc extinguishes. The arc will not restrike if the insulation strength between the contacts can be built up more rapidly than the rate at which the voltage between the contacts is rising. The number of restrikes which occur before this is achieved varies with the type of breaker.

The rate of increase of insulation strength between the contacts depends on:

(i) the speed and efficiency of replacement of the hot ionized oil, air or gas with cool un-ionized medium,

(ii) the speed of separation of the contacts,

(iii) the speed of deflection of the arc to a new, cold path longer than the straight line distance between the contacts.

After each arc extinction, there is an extremely rapid rise of voltage across the contacts. This voltage, called the *restriking voltage*, is a high frequency transient caused by the rapid redistribution of energy between the electromagnetic and electrostatic fields associated with the system. The theory of high frequency transients is more fully dealt with in Section 9.

The rate of rise of restriking voltage depends on the amount of resistance, inductance and capacitance in the circuit. An important part of the capacitance of the circuit is the capacitance between the circuit breaker contacts. As the contacts move further apart, the capacitance between them falls. Each time the arc extinguishes, the energy stored in the inductance of the circuit ($\frac{1}{2}LI^2$) is transferred to the capacitance ($\frac{1}{2}CV^2$). After each successive arc extinction, C is less so that V must be greater. Therefore the rate of rise of restriking voltage increases as shown in graph 3.

After each extinction, the voltage required to restrike the arc increases considerably and the voltage drops across successive arcs increase slightly.

The *recovery voltage* is the voltage that appears across the circuit breaker contacts after final arc extinction. It is less than the normal system voltage until the armature reaction effect ceases.

The power in the arc increases as the arc voltage drop increases. In oil circuit breakers, the heat thus generated increases the tank oil pressure and its value is then also recorded on the test oscillogram.

The circuit shown in figure 4.14 may also be used to perform a MAKE–BREAK test on breaker *B*. Breaker *A* is then closed before *B* and the resulting test oscillogram is distinguishable from that in figure 4.15 because there will now be a wave trace of alternator voltage across the circuit breaker contacts up to the instant of short circuit.

Effect of Circuit Power Factor

If the power factor of the circuit is unity, the voltage is zero when the current is zero and the arc is less likely to be restruck than when a zero power factor circuit is interrupted. In the latter case, the voltage is a maximum when the current is zero and the arc is then restruck much more easily. In figure 4.15, where the power factor is 0·174 lagging, it can be seen that the voltage is very near a peak value at each arc extinction. In practice, circuit breakers are usually tested at 0·1 power factor lagging.

Current Chopping

This occurs when the arc is extinguished before a natural current zero is reached. This phenomenon may occur in any circuit breaker but is more likely in impulse oil breakers and air blast and gas blast breakers. In these types, the arc is blown out as soon as possible with a jet of insulating medium having a pressure which is independent of the current being broken. If this current is considerably less than rated current, the arc may be blown out too soon. In the self-blast oil breaker, the jet pressure does depend on the current being interrupted and there is therefore less likelihood of arc extinction before a natural current zero.

When the current is 'chopped', it falls instantaneously to zero and the energy associated with the inductance of the system $(\frac{1}{2}LI^2)$ is very much more rapidly transferred to the capacitance than when the arc extinguishes at a natural current zero. This results in a corresponding increase in the rate of rise of restriking voltage.

If the arc does not restrike, a high frequency voltage surge is transmitted into the system. The amplitude of this surge may be up to twice that of the normal system voltage and the wavefront of the surge is usually so steep as to severely over-stress the system insulation.

The severity of the surge is attenuated if the arc restrikes almost instantaneously. This is more likely in air blast than in oil or gas blast breakers because the dielectric strength of air is less than that of oil or SF_6.

In most air blast breakers the arc may restrike several times before the next natural current zero. These short 'bursts' of current relieve the electric stress on the system insulation, generating several smaller voltage surges rather than one large surge.

In most impulse oil breakers and gas blast breakers, and in some air blast breakers, it is unlikely that the arc will restrike once it has been 'chopped'. In such cases, other means of reducing the stress on system insulation must be found. One method which can be used is resistance switching.

Resistance Switching

Above 66 kV, multi-break circuit breakers are used. In order to maintain equal voltages across the contact gaps, equal resistors in the order of 100 Ω are connected across each gap. These resistors are shorted out by the main contacts themselves when the breaker is closed. When the breaker opens, an auxiliary contact breaks the resistor current after the main arcs are extinguished.

The use of these resistors also has the following effects:

(i) The system power factor is improved during the main arcing period so that the main arcs are more easily extinguished. Operating oil, air or gas pressure, contact clearance and overall cost can thus be reduced.

(ii) The value to which the restriking voltage rises after main arc extinction is reduced since some of the electromagnetic energy of the system is dissipated in heat in the resistors.

(iii) The high frequency restriking voltage transient which occurs after final main arc extinction (marked 'x' in graph 3 of figure 4.15) is damped out by the resistors. If the correct value of resistor is used, this restriking transient can be given an exponential rather than oscillatory growth to the recovery voltage.

Capacitance Switching

As well as using resistors to equalize the voltages across the contact gaps of multi-break circuit breakers, capacitors may be used. These improve the circuit power factor and reduce the restriking voltage by increasing the capacitance between each pair of contacts.

A capacitor is connected permanently across each pair of circuit breaker contacts whilst the resistors are connected in series with auxiliary interruptors as previously described. Thus, when the circuit breaker is open, only the capacitors are left in circuit. These serve to equalise the distribution of voltage across the contact gaps under surge conditions whilst passing negligible current under normal conditions.

Determination of Breaking Current at the Instant of Contact Separation

In practice, tests must be performed to prove that a circuit breaker is capable of breaking asymmetrical as well as symmetrical S/C currents.

A typical S/C current oscillogram is shown in figure 4.16.

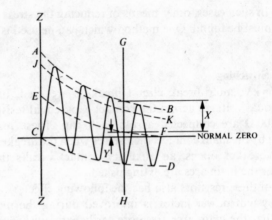

Fig. 4.16

In this oscillogram:

ZZ = instant at which short circuit occurs.

$ABCD$ = envelope of current wave.

EF = displacement of current wave zero line from normal zero line.

GH = instant of contact separation.

JK = r.m.s. value of the sinusoidal component of the current measured from EF.

X = peak value of sinusoidal component of current at instant of contact separation. (This is the distance between the points of intersection of AB with GH and of EF with GH.)

Y = d.c. component of current at instant of contact separation. This is the distance between the points of intersection of EF with GH and of the normal zero line with GH.)

A test is said to be asymmetrical if Y/X is greater than 0·5 and symmetrical if Y/X is less than 0·2. In tests on three-phase circuit breakers, there will be different degrees of asymmetry on each phase. A test is then only considered to be symmetrical if Y/X for each phase is less than 0·2.

For each phase, the breaking current is equal to $\sqrt{\left\{\left[\dfrac{X}{\sqrt{2}}\right]^2 + Y^2\right\}}$.

Determination of Making Current

The capacity of a circuit breaker in this respect is important because the breaker may accidentally be closed onto a short circuit when in service. Also, some breakers are automatically reclosed shortly after a short circuit in order to test whether the fault was of short duration and has cleared itself.

In a MAKE–BREAK test, the breaker under test is purposely closed onto a short circuit.

A typical S/C making current oscillogram is shown in figure 4.17.

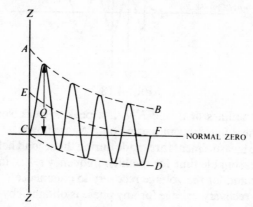

FIG. 4.17

In this oscillogram:

ZZ = instant at which breaker is closed onto short circuit.

$ABCD$ = envelope of current wave.

EF = displacement of current wave zero line from normal zero line.

Q = peak current made. (This is the *major* peak value of S/C current measured from the normal zero line.)

In some tests, a minor peak value occurs before the first major peak. In such cases, the minor peak is ignored.

Determination of Recovery Voltage

The recovery voltage is an indication of the severity of the test.

The recovery voltage will be less than the normal system voltage due to the voltage drops caused by armature reaction, leakage reactance and resistance in the alternator.

A typical recovery voltage oscillogram is shown in figure 4.18.

In this oscillogram, line LL is drawn through the point of final arc extinction, this point being determined from an examination of the three corresponding current waveforms.

Lines MM and NN are drawn at half-cycle intervals from LL.

The peak to peak recovery voltages ($= V_1$, V_2, etc.) are measured during the second complete half-cycle after final arc extinction, that

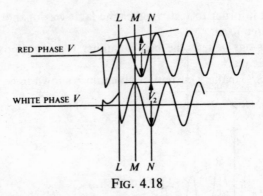

RED PHASE V

WHITE PHASE V

FIG. 4.18

is, between the lines MM and NN. If a peak to peak voltage occurs exactly on these lines, it is measured on NN, as shown.

The above measurements are made during the second half-cycle so as to allow a reasonable time for the high frequency restriking transients to disappear and for the voltage recovery to commence.

The r.m.s. recovery voltage for any phase is obtained by dividing the peak to peak value by $2\sqrt{2}$.

Average recovery line voltage is $\dfrac{(V_1 + V_2 + V_3) \times \sqrt{3}}{2\sqrt{2} \times 3}$, for a three-phase breaker.

Example 4-2. The portions of the test oscillograms shown in figure 4.19 were obtained during a make–break test on a circuit breaker.

Estimate:
(a) the line voltage rating of the breaker,
(b) the peak making current for the red phase only,
(c) the a.c. and d.c. components of the breaking current at the instant of contact separation for the white phase only. Hence determine whether the test is symmetrical or asymmetrical and estimate the breaking current.

(a) Peak to peak phase system voltage $= A = 18\,\text{kV}$.

R.m.s. phase system voltage $= \dfrac{18}{2\sqrt{2}} = 6\cdot35\,\text{kV}$.

Line voltage rating of breaker $= \sqrt{3} \times 6\cdot35 = \mathbf{11\,kV}$.
(b) Peak making current $= B = \mathbf{26\cdot8\,kA}$.
(c) a.c. component of breaking current $= X = 19\,\text{kA}$.
    d.c. component of breaking current $= Y = 11\,\text{kA}$.

$\dfrac{Y}{X} = \dfrac{11}{19} = 0\cdot578$, therefore the test is asymmetrical.

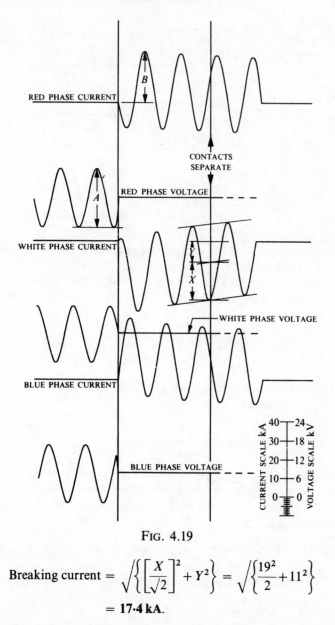

FIG. 4.19

$$\text{Breaking current} = \sqrt{\left\{\left[\frac{X}{\sqrt{2}}\right]^2 + Y^2\right\}} = \sqrt{\left\{\frac{19^2}{2} + 11^2\right\}}$$

$$= 17{\cdot}4 \text{ kA}.$$

Example 4-3. The portions of the circuit breaker oscillograms shown in figure 4.20 were obtained towards the end of a break test.

Estimate the r.m.s. recovery voltage for each phase and hence the average recovery line voltage.

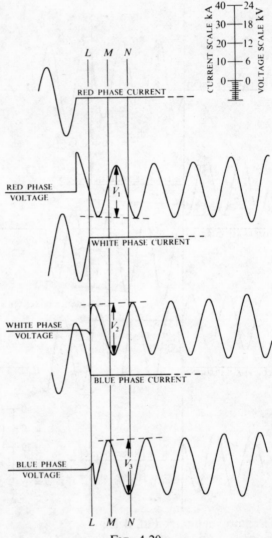

FIG. 4.20

R.m.s. recovery voltage for red phase

$$= \frac{V_1}{2\sqrt{2}} = \frac{16\cdot5}{2\sqrt{2}} = \mathbf{5\cdot84\,kV}.$$

R.m.s. recovery voltage for white phase

$$= \frac{V_2}{2\sqrt{2}} = \frac{16\cdot2}{2\sqrt{2}} = \mathbf{5\cdot73\,kV}.$$

R.m.s. recovery voltage for blue phase

$$= \frac{V_3}{2\sqrt{2}} = \frac{17\cdot4}{2\sqrt{2}} = \textbf{6·15 k V.}$$

Average recovery line voltage

$$= \frac{(5\cdot84 + 5\cdot73 + 6\cdot15) \times \sqrt{3}}{3} = \textbf{10·2 k V.}$$

EXAMPLES 4

1. Sketch an arc-control device suitable for use in a large, self-blast oil circuit breaker. Describe, in detail, the process of arc extinction.

State the essential differences between a self-blast oil circuit breaker and an impulse oil circuit breaker.

Briefly describe the process of arc extinction in a 500-MVA air-break breaker.

Compare air-break and oil circuit breakers on the scores of maintenance and safety.

2. With the aid of sketches showing constructional details, describe the operation of:

(a) A 66-kV, air-blast circuit breaker in which the contact chamber is not maintained at pressure.

(b) A 400-kV, air-blast circuit breaker employing full air pressure in both the open and closed positions.

Comment on any important differences in the designs of these two breakers.

3. Compare, with reasons, the air-blast and the oil circuit breaker on the scores of:

(a) suitability for very high voltage working,

(b) suitability for very high breaking capacities,

(c) suitability for frequent operation,

(d) performance on light loads,

(e) initial cost.

4. State the advantages gained from using compressed sulphur hexafluoride instead of compressed air in a blast circuit breaker.

What disadvantages are associated with the use of SF_6?

5. A 50-Hz sinusoidal voltage of peak value 500 V is applied to a series circuit having a resistance of $0\cdot1\ \Omega$ and an inductive reactance of $1\ \Omega$.

Calculate the instant of switch closure in the voltage cycle for which the exponential component of current will have:

(a) its greatest positive value,

(b) its greatest negative value,

(c) zero value.

Assuming that the switch is closed at the instant which gives condition (a), calculate the sinusoidal, exponential and total values of current at the instant 0·01 second after switch closure.

(Answers (a) **354·3°**, (b) **174·3°**, (c) **84·3° or 264·3°, 500 A, 365 A, 865 A.**)

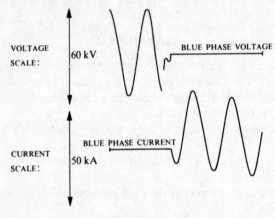

FIG. 4.21

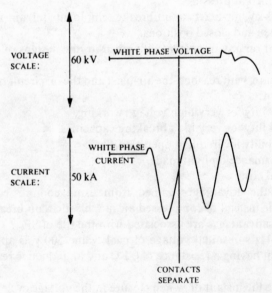

FIG. 4.22

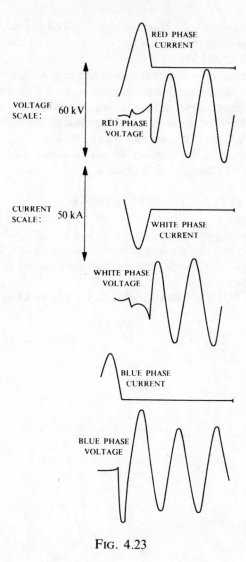

FIG. 4.23

6. Briefly discuss the significance of the following terms with reference to circuit breaker performance:
   (a) rate of rise of restriking voltage,
   (b) rate of rise of insulation strength between the contacts,
   (c) power factor of circuit to be interrupted,
   (d) current chopping,
   (e) resistance switching.

7. Using the test oscillogram shown in figure 4.21, estimate the peak making current and the line voltage rating of the circuit breaker.
(Answers **30 kA, 33 kV.**)

8. Using the test oscillogram shown in figure 4.22, estimate the a.c. and d.c. components of breaking current at the instant of contact separation. Hence determine whether the test is symmetrical or asymmetrical and estimate the breaking current.
(Answers **20 kA, 13·75 kA, asymmetrical, 19·7 kA.**)

9. Using the test oscillogram shown in figure 4.23, estimate the r.m.s. recovery voltage for each phase and hence the average recovery line voltage.
(Answers **19·1 kV, 18·7 kV, 18·9 kV, 32·8 kV.**)

10. Using the test oscillogram shown in figure 4.19, estimate:
(a) The making current for the white and blue phases only.
(b) The a.c. and d.c. components of breaking current at the instant of contact separation, and hence the breaking current, for the red and blue phases only.
(Answers (a) **36·5 kA, 33 kA**, (b) **20 kA, 4·5 kA, 14·8 kA, 20 kA, 8 kA, 16·3 kA.**)

5

Underground Cables

Conductor Materials

Copper is the most common. It must be at least 99·5 per cent pure to prevent chemical action. The conductors are usually stranded to improve flexibility.

The most common way of jointing cable conductors is to insert the ends into a metal tube and solder the whole solid. This is a simple process with copper conductors and, during recent years, confidence has been growing in the techniques used for soldering aluminium.

There has therefore been a steady increase in the use of aluminium as a cable conductor. It is lighter and cheaper than copper, the density of aluminium being about one-third that of copper. Aluminium has a lower conductivity, however (about 60 per cent of that of copper), so that a larger cross-sectional area of aluminium is required for the same transmission efficiency.

Both solid and stranded aluminium conductors are in present use, the former being cheaper and easier to joint but less flexible than the latter.

Insulating Materials

Impregnated paper is the most common. It may be made from wood pulp or rag or manila hemp. The latter is derived from the leaves of the manila plant which grows mainly in the Philippines.

The fibres in any paper have a lower electrical resistance and dielectric strength than the remainder and should therefore be as short as possible. Manila fibres are shorter than those of wood or rag so that manila paper is preferred for use in cables. The paper is wrapped around the conductors in concentric layers.

Impregnation of the paper with mineral oil greatly improves its dielectric strength. Typical values of breakdown stress are 70 kV peak/cm before impregnation and 600 kV peak/cm after impregnation.

Resin is often added to the impregnating oil to increase its viscosity and so reduce the drainage from the upper regions of the paper which occurs at working temperatures.

The relative permittivity of impregnated paper is in the order of three.

In terms of their electrical and thermal properties, the new synthetic materials, such as polyvinylchloride (PVC), and polythene, have few technical advantages over impregnated paper when used for insulating underground cables in domestic and commercial power distribution systems. Improvements in the techniques used to impregnate the paper have kept pace with the development of other insulating materials.

In power distribution systems used in industry, however, the picture is entirely different. Here, armoured PVC insulated cables have virtually eliminated impregnated paper, varnished cambric, and vulcanized india-rubber for the following reasons:

(a) PVC has a more attractive appearance, is lighter in weight and easier to handle.

(b) PVC is non-hygroscopic and is therefore unaffected by the ingress of moisture at terminations. These need not therefore be sealed except in very adverse conditions.

(c) PVC is flame retardant and has a greater ability to withstand mechanical damage than paper. Thus PVC is more suitable for use in hazardous situations such as mines and quarries.

One serious disadvantage in using thermoplastics such as PVC is that the maximum permissible operating temperature is 70°C compared with 80°C for paper. This is not so important in industrial applications however, because currents can be more accurately determined and overload conditions more precisely controlled than in public supply systems.

By the addition of special plasticizers and stabilizers, PVC can be worked up to 85°C but this leaves absolutely no overload margin. Butyl rubber is more expensive than PVC but can be run continuously at 85°C and sustain overloads in addition. This type of cable insulation is used for special applications where thermal difficulties occur, such as aboard ships and in high power electrical test installations.

Sheathing and Armouring Materials

Since paper insulation is hygroscopic, a lead or aluminium sheath is extruded over it to prevent the ingress of moisture.

In situations where mechanical damage is likely, armouring is also required. Metal armouring cannot be applied directly over the lead because the armouring would bite into the lead, particularly when the cable is bent. A bedding of hessian or fabric tape is therefore first applied over the lead. The armouring may consist of two layers of steel tape so wound that the upper layer covers the joint in the lower layer. A more flexible cable results, however, if stranded steel wire armouring is used instead. For small cables, a single layer may suffice, but for larger cables a double layer of small diameter steel wires is more flexible than a single layer of larger wires. An outer serving of hessian or jute dressed with a preservative bituminous compound is applied over the armouring.

In conditions where steel armouring is unnecessary, the lead sheath is usually reinforced with copper, bronze, or brass tape. Outer servings of PVC, self-vulcanized rubber and hessian tapes are then applied.

In conditions where a conducting sheath is unnecessary, a PVC sheath may give sufficient mechanical protection. PVC sheaths are also used, instead of a hessian serving, as an outer protective covering over aluminium sheaths or stranded steel wire armouring.

Types of Cable

A cross-section through the famous Ferranti 11-kV cable is shown in figure 5.1.

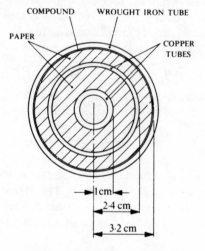

FIG. 5.1

This cable was in use in Deptford, London from 1890 to 1933 and was the first concentric, impregnated paper insulated cable. The insulated conductors were pushed into wrought iron pipes which were then filled with compound. The cable was made in short lengths of 6 m and jointed mechanically using unskilled labour.

In contrast, a cross-section through a modern 440-V, three-phase, four-wire, distribution cable is shown in figure 5.2.

Each conductor has a cross-sectional area of 1.94 cm^2.

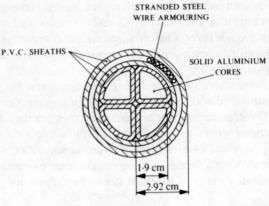

Fig. 5.2

A cross-section through an 11-kV, single-core, paper insulated, lead-sheathed cable is shown in figure 5.3.

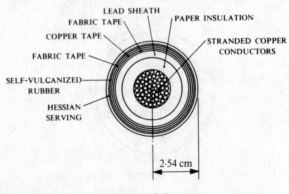

Fig. 5.3

The cross-sectional area of the core is 2·58 cm².

A serious difficulty which occurs with this type of cable is due to the inelasticity of the lead sheath. When the cable is on load, the insulation and lead sheath expand, but when the cable cools the sheath does not return to its original dimensions. During several years of heating and cooling cycles, voids are formed between the layers of paper.

Once a void is formed, the voltage across it is greater than that across an equivalent thickness of paper. This is because the relative permittivity of the void is less than that of the paper. The void and paper layers may be considered as series connected capacitors. Since the void has a lower capacitance than an equivalent thickness of paper, the void has a higher voltage across it.

In time, the voltage across the void will be sufficient to ionize the gas trapped within it. The void is then made larger and other voids are formed by the heat generated in the arc. During the life of the cable, therefore, this cumulative process causes a gradual deterioration of insulation, leading eventually to complete breakdown.

The formation of voids can be prevented or delayed in several ways. In the above cable, the reinforcing copper tape helps to reduce the inelasticity of the lead sheath. For higher voltages, the cable may be filled with insulating oil also, as shown in figure 5.4.

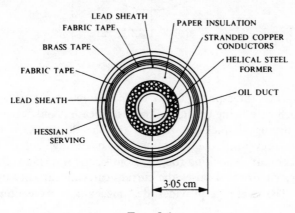

FIG. 5.4

The cable shown operates at 22 kV and the cross-sectional area of the annular conducting core is 2·58 cm². A pressure of 35 to 70 kN/m² is maintained inside the cable by means of oil reservoirs along the route. Any expansions or contractions of the cable insulation simply result in changes in level in these reservoirs.

The oil pressure makes the formation of voids less likely, and any which do form are filled with oil having a high relative permittivity. Because of this, the long-time breakdown strength of an oil-filled cable is roughly twice that of the equivalent paper-insulated solid cable. Also some benefit is derived from the fact that the oil acts as a coolant. The disadvantages of oil-filling are higher initial cost and more complicated jointing.

Another method of preventing cable breakdown due to void formation is to place the cable in a steel pipe containing nitrogen gas at about 1,380 kN/m², as shown in figure 5.5.

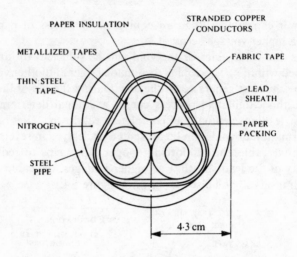

FIG. 5.5

A three-core, three-phase, 66-kV cable is shown, the cross-sectional area of each core being 0·97 cm². The lead sheath is only about three-quarters the usual thickness so that the sheath acts as a pressure membrane, preventing the formation of voids during cooling. The gas acts as a coolant. Gas-filling roughly doubles the working voltage of a cable of given size and raises the current-carrying capacity by about 1·5 times. The steel pipe provides ideal mechanical protection for the cable.

Alternatively, the compressed nitrogen may be contained in a space left between the lead sheath and the paper insulation. The pressure is then maintained by the subdivision of this space into a series of gas cushions by means of helical spacers. If this type of cable is cut for jointing or accidentally damaged, the gas is lost from a short length only. The gas pressure need not be maintained from an external source, nor is an outer steel pipe required.

Lower voltage, three-phase cables may be of the belted type as shown in figure 5.6.

A three-core, three-phase, 6·6-kV cable is shown, the cross-sectional area of each core being 0·97 cm². The cable derives its name from the use of an insulating belt of impregnated paper which surrounds all three cores.

A serious difficulty which occurs with this type of cable is due to the distribution of the electric stress throughout the insulation. The electric field set up when this type of cable is connected to a three-phase supply is as shown in figure 5.7.

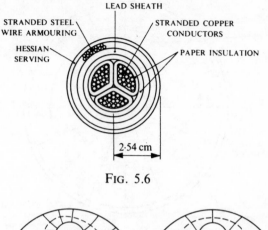

FIG. 5.6

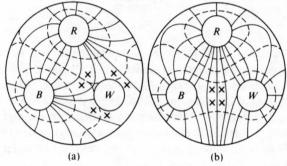

(a)   (b)

FIG. 5.7

Figure (a) is drawn for the instant in the cycle when $v_R = +0.866V_m$, $v_W = 0$, and $v_B = -0.866V_m$.

Figure (b) is drawn for the instant in the cycle when $v_R = +V_m$, and v_W and v_B each $= -0.5V_m$.

In both figures, the dotted lines represent lines of equipotential and the full lines represent lines of electric field or stress. It can be seen that the shape of the electric field changes from instant to instant. This is quite different from the field set up in a single-core lead-sheathed cable which is as shown in figure 5.8.

Here the lines of equipotential are concentric circles and the lines of electric stress are radial. The electric field does not change its shape but merely pulsates and reverses.

The electrical resistance of paper insulation is much greater across the layers than along them. This is because a lattice of lower resistance paths is formed along each surface by the fibres in the paper. The breakdown stress is also greater across the layers than along them for

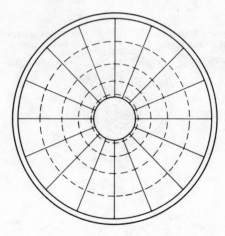

FIG. 5.8

the same reason. Thus paper insulation is used to best advantage if the lines of equipotential are coincident with the layer surfaces and the lines of electric stress are radial as in figure 5.8.

If the lines of stress are tangential to the paper layers as in the areas marked X in figure 5.7, then there is a tendency for leakage currents to flow along the layers. The heat thus generated may lead to the formation of voids and lead to breakdown. For this reason, the belted cable is not used at voltages higher than 11 kV line.

Tangential stresses can be eliminated by screening each core separately as in the Hochstadter or 'H' type cable shown in figure 5.9.

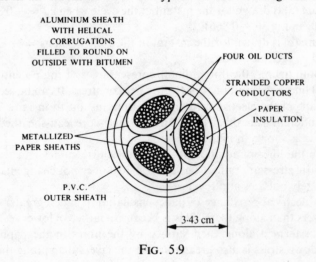

ALUMINIUM SHEATH
WITH HELICAL
CORRUGATIONS
FILLED TO ROUND ON
OUTSIDE WITH BITUMEN

FOUR OIL DUCTS

STRANDED COPPER
CONDUCTORS

PAPER
INSULATION

METALLIZED
PAPER SHEATHS

P.V.C.
OUTER SHEATH

3·43 cm

FIG. 5.9

A three-core, three-phase, 33-kV, oil-filled cable is shown, the cross-sectional area of each core being 1·94 cm². The metallized paper sheaths are in electrical contact with each other and with the overall aluminium sheath. The cable is therefore equivalent to three single-core cables, the stress in each being radial.

The metallized paper sheaths are perforated to enable the oil continuously to impregnate the paper insulation.

Conductor cores of oval section are used to increase the radius and hence reduce the stress at the points where the cores are closest to each other or to the sheath. The aluminium outer sheath is corrugated to improve its flexibility and to increase its cooling surface area.

A similar cable using an outer lead sheath is shown in figure 5.10.

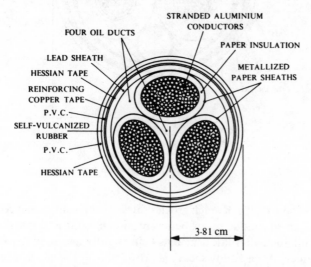

FIG. 5.10

A three-core, three-phase, 33-kV, oil-filled, 'H' type cable is shown, the cross-sectional area of each core being 3·88 cm². The lead sheath and its reinforcing copper tape are protected against corrosion by PVC and rubber sheaths as well as by the usual hessian serving.

An 'H' type, oil-filled cable for 132 kV line is shown in figure 5.11.

The cross-sectional area of each core is 3·88 cm². The outer strands are shaped to create a smoother surface and thus reduce the stress.

Three-core, gas-filled cables are also of the 'H' type, as shown in figure 5.5.

For 275 kV line and above, three separate single-core cables are used. The construction of each cable is similar to that shown in figure 5.4

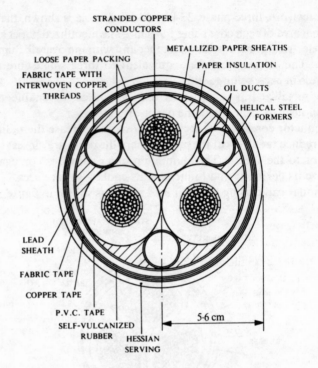

STRANDED COPPER
CONDUCTORS

METALLIZED PAPER SHEATHS

PAPER INSULATION

LOOSE PAPER PACKING

FABRIC TAPE WITH
INTERWOVEN COPPER
THREADS

OIL DUCTS

HELICAL STEEL
FORMERS

LEAD
SHEATH

FABRIC TAPE

COPPER TAPE

P.V.C. TAPE
SELF-VULCANIZED
RUBBER

HESSIAN
SERVING

5·6 cm

FIG. 5.11

except, of course, that a much greater thickness of insulation is required. Six compacted conductor segments are laid up round a 16 mm diameter central oil duct, alternate segments being lightly insulated to minimize 'skin' effects. A lead alloy sheath is extruded over the paper insulation. The sheath is reinforced with bronze tapes and protected overall by an extruded black PVC sheath.

For voltages above 275 kV line, difficulties are encountered due to the increasing magnitude of the power losses through the cable insulation. For runs longer than 40 km, it is necessary to use special insulating materials which cut down these losses by a large factor.

For 400 kV line, research on the development of a single-core cable using lapped polythene tape under gas pressure has reached an advanced stage. An attempt is also being made to develop an 'all-gas' insulated cable in which the conductor is supported inside a steel pipe by insulating spacer discs. Insulation is then provided by filling the pipe with such gases as nitrogen or sulphur hexafluoride, or mixtures of the two, under a pressure of several atmospheres.

Water-cooled Cables

The amount of current that can be passed through a cable is limited by the rise in temperature of the conductors and insulation. One way of increasing the current-carrying capacity is by forced water cooling. The water is pumped through pipes laid next to the cables. It is then cooled in a radiator, with or without forced-draught cooling, and recirculated.

In most cases, water-cooling is only economically worth considering for voltages of 275 kV line and above. There are, however, some special circumstances in which low voltage, water-cooled cables are used. For example, as the rating of alternators increases, it becomes more difficult to provide a satisfactory connection between the alternator and its transformer. For very large currents, it has been found that internally water-cooled cables are less expensive and less bulky than the conventional copper bus-bars.

An internally water-cooled cable is shown in figure 5.12.

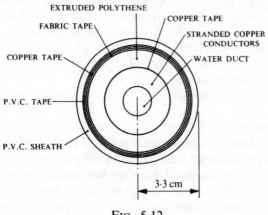

FIG. 5.12

The cable shown is a 13·8-kV, single-core cable, the cross-sectional area of the core being 6·45 cm². The conductors are laid up on a helical former and bound with copper tape. The polythene layer is extruded over this and is coated with colloidal graphite to improve the flexibility of the cable. The usual lappings of fabric, copper, and PVC tapes are protected by an overall extruded PVC sheath.

Two 40-m runs of three single-core cables of this size are in service in Bankside Power Station. The cables are rated at 6,000 A/phase and are used to connect a 120-MW alternator to its transformer.

A similar cable, having a core cross-sectional area of 12.9 cm^2, is in service in a test bay at the Trafford Park Works of G.E.C. Ltd. Here there is a 28-m run of three single-core cables rated at 15,000 A/phase and 25 kV phase. 64 litres of water per minute at 345 kN/m^2 are pumped through each cable.

Direct Current Cables
A given thickness of insulation can withstand a higher constant voltage stress than alternating stress. Therefore d.c. cables can be made smaller and cheaper than a.c. cables. A further point in favour of the introduction of d.c. links into an existing extensive supply system is that they sectionalize the network and thus reduce the short circuit current and MVA levels.

There are, however, definite drawbacks to the use of d.c. Firstly, the costs of conversion from a.c. to d.c. and back again are so high that for short distances, d.c. cannot compete economically with a.c. For a load of 1,200 MW the 'break-even' distance is between 40 and 57 km for a cable and about 1,450 km for an overhead line. Secondly, d.c. lends itself more readily to point-to-point transmission than to a network. For example, if a d.c. line is 'tapped' at some intermediate point, considerable difficulties arise from the inherent nature of the valve converters used at each end. At present, therefore, all existing and planned d.c. links are two-terminal only.

High voltage d.c. transmission is also discussed in Section 3.

Superconduction
A more radical approach to the problem of improving cable performance is possible with the superconducting cable.

Many metals and alloys, when cooled to a temperature approaching absolute zero, become superconducting or capable of carrying an electric current without any resistive losses whatever. When materials like lead or tin are made superconducting, the current is carried only on the surface of the material. Such materials are equally suitable for a.c. or d.c. transmission.

With the more recently prepared alloys of niobium and tin, or zirconium, however, it has been possible to achieve superconducting direct current distribution throughout the cross-sectional area of the conductor. The value of current which can be carried is then limited by the magnetic field set up inside the conductor. Nevertheless, direct current densities in the order of $100,000 \text{ A/cm}^2$ are possible. On alternating current, however, the density is much lower due to the generation in the conductor of an appreciable amount of heat.

An attempt is being made to develop a superconducting cable using liquid helium as the cooling agent, surrounded by liquid nitrogen as the heat insulating medium. At present, however, the technical difficulties are immense and the running costs of such a low temperature installation are very high.

Inductance of a Concentric Cable

Consider a cable of the type shown in figure 5.1.

Let each conductor carry I amperes in opposite directions,

the external radius of the inner conductor = r m,

the internal radius of the outer conductor = R m,

the length of the cable = l m, as shown in figure 5.13.

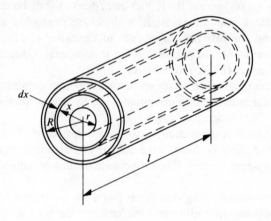

FIG. 5.13

Consider an elementary cylinder of radius x metres and radial thickness dx metres.

The length of the path of the magnetic flux in this cylinder = $2\pi x$ metres and the cross-sectional area of the path of this flux = $dx.l$ m^2.

Let the flux density at radius $x = B$ Wb/m^2 and the flux set up in the elementary cylinder = $d\Phi$ Wb, then $d\Phi = B.dx.l$ Wb.

Let the magnetizing force at radius $x = H$ A.t/m, then

$$H = I/2\pi x \text{ A.t/m.}$$

But $$B = \mu_0 H \text{ Wb/m}^2,$$

and $$\frac{d\Phi}{dx.l} = \frac{\mu_0 I}{2\pi x} \text{ Wb/m}^2,$$

so that
$$d\Phi = \frac{\mu_0 Il}{2\pi x}. dx \text{ Wb.}$$

Therefore total flux linkages $= \frac{\mu_0 Il}{2\pi}. \int_r^R \frac{1}{x}. dx = 2.10^{-7}. Il. \log_e \frac{R}{r}.$

But inductance (L henrys) = flux linkages/ampere,

which is
$$L = 2.10^{-7}. l. \log_e R/r \text{ H.}$$

or
$$L = 0.2 \log_e R/r \text{ mH/km.}$$

This expression ignores the inductances due to the fluxes set up inside the conductors themselves. Both of these are negligible at high frequencies and the internal inductance of the outer conductor is also negligible at 50 Hz. An expression for the internal inductance of the inner conductor will be derived later.

There is no magnetic field set up outside the outer conductor because the m.m.f.'s due to the two conductors are equal and opposite in this region.

The above expression cannot easily be applied to the single-core, lead-sheathed cable because of the difficulty in determining the correct value of the upper limit R. The inductance of such a cable will depend on:

(i) The amount of magnetic screening afforded by the lead sheath. This depends on the radius and thickness of the lead sheath and the current being carried by the conductor.

(ii) The amount of armouring and whether it is of a ferrous material.

(iii) The proximity of the cable to other conductors and ferrous objects.

Taking the extreme case of a single conductor isolated in air, $R =$ infinity so that the inductance is theoretically infinite. In practice, of course, there is usually at least one other parallel conductor in the vicinity. The inductance of parallel conductors is dealt with in Section 7.

Internal Inductance

Consider the solid conductor shown in figure 5.14.

If uniform current distribution throughout the cross section of the conductor is assumed, then the current flowing in the inner shaded portion is $(x^2/r^2). I$ amperes.

This current sets up the flux in the elementary cylinder shown.

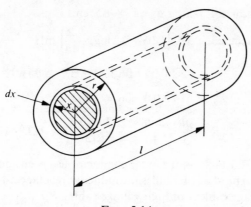

FIG. 5.14

Substituting this new value of current into the previous expression for $d\Phi$:

$$d\Phi = \frac{\mu_0 I x l}{2\pi r^2}.dx \text{ Wb.}$$

This flux does not link with the whole conductor, but only with x^2/r^2 of it. Therefore

$$\text{total flux linkages} = \frac{\mu_0 I l}{2\pi r^4}.\int_0^r x^3.dx = \tfrac{1}{2}.10^{-7}.I.l,$$

and $\qquad L = \tfrac{1}{2}.10^{-7}.l \text{ H.}$

or $\qquad L = 0.05 \text{ mH/km.}$

Thus the internal inductance is independent of conductor radius.

The internal inductance of a stranded conductor is greater than that of a solid conductor. This is due mainly to the helical paths of the currents in the strands. The effect of stranding is illustrated in the following table:

Number of strands	solid	61	37	19	7	3
Internal inductance (mH/km)	0.05	0.052	0.053	0.056	0.064	0.078

Example 5-1. The solid inner conductor of a concentric cable has a diameter of 2.28 cm and the outer conductor has an internal radius of 2.28 cm.

Calculate the total inductance of 32.2 km of this cable.

Compare the inductive reactance at 50 Hz with the resistance of the inner conductor, taking $\rho = 1.78\ \mu\Omega$. cm.

$$\text{Total inductance} = 32.2\left(0.05 + 0.2 \log_e \frac{2.28}{1.14}\right) \text{ mH}$$

$$= 32.2(0.05 + 0.1386) \text{ mH} = \textbf{6.06 mH}.$$

$$X_L = 314 \times 0.00606 = 1.9\ \Omega.$$

$$R = \frac{\rho l}{a} = \frac{1.78 \times 32.2 \times 10^5}{10^6 \times \pi \times 1.14^2} = 1.4\ \Omega.$$

When the resistance of the outer conductor has been added, the total resistance will be about 1·5 times the inductive reactance. This is typical of a low voltage cable. For high voltage cables, R/r will be greater and the inductive reactance will be higher than the total resistance.

Skin Effect

On d.c., the current density is uniform throughout the cross section of the conductor. This is not true on a.c.

Consider a solid conductor to be made up of a number of concentric cylinders, each carrying a portion of the alternating current. Each cylinder will set up its own alternating flux. The outermost cylinder will be cut by the external fluxes of the other cylinders only. A cylinder nearer the centre will be cut by the internal and external fluxes of the cylinders outside it and by the external fluxes of the cylinders inside it. Thus the inner cylinders have a higher inductance and reactance than the outer cylinders and this causes most of the current to flow in the outer cylinders. This phenomenon is known as the 'skin effect'. It causes the resistance of a solid conductor to be greater on a.c. than on d.c. Since inductive reactance is directly proportional to frequency, the skin effect is much greater at high frequencies than at 50 Hz.

For a steel-cored, aluminium conductor of the type used in overhead lines, hardly any current will flow in the steel due to its higher resistivity and to the intensification of the internal magnetic field by the high permeability of the steel.

In an underground cable, the central conductor strands are sometimes omitted since they carry little current. The channel thus formed may then be used as an oil or water duct as in figures 5.4 and 5.12.

The skin effect also depends on the conductor diameter, as shown in the following table:

Diameter of solid copper conductor (cm)	< 1·3	1·9	2·5	3·8
Increase in resistance from 0 to 50 Hz (%)	0	2·5	8	25

Stranding the conductor considerably reduces the skin effect.

The value of 0·05 mH/km for the internal inductance of a solid conductor is based on the assumption that the current density is uniform throughout the cross section of the conductor. Due to the skin effect, however, more current flows in the outer regions so that the current flowing in the shaded portion of the conductor in figure 5.14 is less than $(x^2/r^2)I$ amperes. The internal inductance is therefore slightly less than 0·05 mH/km at 50 Hz, and much less at higher frequencies.

Capacitance of a Single-core Cable

Consider a length of one metre of the cable shown in figure 5.15.

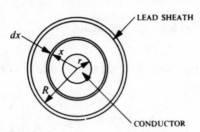

FIG. 5.15

Let the dimensions be in metres and a potential difference of V volts between the conductor and sheath give charges of $+q$ and $-q$ coulombs respectively.

The number of lines of electric flux emanating radially from the conductor is q.

At radius x, the surface area of a concentric cylindrical element is equal to $2\pi x \cdot l$ m^2.

The electric flux density at radius $x = D = q/2\pi x$ coulombs/m^2.

But the absolute permittivity of the insulation $= \varepsilon = D/E$, where E is the electric force or electric stress or potential gradient measured in volts/metre, at radius x.

Hence
$$E = \frac{q}{2\pi x \varepsilon} \text{ V/m.} \tag{1}$$

Let the potential gradient at radius $x = dV/dx$,

then
$$V = \int_r^R \frac{q}{2\pi x \varepsilon} \cdot dx = \frac{q}{2\pi \varepsilon} \cdot \log_e \frac{R}{r} \text{ V.} \tag{2}$$

The capacitance per metre length $= C = \dfrac{q}{V} = \dfrac{2\pi \varepsilon}{\log_e(R/r)}$ F.

But $\varepsilon = \varepsilon_0 \varepsilon_r$, where $\varepsilon_0 = 1/(36\pi . 10^9)$, and ε_r = the relative permittivity of the insulation.

Hence
$$C = \frac{10^{-9} . \varepsilon_r}{18 . \log_e(R/r)} \text{ F/m,}$$

or
$$C = \frac{\varepsilon_r}{18 \log_e(R/r)} \mu\text{F/km.}$$

Dielectric Stress in a Single-core Cable

Substituting equation (1) into equation (2) in order to eliminate q gives

$$V = E . x . \log_e \frac{R}{r}, \quad \text{and hence} \quad E = \frac{V}{x . \log_e(R/r)}.$$

The dielectric stress will be a maximum when $x = r$ and a minimum when $x = R$. Hence

$$E_{max} = \frac{V}{r . \log_e(R/r)} \quad \text{and} \quad E_{min} = \frac{V}{R . \log_e(R/r)}.$$

To obtain the smallest value of E_{max} for a cable of given overall size, consider R fixed and r variable.

The denominator of the expression for E_{max} must be a maximum.

Let this denominator = A, then $A = r(\log_e R - \log_e r)$ and

$$\frac{dA}{dr} = r\left(-\frac{1}{r}\right) + \left(\log_e \frac{R}{r}\right) . 1.$$

Now A will be a maximum when $dA/dr = 0$.

Then $\log_e(R/r) = 1$ and $R = 2.718r$.

The value of r which satisfies this condition is called the 'optimum radius of the conductor'.

Example 5-2. The conductor of a 50-kV, single-core, lead-sheathed cable has a diameter of 3 cm and the internal diameter of the lead sheath is 5 cm. Insulation having a relative permittivity of three is used throughout.

Calculate:

(i) The capacitance of 6·44 km of this cable.

(ii) The maximum and minimum values of stress.

(iii) The optimum value of conductor radius to give the smallest value of maximum stress.

(iv) The maximum stress for a conductor of radius 0·8 cm, if the dimensions of the lead sheath remain unaltered.

(i) $C = \dfrac{\varepsilon_r}{18 \log_e(R/r)} \mu F/km = \dfrac{3 \times 6\cdot44}{18 \log_e 1\cdot667} \mu F = \mathbf{2\cdot1\ \mu F}.$

(ii) $E_{max} = \dfrac{V}{r \cdot \log_e(R/r)} = \dfrac{50}{1\cdot5 \log_e 1\cdot667} = \mathbf{65.2\ kV\ r.m.s./cm}.$

$E_{min} = \dfrac{V}{R \cdot \log_e(R/r)} = \dfrac{50}{2\cdot5 \log_e 1.667} = \mathbf{39\cdot1\ kV\ r.m.s/cm}.$

(iii) Optimum radius of the conductor $= \dfrac{R}{2\cdot718} = \dfrac{2\cdot5}{2\cdot718} = \mathbf{0\cdot92\ cm}.$

$$\left[E_{max} \text{ would then} = \frac{50}{0\cdot92 \log_e(2\cdot5/0\cdot92)} = 54\cdot4\ kV\ r.m.s./cm. \right]$$

(iv) $E_{max} = \dfrac{50}{0\cdot8 \log_e(2\cdot5/0\cdot8)} = \mathbf{54\cdot9\ kV\ r.m.s./cm}.$

Insulation Resistance of a Single-core Cable

Consider a length of *l* cm of the cable shown in figure 5.15.

Let the dimensions be in cm and the resistivity of the insulation $= \rho$ ohm.cm.

The resistance of the cylindrical element in the radial direction

$$= \frac{\rho \cdot dx}{2\pi x l}\ \Omega.$$

The total insulation resistance between the core and the lead sheath

$$= \frac{\rho}{2\pi l} \int_r^R \frac{1}{x} \cdot dx = \frac{\rho}{2\pi l} \log_e \frac{R}{r}\ \Omega.$$

Note that the insulation resistance is inversely proportional to the length of the cable.

Example 5-3. A 6·6-kV, 50-Hz single-core, lead-sheathed cable has a conductor radius of 1 cm and a lead sheath of internal radius 2 cm. The resistivity of the insulation is $1\cdot3 \times 10^8$ MΩ.cm and the cable is 16·1 km long.

Calculate:

(a) the insulation resistance.

(b) the power loss due to leakage current flowing through the insulation resistance.

(a) Length of cable = 1,610,000 cm.

$$\text{Insulation resistance} = \frac{\rho}{2\pi l}\log_e\frac{R}{r} = \frac{1\cdot3 \times 10^8}{2\pi \times 1,610,000} \times \log_e 2$$

$$= \mathbf{8\cdot91 \ M\Omega}.$$

(b) Power loss due to leakage current $= \dfrac{V^2}{R} = \dfrac{6,600^2}{8\cdot91 \times 10^6} = \mathbf{4\cdot89 \ W}.$

Dielectric Hysteresis Loss

This is the energy loss caused by the alternating electric field in the dielectric of an a.c. cable. The alternations cause continual changes in the orbital paths of the electrons in the atomic structure of the insulating material. These changes result in a loss of energy which is dissipated in heat.

Dielectric hysteresis loss cannot be measured separately. The total dielectric losses, consisting of dielectric hysteresis loss and the power loss due to leakage current flowing through the insulation resistance, may be measured by means of the Schering Bridge. These losses vary with voltage and frequency and also depend on the state of the cable dielectric. The test must therefore be carried out at rated voltage and frequency.

Throughout the life of a paper-insulated cable, the formation of voids will reduce the insulation resistance and increase the leakage current and its associated power loss. This will cause a gradual increase in the loss angle of the cable during service. Measurement of the loss angle at regular intervals therefore gives a good indication of the rate of deterioration of the cable dielectric.

Determination of Cable Loss Angle by Means of the Schering Bridge

A connection diagram for the Schering Bridge is shown in figure 5.16.

Arm ① is a variable, standard capacitor in parallel with a non-inductive, variable, standard resistor.

Arm ② is a non-inductive, standard resistor.

Arm ③ is a standard capacitor.

Arm ④ is the cable under test.

Ⓓ is the detector arm.

E is derived from the secondary of a high voltage transformer.

The impedances are so chosen that the voltages across arms ① and ② are low compared with those across arms ③ and ④. Hence the adjustable arm is only at 200 to 300 volts with respect to earth whilst the cable has rated voltage at rated frequency applied to it.

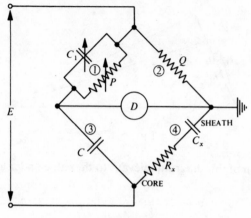

Fig. 5.16

The bridge is balanced when $\dfrac{\overline{Z}_2}{\overline{Z}_1} = \dfrac{\overline{Z}_4}{\overline{Z}_3}$.

Now
$$\frac{1}{\overline{Z}_1} = \frac{1}{-j/\omega C_1} + \frac{1}{P} = j\omega C_1 + \frac{1}{P}, \quad \overline{Z}_2 = Q,$$

$$\frac{1}{\overline{Z}_3} = j\omega C, \quad \overline{Z}_4 = \frac{1}{j\omega C_x} + R_x.$$

Hence
$$Q\left(j\omega C_1 + \frac{1}{P}\right) = \left(\frac{1}{j\omega C_x} + R_x\right)j\omega C,$$

or
$$j\omega C_1 Q + \frac{Q}{P} = \frac{C}{C_x} + j\omega C R_x.$$

Equating the horizontal terms gives

$$\frac{Q}{P} = \frac{C}{C_x}, \quad \text{or} \quad C_x = \frac{CP}{Q}.$$

Hence C_x is balanced by adjusting P.

Equating the vertical terms gives

$$C_1 Q = C R_x, \quad \text{or} \quad R_x = \frac{C_1 Q}{C}.$$

Hence R_x is balanced by adjusting C_1.

The complete vector diagram for the balanced condition is shown in figure 5.17.

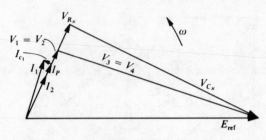

FIG. 5.17

The portion of this diagram relevant to the cable under test is shown in figure 5.18.

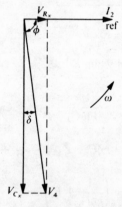

FIG. 5.18

In this diagram, ϕ is the phase angle and δ the loss angle of the cable. $\cos \phi = V_{R_x}/V_4$. Since δ is usually of the order of a few minutes only, $V_4 \simeq V_{C_x}$, so that

$$\cos \phi \simeq \frac{V_{R_x}}{V_{C_x}} = \frac{R_x}{X_{C_x}} = \omega C_x R_x.$$

Also, $\cos \phi = \sin \delta \simeq \tan \delta \simeq \delta$ in radians.

Hence δ in radians $\simeq \omega C_x R_x$.

The total dielectric loss $= V_4 I_4 \cos \phi \simeq V_4 \cdot (V_4/X_{C_x}) \cdot \delta = V_4^2 \omega C_x \delta$ W.

Of this, the loss due to the leakage current flowing through the insulation resistance can be calculated as shown in example 5-3.

The remainder is the dielectric hysteresis loss.

Example 5-4. The Schering Bridge shown in figure 5.16 was used to test the cable described in example 5-3. Balance was obtained with the following values: $C_1 = 0.014\,\mu F$, $P = 454\,\Omega$, $Q = 25\,\Omega$, and $C = 0.25\,\mu F$.

Calculate the values of C_x and R_x, the loss angle, the total dielectric loss and the dielectric hysteresis loss.

$$C_x = \frac{CP}{Q} = \frac{0.25 \times 454}{25} = \textbf{4·54}\,\boldsymbol{\mu}\textbf{F}. \qquad R_x = \frac{C_1 Q}{C} = \frac{0.014 \times 25}{0.25} = \textbf{1·4}\,\boldsymbol{\Omega}.$$

This value of resistance is, of course, the theoretical value of an equivalent series resistor and not the insulation resistance of the cable.

$$\delta = \omega C_x R_x = 314 \times 4.54 \times 10^{-6} \times 1.4 = \textbf{0·002 radians or 7 minutes}.$$

Total dielectric loss $= V_4^2 \omega C_x \delta^c = 6,600^2 \times 314 \times 4.54 \times 10^{-6} \times 0.002$

$$= \textbf{124 W}.$$

From example 5-3, the loss due to leakage current flowing through the insulation resistance ≈ 5 W, so

Dielectric hysteresis loss $= 124 - 5 = \textbf{119 W}$.

These values are typical for a new cable. If the dielectric deteriorates during service, the leakage current and the power loss associated with it increase and so does the loss angle. The formation of voids causes a reduction in C_x and an increase in R_x. The latter is greater than the former so that their product increases with time as shown in figure 5.19.

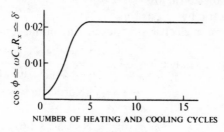

Fig. 5.19

The variation of instantaneous breakdown strength with time for a paper-insulated cable is as shown in figure 5.20.

For a properly designed cable, working under the correct conditions of voltage and temperature, the stable conditions shown in the right-hand portions of these two graphs should be maintained indefinitely.

Example 5-5. Data for a 19·1-kV, 50-Hz, single-core, lead-sheathed, paper-insulated cable are as follows:

Conductor diameter 2 cm.

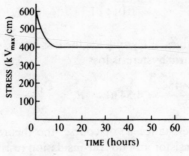

FIG. 5.20

Internal diameter of lead sheath 5 cm.

Length 1·61 km.

The insulation used is uniform throughout and has a resistivity of $1·4 \times 10^8$ megohm.cm and a relative permittivity of 3·5.

The loss angle at rated voltage and frequency is 6 minutes (0·0017 radians).

Calculate:

(a) The insulation resistance.

(b) The capacitance.

(c) The power loss due to leakage current flowing through the insulation resistance.

(d) The total dielectric loss.

(e) The dielectric hysteresis loss.

(f) The maximum electric stress occurring in the dielectric.

(a) Insulation resistance $= \dfrac{\rho}{2\pi l} \log_e \dfrac{R}{r} = \dfrac{1·4 \times 10^8}{2\pi \times 1{,}610 \times 100} \times \log_e 2·5$

$= \mathbf{127\ M\Omega}.$

(b) Capacitance $= \dfrac{\varepsilon_r}{18 \log_e(R/r)}\ \mu\text{F/km} = \dfrac{3·5 \times 1·61}{18 \log_e 2·5} = \mathbf{0·343\ \mu F}.$

(c) Power loss due to leakage current $= \dfrac{V^2}{R} = \dfrac{19{,}100^2}{127 \times 10^6} = \mathbf{2·88\ W}.$

(d) Total dielectric loss $= V^2 \omega C \delta^c$

$= 19{,}100^2 \times 314 \times 0·343 \times 10^{-6} \times 0·0017$

$= \mathbf{66·8\ W}.$

(e) Dielectric hysteresis loss $= 66·8 - 2·9 = \mathbf{63·9\ W}.$

(f) Maximum stress $= \dfrac{V}{r \cdot \log_e(R/r)} = \dfrac{19 \cdot 1}{1 \times \log_e 2 \cdot 5}$

$= \mathbf{20 \cdot 8 \ kV \ r.m.s./cm}.$

Reduction of Maximum Stress

The maximum value of stress occurs at the conductor surface and may be reduced in the following ways:

(i) The conductor radius may be made larger than that required to carry the current, as in figures 5.1, 5.4, and 5.12.

(ii) The conductor radii may be increased at the points where the cores are closest to each other, as in figures 5.2, 5.6, 5.9, and 5.10.

(iii) The outer strands of the conductors may be specially shaped to present a smoother surface, as in figure 5.11.

(iv) The internal radius of the lead sheath may be increased. This will obviously make the cable more bulky. Moreover, if homogeneous insulation is used, the outer layers will be considerably understressed.

(v) Graded insulation may be used, the relative permittivity of the insulation nearest the core being greater than that of the outer layers. Better quality paper is also sometimes used for the inner layers because of its greater mechanical strength.

(vi) Conducting intersheaths may be spaced at intervals throughout the dielectric. These intersheaths are maintained at potentials other than those they would naturally assume.

Methods (v) and (vi) are not widely used in practice due to difficulties which will be discussed later. The design of modern, very high voltage cables is based on oil or gas filling rather than on methods (v) and (vi).

Use of Graded Insulation

Example 5-6. A 100-kV, single-core, lead-sheathed cable has a conductor radius of 1 cm and an internal sheath radius of 4 cm. The first centimetre of radial thickness of insulation has a relative permittivity of five and that of the remainder is three.

Calculate the maximum and minimum values of stress for each dielectric and compare these values with those for a cable having the same dimensions and homogeneous insulation.

Let the capacitance of the inner dielectric be C_1 and that of the outer dielectric be C_2, then

$$\frac{C_1}{C_2} = \frac{5}{3} \times \frac{\log_{10}(4/2)}{\log_{10}(2/1)} = \frac{V_2}{V_1}.$$

Therefore $1.667V_1 = V_2$. But $V_1 + V_2 = 100\,\text{kV}$,

so that $$V_1 = \frac{100}{2.667} = 37.5\,\text{kV}.$$

Hence maximum stress in inner dielectric

$$= \frac{37.5}{1\,.\,\log_e 2} = \mathbf{54.1\ kV\ r.m.s./cm},$$

and minimum stress in inner dielectric

$$= \frac{37.5}{2\,.\,\log_e 2} = \mathbf{27.1\ kV\ r.m.s./cm}.$$

Maximum stress in outer dielectric

$$= \frac{62.5}{2\,.\,\log_e 2} = \mathbf{45.1\ kV\ r.m.s./cm}.$$

Minimum stress in outer dielectric

$$= \frac{62.5}{4\,.\,\log_e 2} = \mathbf{22.5\ kV\ r.m.s./cm}.$$

With homogeneous insulation,

$$\text{maximum stress} = \frac{100}{1\,.\,\log_e 4} = \mathbf{72.1\ kV\ r.m.s./cm},$$

$$\text{minimum stress} = \frac{100}{4\,.\,\log_e 4} = \mathbf{18\ kV\ r.m.s./cm}.$$

Thus the use of graded insulation reduces the maximum stress by 18 kV r.m.s./cm. In order to achieve this reduction with homogeneous insulation and the same conductor radius, the internal radius of the sheath would have to be increased by 2·35 cm.

The variation of stress throughout the dielectrics is shown in figure 5.21.

The curves between the maximum and minimum values are hyperbolic.

One difficulty with graded insulation is that of obtaining materials whose relative permittivities differ by a significant amount. By using various additives, the relative permittivity of impregnated paper can be varied between 2·8 and 4 and that of rubber between 4·2 and 6·1. Thus rubber can be used for the inner dielectric but it is much more expensive than impregnated paper.

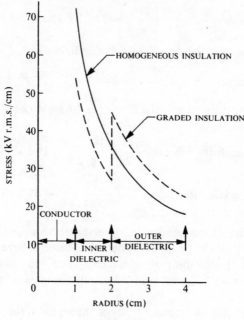

FIG. 5.21

A second difficulty is the possibility of changes in relative permittivity during service. Such changes may alter the stress distribution to such an extent that breakdown occurs.

In practice, it is found that the use of graded insulation for electric stress attenuation is only worth considering for very high voltage cables in which R/r is greater than three. This criterion also applies to the use of conducting intersheaths.

Use of Conducting Intersheaths

Example 5-7. A 100-kV, single-core, lead-sheathed cable has a conductor radius of 1 cm and an internal sheath radius of 4 cm. There is a conducting intersheath at a radius of 2·5 cm. The insulation is homogeneous and has a relative permittivity of 3·5.

Calculate:

(a) The maximum stress and the intersheath potential when it is not connected to the supply transformer.

(b) The stress at the conductor surface and on either side of the intersheath when its potential is maintained at 44 kV with respect to the conductor.

(a) Maximum stress $= \dfrac{100}{1 \, . \, \log_e 4} = $ **72·1 kV r.m.s./cm**.

Hence the p.d. between core and intersheath $= 72 \cdot 1 \times 1 \times \log_e 2 \cdot 5$

$= $ **66·1 kV r.m.s.**

(b) Stress at conductor surface $= \dfrac{44}{1 \, . \, \log_e 2 \cdot 5} = $ **48 kV r.m.s./cm**.

Stress inside intersheath $= \dfrac{44}{2 \cdot 5 \, . \, \log_e 2 \cdot 5} = $ **19·2 kV r.m.s./cm**.

Stress outside intersheath $= \dfrac{56}{2 \cdot 5 \, . \, \log_e 1 \cdot 6} = $ **47·7 kV r.m.s./cm**.

Thus the use of the conducting intersheath reduces the maximum stress by 24·1 kV r.m.s./cm. In order to achieve this reduction with homogeneous insulation, no intersheath, and the same conductor radius, the internal radius of the lead sheath would have to be increased by 4·02 cm.

The hyperbolic variation of stress throughout the dielectrics is shown in figure 5.22.

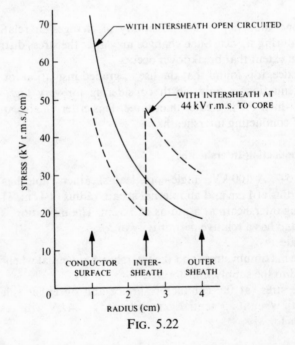

FIG. 5.22

The difficulties associated with the use of conducting intersheaths are as follows:

(i) Cable jointing is more complex.

(ii) Mechanical damage may open circuit all or part of the intersheath during service. The stress at the conductor surface may then rise to a value high enough to cause breakdown.

(iii) An extra tapping is required on the supply transformer to maintain each intersheath at an appropriate potential.

(iv) The capacitance currents are greater with an intersheath than without, as shown in example 5-8. (The additional charging kVAr is derived from the supply transformer.) The charging currents flowing in the intersheaths and outer sheath of a long cable may be large enough to cause overheating.

Because of these difficulties, the use of intersheaths is comparatively rare. When used, there is usually one intersheath only.

Example 5-8. A 120-kV, 50-Hz, single-core, lead-sheathed cable has a conductor radius of 1 cm and an internal sheath radius of 4·2 cm. There is a conducting intersheath at a radius of 2 cm. The insulation is homogeneous and has a relative permittivity of 3·8. The cable is 6·44 km long.

Calculate:

(a) The capacitance of each dielectric.

(b) The total capacitance.

(c) The maximum stress when the intersheath is open circuited.

(d) The potential at which the intersheath must be maintained in order to reduce the stress at the conductor surface to 55 kV r.m.s./cm.

(e) The capacitance currents and total charging kVAr for conditions (c) and (d).

(a) Capacitance of inner dielectric $= \dfrac{3\cdot8 \times 6\cdot44}{18 \log_e 2} = \mathbf{1\cdot96\,\mu F}$.

Capacitance of outer dielectric $= \dfrac{3\cdot8 \times 6\cdot44}{18 \log_e 2\cdot1} = \mathbf{1\cdot83\,\mu F}$.

(b) Total capacitance $= \dfrac{1\cdot96 \times 1\cdot83}{1\cdot96 + 1\cdot83} = \mathbf{0\cdot946\,\mu F}$.

Alternatively, total capacitance $= \dfrac{3\cdot8 \times 6\cdot44}{18 \log_e 4\cdot2} = \mathbf{0\cdot946\,\mu F}$.

(c) Maximum stress $= \dfrac{120}{1 \,.\, \log_e 4\cdot2} = \mathbf{83\cdot6\ kV\ r.m.s./cm}$.

(d) P.d. between core and intersheath

$$= 55 \times 1 \times \log_e 2 = \textbf{38·1 kV r.m.s.}$$

(e) With intersheath open circuited:
Capacitance current

$$= 2\pi f C V = 314 \times 0.946 \times 10^{-6} \times 120 \times 10^3 = \textbf{35·7 A.}$$

This current is shown in figure 5.23(a).

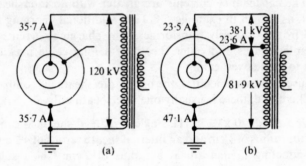

FIG. 5.23

Total charging kVAr $= 120 \times 35.7 = \textbf{4280}$.
With intersheath at 38·1 kV with respect to the core:
Capacitance current in inner dielectric

$$= 314 \times 1.96 \times 10^{-6} \times 38.1 \times 10^3 = \textbf{23·5 A.}$$

Capacitance current in outer dielectric

$$= 314 \times 1.83 \times 10^{-6} \times 81.9 \times 10^3 = \textbf{47·1 A.}$$

These currents are shown in figure 5.23(b).
Total charging kVAr $= (38.1 \times 23.5) + (81.9 \times 47.1) = \textbf{4750}$.

Capacitance of a Three-core, Belted Cable

The three-core, 'H' type cable is equivalent to three separate single-core cables as far as stress and capacitance are concerned.

In the three-core, belted-type cable, however, there are capacitances of C_c μF between conductors and capacitances of C_s μF between each conductor and the sheath. These capacitances are shown in figure 5.24.

This arrangement of capacitances is equivalent to a star system connected in parallel with a delta system as shown in figure 5.25.

Let the delta system of capacitances C_c be replaced by an equivalent star system of capacitances C, as shown in figure 5.26.

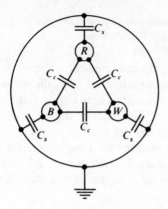

FIG. 5.24

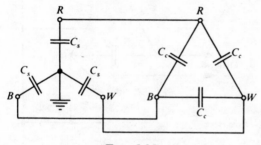

FIG. 5.25

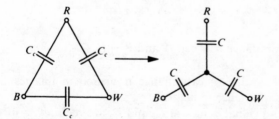

FIG. 5.26

For equivalence, the capacitance between R and W must be the same in each of these systems.

In the delta system, the capacitance between R and $W = C_c + C_c/2$ $= 3C_c/2$.

In the star system, the capacitance between R and $W = C/2$, so that $C = 3C_c$.

Thus the cable is equivalent to a star system of capacitances, each of value $C_s\,\mu F$, in parallel with a second star system of capacitances, each of value $3C_c\,\mu F$.

The effective capacitance to neutral is therefore $C_s + 3C_c\,\mu F$.

The effective capacitance to neutral is difficult to calculate accurately due mainly to inhomogeneities in the insulation. In practice, therefore, it is usual to measure this quantity on a finished length of cable by means of the Schering Bridge.

The test is performed at the working voltage, frequency and temperature. One core is connected to the sheath and the capacitance between the other two cores is then measured as shown in figure 5.27.

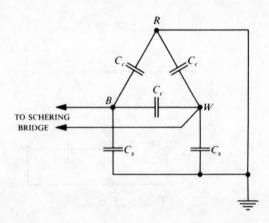

FIG. 5.27

The capacitance between W and $B = C_c + \dfrac{C_s + C_c}{2} = \dfrac{C_s + 3C_c}{2}$.

Thus the value of capacitance measured in this test is half the effective capacitance to neutral.

If the individual values of C_s and C_c are required, a further test is performed in which the three cores are connected together and the capacitance between them and the lead sheath is then measured. In this test, the capacitances C_c are shorted out and the three capacitances C_s are connected in parallel. Thus the value of capacitance measured in this test is $3C_s$.

Example 5-9. In a test on a three-core, 50-Hz, 11-kV, belted-type cable a capacitance of $1{\cdot}1\,\mu F$ was measured between two cores when the third was connected to the lead sheath.

In a further test on the same length of cable, a capacitance of $1 \cdot 2$ μF was measured between the three cores connected together and the lead sheath.

Calculate:

(a) The effective capacitance to neutral.

(b) The charging current per core.

(c) The total charging kVAr.

(d) The capacitance between each conductor and the sheath and between each pair of conductors.

(a) Effective capacitance to neutral $= 2 \times 1 \cdot 1 = \mathbf{2 \cdot 2 \, \mu F}$.

(b) Charging current per core $= 314 \times 2 \cdot 2 \times 10^{-6} \times 6,350 = \mathbf{4 \cdot 39 \, A}$.

(c) Total charging kVAr $= \sqrt{3} \times 11 \times 4 \cdot 39 = \mathbf{83 \cdot 6}$.

(d) Capacitance between each conductor and the sheath $= C_s$ $= 1 \cdot 2/3 = \mathbf{0 \cdot 4 \, \mu F}$.

Capacitance between each pair of conductors $= C_c$.

Value of capacitance measured in first test $= \dfrac{C_s + 3C_c}{2} = 1 \cdot 1 \ \mu\text{F}$, and

therefore $\qquad C_c = \dfrac{2 \cdot 2 - 0 \cdot 4}{3} = \mathbf{0 \cdot 6 \, \mu F}$.

EXAMPLES 5

1. Draw fully labelled, cross-sectional sketches of the following types of underground cable:

(a) Two-conductor concentric.

(b) Three-core belted.

(c) Single-core oil-filled.

(d) Three-core, 'H' type, gas-filled.

(e) Single-core, water-cooled.

Give reasons for the choice of the materials used and state the advantages and disadvantages of each type.

2. A two-conductor, concentric cable is $8 \cdot 05$ km long and has an inner conductor of external radius $0 \cdot 635$ cm and an outer conductor of internal diameter $3 \cdot 81$ cm. The dielectric between the conductors is homogeneous and has a relative permittivity of four. The overall protective sheath is non-metallic and the conductors are of copper. The cable is connected to a 66-kV, 50-Hz, single-phase supply.

Calculate:

(a) The total inductance and capacitance of the cable.

(b) The charging current, ignoring the inductance.

(c) The charging kVAr, ignoring the inductance.

(Answers (a) **1·85 mH, 1·63 μF**, (b) **33·7 A**, (c) **2,230 kVAr**.)

3. Derive an expression for the line-to-neutral capacitance (μF/km) for a three-core 'H' type cable.

A 16·1-km length of 33-kV, 50-Hz, three-core, 'H' type cable has conductors of radius 0·635 cm and insulation of radial thickness 0·762 cm and relative permittivity 3.

Calculate the charging current per core and the total charging kVAr. (Answers **20·4 A, 1,160 kVAr.**)

4. In a 66-kV, three-core, 'H' type, oil-filled cable the diameter of each metallized paper sheath is to be 3 cm.

Calculate the optimum conductor diameter and the corresponding value of maximum stress.

(Answers **1·1 cm, 69·3 kV r.m.s./cm.**)

5. A single-core, lead-sheathed cable has a conductor of external diameter 3 cm and an internal sheath radius of 4·25 cm. The cable is to be insulated with two dielectrics, the relative permittivity of the insulation nearest the core being 5 and that of the remainder being 3. The maximum values of stress are to be 38 and 26 kV max/cm respectively.

Calculate the radial thickness of each dielectric and the greatest r.m.s. voltage which may be applied between the core and the sheath. (Answers **2·15 cm, 0·6 cm, 46 kV r.m.s.**)

6. Derive an expression for the electric stress at any point in the dielectric of a single-core cable with a concentric sheath or screen.

Three such cables are used for a three-phase, 132-kV feeder. Each cable has two dielectrics of equal thickness, the radius of the core being 1 cm and that of the metallized paper screen being 2 cm.

Calculate:

(a) The ratio of the relative permittivities of the two dielectrics for each to have the same value of maximum stress.

(b) The voltage across each dielectric.

(c) The value of the maximum stress.

(d) The maximum stress if a single dielectric were used.

(Answers (a) **Inner/outer = 1·5/1**, (b) **36·8 kV r.m.s. inner, 39·2 kV r.m.s. outer**, (c) **91 kV r.m.s./cm**, (d) **110 kV r.m.s./cm.**)

7. A 66-kV, 50-Hz, three-phase, 'H' type cable has a conductor radius of 1 cm and a screen radius of 2 cm. The cable is 8·05 km long and the relative permittivity of the dielectric is 3.

Calculate the capacitance and the maximum stress.

If a metal intersheath is inserted midway between sheath and core, and is maintained at a potential of half of that between sheath and core, calculate the new maximum stress and the charging current entering or leaving each intersheath.

(Answers **1·95 µF line to neutral, 55 kV r.m.s./cm, 47 kV r.m.s./cm, 8·1 A.**)

8. A 66-kV, 50-Hz, three-phase, 'H' type cable has a conductor radius of 1 cm and a radial insulation thickness of 2 cm. The cable is 40·25 km long and the relative permittivity of the insulation is 3.

Calculate the charging current per core.

If a conducting intersheath is inserted in the dielectric at a radius of 2 cm, calculate the potential at which the intersheath must be maintained relative to the core so that the intersheath charging current is 35 A.

(Answers **73 A, 19·8 kV r.m.s.**)

9. A 38·1-kV, single-core, lead-sheathed cable has a conductor radius of 1 cm, a conducting intersheath of radius 2·5 cm and an internal sheath radius of 4 cm. The relative permittivity of the dielectric is 3·5.

Calculate the potential at which the intersheath must be maintained relative to the outer sheath so that the charging current flowing in the conductor is equal to that flowing in the intersheath.

State the disadvantages associated with the use of conducting intersheaths.

(Answer **19·3 kV r.m.s.**)

10. An 11-kV, 50-Hz, three-core, belted type cable is 8·05 km long. The capacitance measured between two cores whilst the third was connected to the lead sheath was 0·249 µF/km.

Calculate the charging current per core and the total charging kVAr.

(Answers **8 A, 152 kVAr.**)

11. Data for a 6·6-kV, 50-Hz, single-core, lead-sheathed cable are as follows:

Conductor diameter 2 cm.

Internal diameter of lead sheath 4 cm.

Length 4·83 km.

The insulation used is uniform throughout and has a resistivity of $1·3 \times 10^8$ megohm.cm and a relative permittivity of 3·5.

The loss angle at rated voltage and frequency is 7 minutes (0·002 radians).

Calculate:

(a) The insulation resistance.

(b) The capacitance.

(c) The power loss due to leakage current flowing through the insulation resistance.

(d) The total dielectric loss.

(e) The dielectric hysteresis loss.

(f) The maximum electric stress occurring in the dielectric.

(Answers (a) **29·7 megohms,** (b) **1·35 µF,** (c) **1·47 W,** (d) **36·9 W,** (e) **35·4 W,** (f) **9·52 kV r.m.s./cm.**)

12. Explain why the loss angle of a paper-insulated, lead-sheathed cable may vary during its operating life.

Show how the loss angle may be measured by means of the Schering Bridge.

Define the term 'dielectric hysteresis loss' and explain its cause.

State the difficulties associated with capacitance grading by means of dielectrics of different relative permittivities.

6

Insulators

Materials

Many insulators are made from hard porcelain containing 50 per cent kaolin (china clay), 25 per cent felspar and 25 per cent quartz. It is essential that the porcelain be free from blowholes and impurities, otherwise its dielectric strength is impaired. Since porcelain is hygroscopic, it must be made impervious to moisture by means of glaze.

The dielectric strength of mechanically sound porcelain is of the order of 60 to 70 kV peak/cm. The ultimate mechanical strength varies between 276 and 450 MN/m² in compression and 10·3 to 86·1 MN/m² in tension, depending on the composition.

Difficulty has been experienced in manufacturing large thicknesses of homogeneous porcelain but improvements in design and manufacture have enabled larger one-piece insulators to be made than was previously possible. For voltages above 33 kV, however, the cost increases rapidly and it is usually better for an insulator to take the form of several identical units in series.

Insulators are also made from glass. Glass has a dielectric strength of the order of 140 kV peak/cm, is mechanically stronger than porcelain in compression, and has about the same strength as porcelain in tension. Moisture condenses more readily on glass than on glazed porcelain and it is difficult to manufacture large glass insulators due to the internal stresses caused by the cooling of large irregular masses. Up to the present time it has not been possible successfully to develop a large pin type glass insulator although glass suspension insulators are very common. These have the following advantages over porcelain:

(i) Blowholes and other inhomogeneities can be seen.

(ii) After an overvoltage surge, a faulty insulator can be more readily identified because glass shatters whilst porcelain merely cracks when electrical breakdown occurs.

(iii) Glass has a lower coefficient of thermal expansion which minimizes strains caused by ambient temperature changes.

(iv) Glass insulators become less overheated in sunlight since most of the heat rays pass through instead of being absorbed.

Pin Type Insulators

These are used to support overhead lines. A typical 11-kV insulator of this type is shown in figure 6.1.

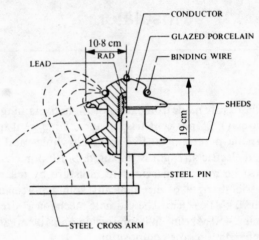

FIG. 6.1

In this figure, lines of equipotential are shown chain-dotted and lines of electric flux are shown dotted. The upper surfaces of the sheds are shaped to coincide with lines of equipotential so that there will be no potential difference between points in these surfaces and therefore no tendency for leakage currents to flow along them. The sheds are widely spaced so as to derive maximum benefit from the washing action of rain. The lower surface of the upper shed has circular corrugations to increase the length of the surface leakage path.

The mechanical design of the insulator must be such that it is strong enough to support a conductor span subjected to ice and wind loading.

Suspension Type Insulators

A typical 11-kV suspension type insulator is shown in figure 6.2.

The upper surface is shaped to follow a line of equipotential and the lower surface is corrugated for the same reasons as in the pin type.

A slot is provided in the cap of each unit to enable a series string to be built up. Each pin is locked into the slot of the next unit by means of a steel cotter pin. More benefit is derived from rain washing when the string is horizontal than when it is vertical.

When used to support high voltage lines, the suspension insulator string has the following advantages over the pin type insulator:

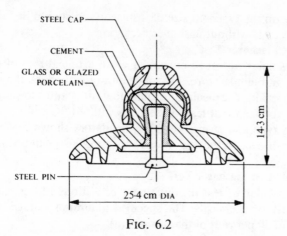

STEEL CAP

CEMENT

GLASS OR GLAZED
PORCELAIN

14·3 cm

STEEL PIN

25·4 cm DIA

FIG. 6.2

(i) The initial cost of the suspension string is lower than that of the equivalent pin type. Also the replacement cost is lower due to the ease with which damaged suspension units may be replaced without replacing the whole string.

(ii) It is easier to manufacture homogeneous dielectrics for the suspension type than for the larger pin types.

(iii) The flexibility of the suspension string reduces mechanical stresses and equalizes tensions in adjacent conductor spans.

(iv) The same suspension unit may be used to support lines of any voltage by varying the number of insulators in the string. If the system voltage is to be increased, more units may be added easily.

The disadvantages of the suspension insulator are:

(i) Up to about 50 kV, the pin type is cheaper.

(ii) The flexibility of the suspension string allows a larger conductor swing. The spaces between conductors must therefore be greater than with the pin type so that the supporting tower arms are longer and therefore slightly more expensive.

Testing of Insulators

Insulators used on overhead lines are subjected to the following tests:

(i) Dry Flashover Test.

The flashover voltage is that at which the insulator surface breaks down, allowing current to flow on the outside of the insulator between the conductor and the cross-arm.

The clean insulator is mounted in the position in which it will be used in service and a gradually increasing voltage of normal system frequency is applied. This voltage is increased to a specified minimum depending on the type and size of insulator and should be held for at least 30 seconds without flashover occurring.

(ii) Wet Flashover Test.

This is similar to test (i) but under clean artificial rain of specified resistance and temperature. The angle and rate at which the rain falls are also specified. The insulator should now withstand a lower specified minimum voltage for at least 30 seconds without flashover.

The pin type and suspension type insulators shown in figures 6.1 and 6.2 flash over in the region of 73 kV r.m.s. (dry) and 50 kV r.m.s. (wet).

(iii) Pollution Flashover Test.

This is similar to test (ii) but under conditions of fog, salt spray, smoke, dust, or chemicals. The specified minimum voltage is now of the order of 50 per cent of that for test (ii).

(iv) Puncture Test.

Puncture occurs when the dielectric of the insulator breaks down and allows current to flow inside the insulator between the conductor and the cross-arm.

An insulator may survive flashover without damage but must be replaced when punctured. The design must therefore always be such that flashover occurs at a lower voltage than puncture.

The insulator is immersed in clean insulating oil to prevent flashover and the applied voltage is gradually increased. The insulator should withstand about 1·3 times its dry flashover voltage without puncture.

(v) Impulse Test.

Whether or not an insulator breaks down depends not only on the magnitude of the applied voltage but also on the rate at which the voltage rises. Since insulators have to withstand steep-fronted lightning and switching surges during service, their design must be such that the flashover voltage on a steep-fronted impulse waveform is greater than that on normal system waveform.

The ratio of these voltages is called the impulse ratio.

$$\text{Impulse ratio} = \frac{\text{impulse flashover voltage}}{\text{power frequency flashover voltage}}.$$

This ratio should not be less than 1·3 for suspension and 1·4 for pin type insulators.

The impulse flashover voltage is obtained by applying impulses having the waveform shown in figure 6.3.

(vi) Mechanical Test.

A suspension unit is subjected to a tension of 1·2 times maximum working load and a pin type insulator is subjected to a bending moment 2·5 times maximum working load. Test (i) is then repeated.

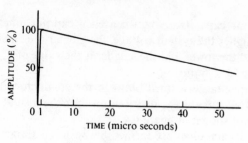

FIG. 6.3

(vii) Temperature Test.

The insulator is immersed alternately in 70°C and 7°C water baths. There are six immersions in all, each having a duration of one hour. The insulator is then dried and test (i) is repeated.

(viii) Porosity Test.

This is a test of the glaze on porcelain insulators.

The insulator is weighed, immersed in water under pressure for 24 hours and then reweighed. Any increase in weight indicates the ingress of water due to imperfect glazing.

Voltage Distribution over an Insulator String

The voltage distribution over a string of identical suspension insulators is not uniform due to the capacitances formed in the air between each cap/pin junction and the earthed metal tower.

The arrangement of capacitances for a string of five insulators is shown in figure 6.4.

C is the capacitance of each insulator and is of the order of 30 $\mu\mu$F.

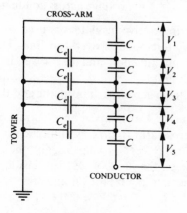

FIG. 6.4

C_e is the air capacitance between each cap/pin junction and the tower. The higher the system voltage, the greater the distance between the string and the tower and the smaller is the value of C_e. It is usually of the order of 3 to 6 $\mu\mu$F.

The air capacitance formed between the conductor and the tower has no effect on the voltage distribution over the insulator string and is therefore not shown in figure 6.4.

Other air capacitances are formed between metal parts at different potentials. For example, there are air capacitances between each cap/pin junction and the conductor. Such capacitances are so small, however, as to have negligible effect on the voltage distribution.

Since the capacitance current for each insulator is $2\pi fCV$ amperes, the voltage developed across each insulator is directly proportional to its capacitance current. This ignores the effect of leakage resistance currents which will be considered later.

It can be seen from figure 6.4 that the capacitance current for the insulator nearest the conductor is greatest because this unit carries the current for the remainder of the network. The currents become progressively lower as the cross-arm is approached and therefore

$$V_1 < V_2 < V_3 < V_4 < V_5.$$

These inequalities are greater the greater the value of C_e.

If the conductor end insulator is electrically stressed to its safe working value, then all the other insulators are understressed and the string is being inefficiently used.

For an insulator string consisting of n series units,

$$\text{string efficiency} = \frac{\text{voltage across string}}{n \times \text{voltage across conductor end unit}}.$$

Example 6-1. A string of five insulators is used to suspend one conductor of a 33-kV, three-phase, overhead line. The air capacitance between each cap/pin junction and the tower is one tenth of the capacitance of each unit.

Calculate the voltage across each insulator and the string efficiency.

Referring to figure 6.4, the capacitance current for the second insulator from the cross-arm is $2\pi fCV_2$ amperes, that for the insulator nearest the cross-arm is $2\pi fCV_1$ amperes, and that for the air capacitance formed between the junction of these insulators and the tower is $2\pi fC_eV_1$ which equals $2\pi f(0.1 \times C)V_1$ amperes.

Using Kirchhoff's Law, $2\pi fCV_2 = 2\pi fCV_1 + 2\pi f(0.1 \times C)V_1$,

or $$V_2 = 1.1V_1.$$

The voltage across the second cap/pin junction to earth capacitance from the cross-arm is $V_1 + V_2$.

Using a similar argument to that above,

$$V_3 = V_2 + 0 \cdot 1(V_1 + V_2).$$

Therefore $V_3 = 1 \cdot 1 V_1 + 0 \cdot 1(V_1 + 1 \cdot 1 V_1) = 1 \cdot 31 V_1.$

Similarly, $V_4 = V_3 + 0 \cdot 1(V_1 + V_2 + V_3),$

or $V_4 = 1 \cdot 31 V_1 + 0 \cdot 1(V_1 + 1 \cdot 1 V_1 + 1 \cdot 31 V_1) = 1 \cdot 651 V_1.$

Similarly, $V_5 = V_4 + 0 \cdot 1(V_1 + V_2 + V_3 + V_4),$

which on substitution gives

$$V_5 = 1 \cdot 651 V_1 + 0 \cdot 1(V_1 + 1 \cdot 1 V_1 + 1 \cdot 31 V_1 + 1 \cdot 651 V_1)$$
$$= 2 \cdot 157 V_1.$$

But $V_1 + V_2 + V_3 + V_4 + V_5 = \dfrac{33,000}{\sqrt{3}}.$

Therefore $V_1 + 1 \cdot 1 V_1 + 1 \cdot 31 V_1 + 1 \cdot 651 V_1 + 2 \cdot 157 V_1 = 19,050 \text{ V},$

or $V_1 = \dfrac{19,050}{7 \cdot 218} = \textbf{2,640 V}.$

$$V_2 = 1 \cdot 1 \times 2,640 = \textbf{2,904 V}.$$

$$V_3 = 1 \cdot 31 \times 2,640 = \textbf{3,458 V}.$$

$$V_4 = 1 \cdot 651 \times 2,640 = \textbf{4,359 V}.$$

$$V_5 = 2 \cdot 157 \times 2,640 = \textbf{5,694 V}.$$

String efficiency $= \dfrac{19,050}{5 \times 5,694} = \textbf{0·669}.$

Guard Ring

This takes the form of a large conducting ring which surrounds at least the line end unit of a suspension insulator string. The ring is connected to the conductor supporting clamp and is therefore at line potential.

The guard ring is used in conjunction with arcing horns attached to the cross-arm, as shown in figure 6.5.

The primary function of this arrangement is to deflect the power arc following flashover away from the insulator surfaces, thus reducing the probability of insulator damage. This device may slightly reduce the

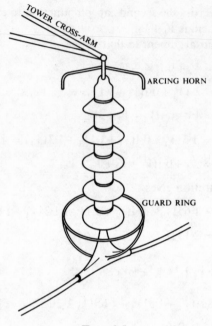

FIG. 6.5

string flashover voltage but this disadvantage is outweighed by an improvement in voltage distribution. This is due to the additional air capacitances between the guard ring and the lower cap/pin junctions. Some of the capacitance current formerly carried by the line end units is now carried by these additional capacitances, as shown in the following example.

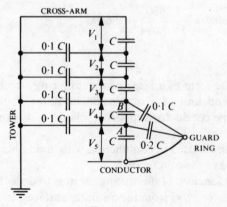

FIG. 6.6

Example 6-2. The fitting of a guard ring to the insulator string described in example 6-1 has the effect of introducing two additional air capacitances, as shown in figure 6.6.

The capacitances between the other cap/pin junctions and the guard ring may be assumed negligible.

Calculate the voltage across each unit and the string efficiency.

The following relationships obtained in example 6-1 are still applicable:

$$V_2 = 1 \cdot 1 V_1. \qquad V_3 = 1 \cdot 31 V_1.$$

Using Kirchhoff's Law on the point B gives

$$V_4 + 0 \cdot 1(V_4 + V_5) = V_3 + 0 \cdot 1(V_1 + V_2 + V_3)$$

or

$$1 \cdot 1 V_4 + 0 \cdot 1 V_5 = 1 \cdot 651 V_1.$$

Hence

$$V_4 = \frac{1 \cdot 651 V_1 - 0 \cdot 1 V_5}{1 \cdot 1}.$$

Similarly for the point A we have

$$V_5 + 0 \cdot 2 V_5 = V_4 + 0 \cdot 1(V_1 + V_2 + V_3 + V_4),$$

from which is obtained

$$1 \cdot 2 V_5 = 1 \cdot 1 V_4 + 0 \cdot 1(V_1 + V_2 + V_3).$$

$$1 \cdot 2 V_5 = 1 \cdot 651 V_1 - 0 \cdot 1 V_5 + 0 \cdot 341 V_1.$$

$$1 \cdot 3 V_5 = 1 \cdot 992 V_1.$$

$$V_5 = 1 \cdot 532 V_1.$$

$$V_4 = \frac{1 \cdot 651 V_1 - 0 \cdot 153 V_1}{1 \cdot 1} = 1 \cdot 361 V_1.$$

But $V_1 + 1 \cdot 1 V_1 + 1 \cdot 31 V_1 + 1 \cdot 361 V_1 + 1 \cdot 532 V_1 = 19,050$ V,

so that

$$V_1 = \frac{19,050}{6 \cdot 303} = \textbf{3,024 V.}$$

$$V_2 = 1 \cdot 1 \times 3,024 = \textbf{3,326 V.}$$

$$V_3 = 1 \cdot 31 \times 3,024 = \textbf{3,961 V.}$$

$$V_4 = 1 \cdot 361 \times 3,024 = \textbf{4,114 V.}$$

$$V_5 = 1 \cdot 532 \times 3,024 = \textbf{4,633 V.}$$

String efficiency $= \dfrac{19,050}{5 \times 4,633} = \textbf{0·823}.$

Thus the guard ring has increased the string efficiency by 0·154.

Example 6-3. Referring to figure 6.7, calculate the values of the air capacitances *p*, *q*, *x*, and *y* required for uniform voltage distribution over the five insulators.

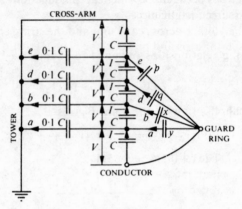

FIG. 6.7

For uniform voltage distribution, the capacitance current (*I*) must be the same for all the insulators.

The capacitance currents for the cap/pin junction to earth capacitances must therefore be supplied through the guard ring to cap/pin junction capacitances as shown.

Hence $y \cdot V = 0 \cdot 1C \cdot 4V$ giving $y = 0 \cdot 4C$.

$x \cdot 2V = 0 \cdot 1C \cdot 3V$ giving $x = 0 \cdot 15C$,

$q \cdot 3V = 0 \cdot 1C \cdot 2V$ giving $q = 0 \cdot 067C$,

and $p \cdot 4V = 0 \cdot 1C \cdot V$ giving $p = 0 \cdot 025C$.

It is not usually possible in practice to achieve completely uniform voltage distribution by means of the guard ring, particularly if the string consists of a large number of units. Increasing the number of units reduces the string efficiency. For example, the efficiency of a string of 25·4 cm diameter standard discs was 0·867 for three units and 0·714 for ten units under the same conditions.

Use of the guard ring does considerably improve the efficiency, however, as shown in example 6-2.

Other Methods of Improving String Efficiency

(i) Larger diameter discs may be used for the one or two units nearest the conductor. The capacitance of the line end units may alternatively be increased by using larger metal caps. The disadvantage of these methods is that stocks of different insulators must be carried.

(ii) The air capacitances between each cap/pin junction and the tower may be reduced by increasing the length of the cross-arm. This method is limited by the reduction in cross-arm rigidity and the increase in tower cost.

(iii) The insulator caps and pins may be made of insulating material instead of steel. There are difficulties in developing materials having all the necessary properties, however, and this method is not widely used.

(iv) It is found in practice that the string efficiency increases when the insulators are wet. This improvement is due to the increase in surface leakage resistance current. This current is the same for all the units and the voltage distribution no longer depends on the capacitance currents only. The dry leakage resistance current may be increased by using high resistance rather than infinite resistance glaze on porcelain insulators. This method is limited by the risk of thermal instability which is discussed later.

Causes of Pollution Flashover

The surface resistance of an insulator is unaffected by deposits of dry dirt but such deposits form continuous conducting layers when wet. Leakage current then flows in these layers and water is first evaporated from those areas where the product of current density and surface resistivity is greatest. This leads to the formation of dry circular insulating bands which continue to increase in width until the leakage current is reduced to a value insufficient to sustain further evaporation.

Further wetting causes the resistance of the remaining wet portions of the insulator to be progressively reduced and small local flashovers occur on sections of the dry bands on which moisture droplets fall. A larger proportion of the total voltage then appears across the wet surfaces and the arcs extend rapidly over the whole surface. Complete flashover may then take place unless interrupted by a voltage zero.

Pollution flashovers often occur in conditions of fog or salt spray, or whenever the insulator is covered by a film of polluted water. This condition is sometimes created during the melting of polluted ice by leakage currents.

Methods of Preventing Pollution Flashover

(i) Insulators may be cleaned by hand. This is expensive and must be carried out very frequently in badly polluted locations. Insulators must be taken out of service whilst being cleaned.

(ii) Insulators may be washed live by means of high pressure hoses.

Expensive equipment is required for this and the water must either be heated or contain a non-conducting anti-freeze in winter.

(iii) Permanent water sprays may be mounted above each insulator string. This method is used extensively in Japan but not widely in Great Britain. If conditions are such that either the insulator surface or the spray water becomes polluted, flashover will be more likely than if no spray were used.

(iv) Pin type insulators for use in badly polluted locations are designed with widely spaced sheds or 'skirts' so as to derive maximum benefit from rain washing. Tension insulator strings with roughly horizontal axes are less likely to become polluted than vertically mounted suspension strings.

(v) Since the wet surfaces of an insulator offer almost no resistance, the tips of the sheds must be so spaced that there is a long leakage path through the air between adjacent sheds and between the lowest shed and the pin.

(vi) Sites for outdoor substations and equipment should be carefully chosen. The rate of pollution may differ considerably for two areas only 100 metres apart.

(vii) Indoor substations effectively eliminate pollution problems but they are usually too expensive a solution.

(viii) Insulators may be coated with water repellent petroleum jelly. This is now used in practically all 132-kV and 275-kV outdoor substations in badly polluted locations. The jelly is soft enough to absorb the dirt particles, insulates them from each other and prevents water coming into contact with them. It must be chemically stable, not soften or slide off during summer, revert to its original state when cooled and not craze or form a skin. It should be easy to put on and remove since it will have to be replaced at intervals of about 12 months, depending on the rate of pollution.

(ix) Oil bath post insulators of the type shown in figure 6.8 may be used.

A stack of five of these insulators, having an overall height of 184 cm, is required for each conductor of a three-phase, 132-kV line. The oil creeps over the whole of the insulator surfaces and has the same effect as greasing. Maintenance costs are much lower, however, and the oil baths may be replenished whilst the insulators are live.

(x) A semi-conducting glaze may be used on porcelain insulators. This type of glaze offers a high rather than infinite resistance to surface leakage currents. Because glaze has a negative temperature coefficient of resistance, the normal leakage current has to be limited to a value of the order of 1 mA. Otherwise the increase in surface temperature

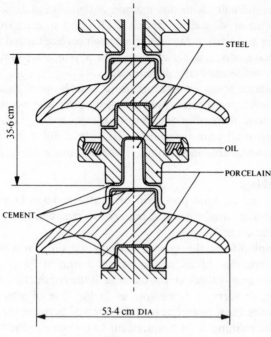

STEEL

OIL

PORCELAIN

CEMENT

35·6 cm

53·4 cm DIA

FIG. 6.8

caused by the flow of leakage current would reduce the glaze resistance to a value at which the temperature would increase cumulatively. Therefore the resistance of the semi-conducting glaze is arranged to be such that the leakage current is just sufficient to dry a wet insulator. Although insulating bands are still formed during drying, they do not interrupt the flow of leakage current through the glaze so that evaporation continues until the insulator is completely dry. In this way, the formation of the alternate wet and dry rings leading to pollution flashover is prevented.

The main difficulty with this method is that the resistance of semi-conducting glaze increases with time due to electrolytic corrosion. Glazes of titania/porcelain and tin-oxide have very slow corrosion rates and these are presently being developed.

(xi) Insulators made from materials other than porcelain or glass are being developed. Polytetrafluoroethylene (PTFE) is more water repellent than either glass or glazed porcelain. Also PTFE has a lower coefficient of friction and therefore stays cleaner longer. Coating insulators with PTFE or silicone rubber roughly doubles their effectiveness.

The main difficulty with this method is that all synthetic materials either track or erode during service. PTFE and silicone rubber have low tracking and erosion rates but the rough surface caused by erosion begins to have a noticeable effect within a year. Non-tracking, low erosion rate resins are being developed.

(xii) Insulated tower cross-arms using resin bonded glass fibre are also being developed. These would reduce the electric stress on insulator strings without increasing the tower size. Also the cross-arms are mainly horizontal and therefore well washed by rain. There are, however, considerable mechanical, tracking, and erosion difficulties.

Hollow Bushings

These are made from porcelain or synthetic resin bonded paper (S.R.B.P.) and are used when it is required to pass conductors through earthed metalwork.

In its simplest form, this type of bushing takes the form of a hollow cylinder surrounded by an earthed metal clamp or flange. The conductor passes axially through the bushing. If the conductors are subject to vibration or thermal expansion, as in the case of alternator and bus-bar connections, clearance must be allowed between them and the bushing. The bushing is then equivalent to two concentric capacitors.

Example 6-4. A conductor, 2 cm in diameter, passes centrally through a cylindrical bushing having internal and external diameters of 2·5 and 10 cm. The bushing is made from synthetic resin bonded paper of relative permittivity 4 and is surrounded by an earthed metal clamp.

Taking the breakdown strength of air as 30 kV peak/cm, calculate the greatest r.m.s. voltage that can be applied between the conductor and the clamp so that ionization does not occur in the air space inside the bushing.

From Section 5, flux density at any radius x

$$= D = \frac{q}{2\pi x} \text{ coulombs/m}^2.$$

Electric stress $= E = \dfrac{D}{\varepsilon} = \dfrac{q}{2\pi x \varepsilon}.$

Maximum stress in the air $= 30 \text{ kV peak/cm} = \dfrac{q}{2\pi \cdot 1 \cdot \varepsilon_0}.$

Maximum stress in the S.R.B.P. $= \dfrac{q}{2\pi \cdot 1 \cdot 25 \cdot 4 \cdot \varepsilon_0}.$

Let these values of stress be E_1 and E_2 respectively, then

$$\frac{E_1}{E_2} = \frac{q}{2\pi . 1 . \varepsilon_0} \times \frac{2\pi . 1.25 . 4 . \varepsilon_0}{q} = 5.$$

Hence $\quad\quad\quad\quad E_2 = 6 \text{ kV peak/cm.}$

Using $V = E . x . \log_e \dfrac{R}{r}$,

$\quad\quad V$ across the S.R.B.P. $= 6 . 1.25 . \log_e 4 = 10.4 \text{ kV peak}$

and $\quad\quad\quad V$ across the air $= 30 . 1 . \log_e 1.25 = 6.7 \text{ kV peak.}$

Thus total applied voltage $= 17.1 \text{ kV peak} = $ **12.1 kV r.m.s.**

Capacitor Bushings

Bushings are required where the connections to a transformer pass through the earthed tank. For the lower voltages, these bushings are of hollow porcelain with rain sheds similar to those on pin type insulators. Above 66 kV, however, the size of this type of bushing becomes excessive and capacitor type bushings may be used. These consist of concentric cylinders of oil-impregnated paper with conducting foil intersheaths. The dimensions of the cylinders are so arranged that the electric stress is more evenly distributed than if a homogeneous bushing were used. For outdoor use, the bushings are housed in hollow porcelain insulators with the usual rain sheds.

Example 6-5. Oil-impregnated paper of relative permittivity 3·5 was used for the capacitor bushing shown in figure 6.9.

The thickness of the conducting foil is negligible and the p.d. between the conductor and earth is 38·1 kV r.m.s.

Calculate:

(a) The capacitance of each cylinder.

(b) The voltage across each cylinder.

(c) The maximum stress in each cylinder.

(d) The maximum stress if a single cylinder of outside radius 4 cm were used.

(a) From Section 5, the capacitance between two concentric cylinders is C,

where $\quad\quad\quad\quad C = \dfrac{10^{-9} . \varepsilon_r}{18 . \log_e (R/r)} \text{ F/m.}$

Therefore $\quad\quad\quad C = \dfrac{10^3 . \varepsilon_r . l}{18 . \log_e (R/r)} \mu\mu\text{F,}$

where l is the length of the shorter of the two cylinders in metres.

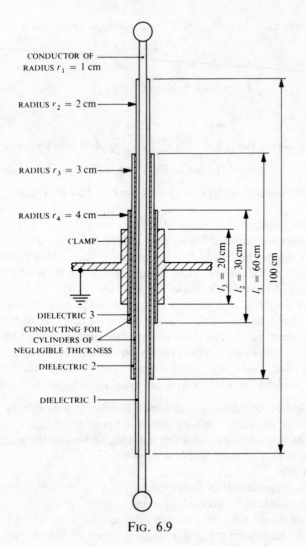

CONDUCTOR OF
RADIUS $r_1 = 1$ cm

RADIUS $r_2 = 2$ cm

RADIUS $r_3 = 3$ cm

RADIUS $r_4 = 4$ cm

CLAMP

$l_3 = 20$ cm

$l_2 = 30$ cm

$l_1 = 60$ cm

100 cm

DIELECTRIC 3
CONDUCTING FOIL
CYLINDERS OF
NEGLIGIBLE THICKNESS

DIELECTRIC 2

DIELECTRIC 1

FIG. 6.9

$$C_1 = \frac{10^3 \times 3\cdot5 \times 0\cdot6}{18 \times \log_e 2} = \mathbf{168\cdot3\,\mu\mu F.}$$

$$C_2 = \frac{10^3 \times 3\cdot5 \times 0\cdot3}{18 \times \log_e 1\cdot5} = \mathbf{143\cdot8\,\mu\mu F.}$$

$$C_3 = \frac{10^3 \times 3\cdot5 \times 0\cdot2}{18 \times \log_e 1\cdot333} = \mathbf{135\cdot3\,\mu\mu F.}$$

(b) Now $C_1 V_1 = C_2 V_2$,

giving $$V_2 = \frac{C_1}{C_2} \times V_1 = \frac{168 \cdot 3}{143 \cdot 8} \times V_1 = 1 \cdot 17 V_1.$$

Also $C_1 V_1 = C_3 V_3$,

giving $$V_3 = \frac{C_1}{C_3} \times V_1 = \frac{168 \cdot 3}{135 \cdot 3} \times V_1 = 1 \cdot 244 V_1.$$

Substituting, $V_1 + 1 \cdot 17 V_1 + 1 \cdot 244 V_1 = 38 \cdot 1 \text{ kV}$

and hence $$V_1 = \frac{38 \cdot 1}{3 \cdot 414} = \mathbf{11 \cdot 16 \, kV},$$

$$V_2 = 1 \cdot 17 \times 11 \cdot 16 = \mathbf{13 \cdot 05 \, kV}$$

and $$V_3 = 1 \cdot 244 \times 11 \cdot 16 = \mathbf{13 \cdot 88 \, kV.}$$

(c) Maximum $$E_1 = \frac{11 \cdot 16}{1 \times \log_e 2} = \mathbf{16 \cdot 1 \, kV \ r.m.s./cm.}$$

Maximum $$E_2 = \frac{13 \cdot 05}{2 \times \log_e 1 \cdot 5} = \mathbf{16 \cdot 1 \, kV \ r.m.s./cm.}$$

Maximum $$E_3 = \frac{13 \cdot 88}{3 \times \log_e 1 \cdot 333} = \mathbf{16 \cdot 1 \, kV \ r.m.s./cm.}$$

(d) Maximum $$E = \frac{38 \cdot 1}{1 \times \log_e 4} = \mathbf{27 \cdot 5 \, kV \ r.m.s./cm.}$$

For the same value of maximum stress in each cylinder of a capacitor bushing,

$$\frac{V_1}{r_1 \times \log_e (r_2/r_1)} = \frac{V_2}{r_2 \times \log_e (r_3/r_2)} = \frac{V_3}{r_3 \times \log_e (r_4/r_3)} \qquad (1)$$

But $C_1 V_1 = C_2 V_2 = C_3 V_3$, so that

$$\frac{l_1 \times V_1}{\log_e (r_2/r_1)} = \frac{l_2 \times V_2}{\log_e (r_3/r_2)} = \frac{l_3 \times V_3}{\log_e (r_4/r_3)} \qquad (2)$$

Dividing (2) by (1) gives

$$l_1 \times r_1 = l_2 \times r_2 = l_3 \times r_3.$$

It can be seen that the dimensions of the capacitor bushing in example 6-5 obey this condition, i.e.

$$60 \times 1 = 30 \times 2 = 20 \times 3.$$

Hence the value of maximum stress for each cylinder is the same.

Example 6-6. A capacitor bushing is to be made from four insulating cylinders of equal radial thickness separated by conducting foil cylinders of negligible thickness. The radius of the conductor is 1·5 cm and the internal radius of the earthed flange is 3·5 cm. The axial length of the innermost foil cylinder is to be 100 cm.

Calculate:

(a) The axial lengths of the other foil cylinders and the earthed flange so that the same value of maximum stress is obtained in each insulating cylinder.

(b) The greatest r.m.s. voltage that can be applied between the conductor and the earthed flange if the maximum value of stress is not to exceed 15 kV r.m.s./cm.

(a) Using the same method of dimensioning as in example 6-5,

$$100 \times 1.5 = l_2 \times 2 = l_3 \times 2.5 = l_4 \times 3.$$

Thus $\qquad$ $l_2 = 75$ **cm**, $l_3 = 60$ **cm and** $l_4 = 50$ **cm.**

(b) $V_1 = 1.5 \times 15 \times \log_e 1.333 = 6.47$ kV.

$V_2 = 2 \times 15 \times \log_e 1.25 = 6.69$ kV.

$V_3 = 2.5 \times 15 \times \log_e 1.2 = 6.84$ kV.

$V_4 = 3 \times 15 \times \log_e 1.167 = 6.95$ kV.

Hence the applied voltage is $6.47 + 6.69 + 6.84 + 6.95 = $ **27 kV.**

EXAMPLES 6

1. Sketch and account for the basic shape of a pin type insulator suitable for 11 kV. Indicate the materials used and discuss their properties.

Describe the electrical and mechanical tests usually applied to such an insulator.

2. Describe the process leading to pollution flashover.

Discuss the methods which may be used to reduce the probability of pollution flashovers in badly polluted locations.

3. A string of four suspension insulators is used to support one conductor of a 33-kV, three-phase, overhead line. The air capacitance between each cap/pin junction and the tower is one sixth of the capacitance of each unit.

Calculate the voltage across each insulator and the string efficiency.

Explain how the voltage distribution may be modified by (a) the fitting of a guard ring, and (b) the use of partially conducting glaze.

Mention another important function of the guard ring and this type of glaze.

(Answers **3·27 kV, 3·81 kV, 5 kV, 7 kV, 0·682.**)

4. A string of six suspension insulators is used to support one conductor of a 66-kV, three-phase, overhead line. The air capacitance between each cap/pin junction and the tower is one tenth of the capacitance of each unit.

Calculate the voltage across each insulator and the string efficiency.

State how and why the string efficiency is modified when the insulators are wet.

(Answers **3·77 kV, 4·15 kV, 4·94 kV, 6·23 kV, 8·14 kV, 10·86 kV, 0·585.**)

5. Sketch and account for the basic shape of a suspension type insulator suitable for 11 kV.

Each conductor of a 66-kV, three-phase, overhead line is to be supported by a string of four suspension units. The air capacitance between each cap/pin junction and the tower is one sixth of the capacitance of each unit.

A guard ring, effective only over the line-end unit, is to be fitted so that the voltage on the two units nearest the line is the same.

Calculate:

(a) The voltage on the line-end unit.

(b) The capacitance, in terms of the cap/pin junction to earth capacitance (C_e), between the guard ring and the cap/pin junction of the two units nearest the line.

(Answers **11·15 kV, 2·42 C_e.**)

6. A string of four suspension insulators is to be used to support an overhead conductor at 20 kV to earth. The air capacitance between each cap/pin junction and the tower ($= C_e$) is one sixth of the capacitance of each unit.

Calculate:

(a) The air capacitances required, in terms of C_e, between each cap/pin junction and a guard ring clamped to the conductor so that the voltage distribution over the string is uniform.

(b) The voltage distribution if the air capacitance between the guard ring and the cap/pin junction nearest the conductor is $2C_e$, that between the guard ring and the next cap/pin junction is C_e and that between the guard ring and the remaining cap/pin junction is negligible.

(Answers (a) **3C_e, C_e, C_e/3**, (b) **4·39 kV, 5·12 kV, 4·96 kV, 5·53 kV.**)

7. A conductor, 4 cm in diameter, passes centrally through a cylindrical bushing having internal and external diameters of 5 and

12 cm. The bushing is made from porcelain of relative permittivity 4 and is surrounded by an earthed metal clamp.

Taking the breakdown strength of air as 30 kV peak/cm, calculate the greatest r.m.s. voltage that can be applied between the conductor and the clamp so that ionization does not occur in the air space inside the bushing.

(Answer **18·75 kV.**)

8. Oil-impregnated paper of relative permittivity 3·5 is used for the capacitor bushing shown in figure 6.10.

An r.m.s. voltage of 54 kV at 50 Hz is applied between the conductor and earth.

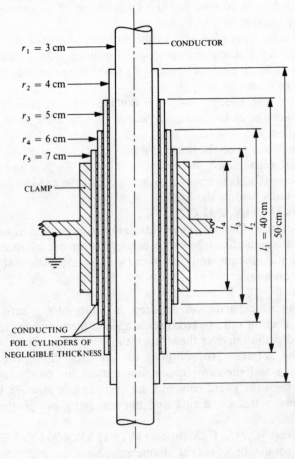

$r_1 = 3$ cm
$r_2 = 4$ cm
$r_3 = 5$ cm
$r_4 = 6$ cm
$r_5 = 7$ cm

CONDUCTOR

CLAMP

CONDUCTING
FOIL CYLINDERS OF
NEGLIGIBLE THICKNESS

l_4 l_3 l_2 $l_1 = 40$ cm 50 cm

FIG. 6.10

Calculate:

(a) The values of l_2, l_3 and l_4 required for the same value of maximum stress in each dielectric.

(b) The capacitance of each cylinder.

(c) The voltage across each dielectric.

(d) The maximum stress.

(e) The total capacitance of the bushing.

(f) The capacitance current.

(Answers (a) **30 cm, 24 cm, 20 cm,** (b) **271 μμF, 261 μμF, 256 μμF, 252 μμF,** (c) **13 kV, 13·4 kV, 13·7 kV, 13·9 kV,** (d) **15 kV r.m.s./cm,** (e) **64·9 μμF,** (f) **1·1 mA.**)

9. A capacitor bushing is to be made from ten insulating cylinders of equal radial thickness separated by conducting foil cylinders of negligible thickness. The radius of the conductor is 2 cm and the internal radius of the earthed flange is 7 cm. The oil-impregnated paper used for the insulating cylinders has a relative permittivity of 3·3 and the innermost foil cylinder has an axial length of 120 cm. The maximum stress is to be 14 kV r.m.s./cm in each dielectric.

Calculate:

(a) The axial lengths of the other foil cylinders and the earthed flange.

(b) The voltage across the innermost dielectric.

(c) The capacitance of the innermost dielectric.

(d) The capacitance current at 50 Hz.

(Answers (a) **96 cm, 80 cm, 68·6 cm, 60 cm, 53·3 cm, 48 cm, 43·6 cm, 40 cm, 36·9 cm,** (b) **6·69 kV r.m.s.,** (c) **986 μμF,** (d) **2·07 mA.**)

7

Overhead Lines

Conductor Materials

Conductors for overhead lines are usually stranded, unless they are of small cross-section, because the continuous swinging and vibration would otherwise produce mechanical fatigue and hence fracture at the insulator clamps.

Because of dirt and oxide films on the surface of each strand, the current flows spirally through the strands rather than axially from strand to strand. The resistance and inductance are therefore slightly higher than those of a solid conductor.

The following materials are used for the conductors of overhead transmission lines:

(i) COPPER has a high electrical conductivity and considerable tensile strength. The conductivity is considerably reduced if impurities are present. Cold working slightly reduces the conductivity but improves the tensile strength. For example, the tensile strength of hard drawn copper wire is 354 MN/m^2 at 1·02 cm diameter and 456 MN/m^2 at 0·163 cm diameter. Copper does not corrode in normal atmospheres and is widely used.

(ii) ALUMINIUM has a density about one-third that of copper, is cheaper than copper, and has a tensile strength in the region of 154–200 MN/m^2. The conductivity of aluminium is about 0·6 times that of copper so that, for the same resistance per unit length, the cross-sectional area of an aluminium conductor is about 1·6 times that of a copper conductor. The weight of the aluminium conductor would be about half that of the copper conductor but, due to the lower tensile strength of aluminium, the advantage is almost negligible. Furthermore, the greater wind and ice loading caused by the larger diameter of the aluminium makes copper superior in adverse conditions. The larger diameter of the aluminium does, however, reduce the electric stress at the conductor surface so that the power loss due to corona is lower than that for an equivalent copper line.

In normal atmospheres, a thin oxide film formed on the surface of aluminium gives high corrosion resistance.

The chief field of application for aluminium is heavy current transmission where the volume of conductor material is high and its cost forms a high proportion of the total cost of the installation.

(iii) STEEL-CORED ALUMINIUM conductors have a core of galvanized steel strands surrounded by one or more layers of aluminium strands. The steel takes the greater part of the mechanical load and the aluminium carries most of the current. This type of conductor is usually cheaper than a copper conductor of equal length and resistance. Steel-cored aluminium is also about 50 per cent stronger and 20 per cent lighter than copper.

For example, a 183-m span length of copper of 0·966 cm^2 section, erected at -5.5°C with a safety factor of 2, an ice load of 0·953 cm radial thickness, and a wind load of 383 N/m^2 of projected area, will have a sag of about 4·3 m at 50°C in still air. Under the same conditions, the sag with an equivalent steel-cored aluminium conductor is about 2·2 m. Hence the supporting towers may be either 2·2 m shorter or spaced further apart, without reducing the ground clearance, if steel-cored aluminium is used. Increasing the span length results in a greater economy than reducing the tower height. Using towers of the same height as those required for the above copper line, the span may be increased to 252 m with steel-cored aluminium without reducing the ground clearance. In this way the number of towers is reduced by 27 per cent. The towers would be more expensive than those for the copper line since the increased span causes a greater mechanical load. However, the increase in individual cost is more than cancelled by the reduction in number. The number of insulators required would also be reduced.

Reducing the number of supports has the additional advantage that the line is made more reliable in operation. This is because the majority of shutdowns during the operation of an overhead line are caused by faults arising at the supports, such as damaged insulators, pollution flashovers, and so on.

Corona losses are lower for a steel-cored aluminium line than for copper because the diameter of a steel-cored aluminium conductor is greater than that of the equivalent copper conductor.

Steel-cored aluminium conductors are very widely used for overhead lines of all voltages.

(iv) COPPER-CLAD STEEL conductors are used for very long spans such as river crossings. Steel wire is enclosed within an annular section of copper and the combination is rolled to form the strands of the conductor. The tensile strength of the composite conductor is much greater than that of the equivalent copper conductor but the conductivity of copper-clad steel is only about 0·35 times that of copper.

(v) CADMIUM COPPER conductors are more expensive than pure copper and are used mainly for long spans of conductors of small cross-section where the cost of the conductor does not form a high proportion of the total cost of the installation. The addition of about one per cent of cadmium increases the tensile strength of copper about 1·5 times but reduces its conductivity by about 15 per cent.

(vi) PHOSPHOR BRONZE conductors are used for exceptionally long spans in atmospheres containing corrosive gases such as ammonia. Phosphor bronze has a much greater tensile strength but a much poorer conductivity than copper. A few strands of cadmium copper are usually added to improve the conductivity.

(vii) GALVANIZED STEEL conductors are used for very long spans, for short sections abnormally stressed due to climatic conditions, for some overhead earth wires, and for some rural distribution lines. The initial cost is much lower than that of any other conductor but the conductivity of steel is low and its inductive reactance high, giving high voltage drops.

Line Supports

For rural distribution lines up to 33 kV with spans of the order of 61 m, wooden poles are initially cheaper than concrete or steel supports. The life of a wooden pole is somewhat uncertain, however,

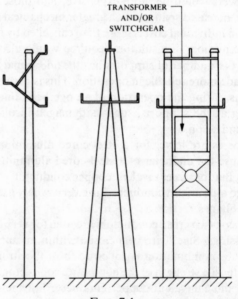

TRANSFORMER
AND/OR
SWITCHGEAR

FIG. 7.1

since it depends on its location and treatment before erection. Winter felled, red fir poles impregnated with creosote under pressure are very widely used in the United Kingdom. Pine, cedar, and chestnut poles are also used. Some typical wooden supports are shown in figure 7.1.

Single poles are common, 'A' type poles are used where greater strength is required and 'H' type poles are used where it is necessary to support switchgear and/or a transformer as well as the line.

Reinforced concrete poles have a higher initial cost but a longer life than wooden poles and are used widely in Europe and America.

The insulators used on wooden and concrete poles are usually of the pin type because they are cheaper than strings of suspension insulators for voltages up to about 50 kV.

For grid lines of the order of 132 kV and above, galvanized or painted steel towers are essential because wide bases are required to withstand the high mechanical stresses encountered. If one or more conductors break, there is a longitudinal pull on the tower in addition to the normal downward and transverse loads. Longitudinal pulls are also exerted when the spans are of unequal length and when the route changes direction. Since such pulls exert a twisting moment on the tower, its strength in the longitudinal direction is usually not less than one quarter of its strength in the transverse direction.

A standard, double-circuit, 132-kV, British grid tower is shown in figure 7.2.

In this and subsequent figures, E indicates the position of the earth wires.

The single, steel-cored aluminium, stranded conductors are supported by strings of standard 25·4 cm diameter, glass or porcelain, suspension or tension units. The number of units in each string varies between nine and twelve and depends on site conditions such as pollution rate.

Larger, stronger towers are required for wide river crossings. For example, one 132-kV, three-phase line crossing the River Thames has a span of 934 m and is supported by towers 149 m high. The usual span length is of the order of 275 to 305 m.

Stronger towers with wider bases are also required at points where the route changes direction by more than 2 degrees.

The tower foundations are of concrete and their complexity depends on the above factors and on the nature of the ground.

For the British 275-kV grid, towers are used of similar design to that shown in figure 7.2 except that all the dimensions are approximately one and a half times larger. Each phase consists of two parallel, steel-cored aluminium conductors held 30·5 cm apart by metal spacers

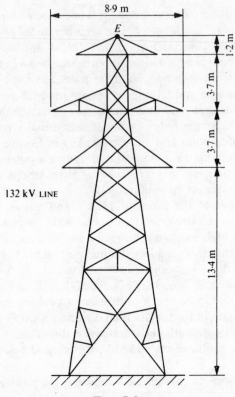

FIG. 7.2

at 122 m intervals. This type of twin conductor is known as a two-bundle conductor. The reasons for the use of bundle conductors will be discussed later. Each phase is supported by twin parallel strings of 2×18, 25.4 cm diameter insulators.

Figure 7.3 shows the comparative sizes of the 220-kV and 500-kV, three-phase, single-circuit towers used on the Southern Californian transmission system.

The position of the insulator strings is shown dotted.

On the 500-kV system, two-bundle conductors are used. These consist of two parallel, 4.48 cm diameter, steel-cored aluminium stranded conductors per phase, spaced 46 cm apart. The vee-string formation of insulators is used for economic reasons, each leg of the vee consisting. of 27, 14.6×25.4 cm diameter units. The two earth wires are insulated for use in communication and protective circuits.

In Britain, 400-kV, three-phase, double-circuit lines are being commissioned. Each phase consists of four 2.28 cm^2, steel-cored

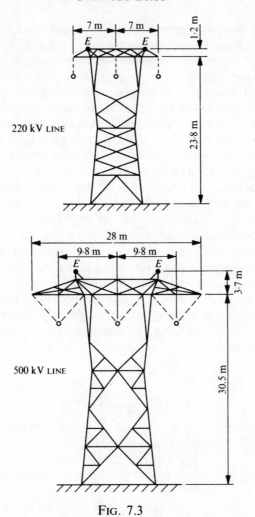

FIG. 7.3

aluminium conductors spaced on the corners of a 30·5 cm square. Metal spacers are used to maintain this formation at intervals of about 76 m. The conductors are supported by twin parallel strings of 2 × 25, 25·4 cm diameter insulators. The standard span length is 366 m, but owing to the varying terrain, spans varying between 168 m and 488 m are not uncommon.

Tests are being carried out on an 800-kV, double-circuit, three-phase, experimental line which has been erected at the C.E.G.B. Research Laboratories at Leatherhead. This line at present consists of one 366 m suspension span and two 183 m tension spans. Each phase of one circuit consists of four steel-cored aluminium conductors, each 2·86 cm in diameter and equivalent to a 2·58 cm² cross-section of copper. The duplex vertical suspension strings contain 2 × 32, 35·6 cm diameter insulators and the roughly horizontal quadruple tension strings contain 4 × 35, 33 cm diameter insulators. Corona loss and radio interference limit the operating voltage of this circuit to about 650 kV. Each phase of the second circuit consists of four steel-cored aluminium conductors, each 3·47 cm in diameter and equivalent to a 3·87 cm² cross-section of copper. The duplex suspension strings contain 2 × 40, 35·6 cm diameter insulators and the quadruple tension strings contain 4 × 43, 33 cm diameter insulators. It is hoped that an operating voltage of 800 kV will be possible with this circuit. In both circuits, the conductors are spaced on the corners of a 30·5 cm square and all the insulators are of toughened glass.

These circuits are being used to investigate problems connected with pollution flashover, corona power loss and radio interference, lightning and switching surges, and conductor spacing.

In Canada 500-kV lines are in operation. The Ontario Hydro-electricity Commission have used lightweight, guyed aluminium towers of the vee type shown in figure 7.4 to support a single-circuit, three-phase, four-bundle conductor line.

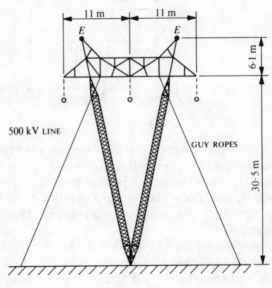

FIG. 7.4

These towers were pre-assembled and flown to the site by helicopter, thus saving a considerable amount of erection time, particularly where the lines were routed through difficult terrain.

By 1970 Quebec had 1,610 circuit kilometres of 735-kV transmission linking the load centres on the St Lawrence River with hydroelectric stations some 805 km distant. Quebec's 1968 load of 6,000 MW is expected to rise to 26,000 MW by 1985, by which time about ten 735-kV circuits will be required.

The first section was commissioned in 1965 and uses four-bundle conductors spaced on the corners of a 45·7 cm square. The phases are spaced 15·3 m apart and this was determined mainly by corona considerations. On river crossings spans are up to 1,800 m, the phase spacing is 24·4 m, and the towers are 168 m high.

A transmission voltage of 1·4 million is proposed for a very long direct-current link in the USSR between the Urals and Siberia.

Conductor Vibration

Mechanical vibrations in overhead conductors and earth wires are of four types:

(i) Swinging of the conductors caused by changes in wind pressure. This is harmless provided that sufficient clearance is left between conductors to prevent flashover. Larger clearances will be required on long spans such as river crossings.

(ii) Dancing of the conductors caused by irregular coatings of sleet in wind. Parts of the conductor are temporarily changed from round to oval section and the wind causes varying amounts of aerodynamic lift throughout the conductor length. The conductors may dance vertically or horizontally with an amplitude great enough to cause them to touch each other. The use of bundle conductors increases the tendency to dance because of torsional oscillations of the bundle and the use of rigid spacers.

(iii) Jumping of the conductors caused by the sudden shedding of ice loads. The worst jumping occurs when ice melts from the centre span of a section after it has fallen from the other spans. Serious jumping also takes place when ice slips down the conductor towards midspan. The distance through which the conductor jumps may be of the order of 6·1 to 15·3 m and nearly 4 per cent of all faults on the British 132-kV and 275-kV lines are due to this cause. Attempts have been made to inhibit conductor jumping by fitting special insulator assemblies at the suspension points and by increasing the mass per unit length of line at midspan. It has not been possible, however, to achieve a sufficient reduction in jump height to prevent the conductors from clashing. In regions subject to ice loads in excess of 1·49 kg/m of single conductor (a radial thickness of ice of about 1·53 cm on a standard 132-kV line), it is therefore necessary to increase the conductor spacing.

(iv) High frequency vibrations caused by the formation of eddies on the leeward side of a conductor. The frequency of the oscillations is of the order of 5 to 100 Hz and their amplitude is about 1·3 centimetres. These vibrations may cause failure of the conductor at the supporting clamps due to metal fatigue. This is less likely when the conductor clamps have been carefully designed or when the conductor has been reinforced for a few metres on either side of the clamp. A more effective method, however, is to prevent the oscillations from reaching the clamps by suspending a Stockbridge damper from each conductor near each point of entry into a clamp. The Stockbridge damper shown in figure 7·5 weighs 5·9 kg and there are other sizes weighing from 1 to 7·3 kg.

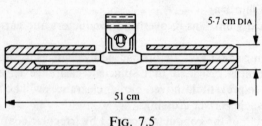

5·7 cm DIA

51 cm

FIG. 7.5

The damper consists of two hollow, cylindrical weights fixed at their outer ends to a length of stranded steel cable. This is fixed to the conductor by means of an aluminium clamp using a single bolt. The two weights are usually of galvanized iron and the damper cable is enclosed in a flexible, water-tight sheath. If necessary, dampers may be fitted whilst a line is live with the aid of special tools.

High frequency vibrations in the conductor cause small oscillations of the weights about their supporting clamp. The energy of these oscillations is converted to heat by the bending of the damper cable and the friction between its strands. In this way the amplitude of the vibrations is reduced to a negligible value.

High frequency vibrations in bundle conductors are considerably smaller than those in single conductors. The use of spacers every 46 to 61 m reduces the amplitude and duration of the vibrations in a two-bundle conductor to about half those in a single conductor, but it is still necessary to clamp Stockbridge dampers to every conductor. The same applies to three- and four-bundle conductors.

Bundle Conductors

On the 275-kV British grid, two-bundle conductors are used. Since the twin conductors of any phase are instantaneously carrying currents in the same direction and are also instantaneously at the same potential, the electromagnetic forces tend to draw the conductors together and the electrostatic forces to force them apart. Since the electromagnetic forces predominate, the spacing between the twin conductors varies from 30·5 cm at the spacers to 20·3 cm midway between the spacers when they are at 122 m intervals.

The advantages derived from the use of two-bundle conductors instead of single conductors per phase are:

(i) The line inductance and inductive reactance are reduced by about 25 per cent. This is due to the reduction in magnetic flux caused by the increased length of the magnetic circuit through the air surrounding each phase.

(ii) The voltage to cause corona is 5 to 10 per cent higher. This is due to the reduction in electric stress at the conductor surfaces caused by the increase in the effective radius from which the electric flux emanates.

(iii) More current may be carried per unit mass of conductor. For the same total cross-sectional area of conductor, the surface area is increased by about 1·4 times (see 'skin effect').

(iv) The amplitude and duration of high frequency vibrations may be halved.

Greater improvements than those listed above are derived from using three- or four-bundle conductors.

The disadvantages of bundle conductors are:

(i) Increased ice and wind loading.

(ii) Suspension is more complicated and duplex or quadruple insulator strings may be necessary.

(iii) The tendency to dance is increased.

For transmission voltages above about 250 kV line, the advantages outweigh the disadvantages. It is usual to use two-bundle conductors in the region of 275 kV line and four-bundle conductors at 400 kV line and above.

Calculation of Line Tension—Catenary Method

A uniform conductor suspended in still air from two supports takes the form of a catenary, as shown in figure 7.6.

Let the OX axis be some unknown distance AO m from the point A.

Let the mass per metre run of conductor be w kg and the curved length of portion AP, s m.

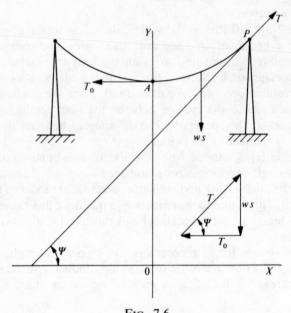

FIG. 7.6

Then, for equilibrium of this portion, a triangle of forces is formed by the tension at the point P ($= T$ kg), the mass ws kg and the tension at the point A ($= T_0$ kg), as shown in figure 7.6.

Now let $T_0 = wc$ = the mass of some unknown length of conductor = c m. Then

$$T^2 = (wc)^2 + (ws)^2 = w^2 \cdot (c^2 + s^2),$$

and therefore $\qquad T = w \cdot \sqrt{(c^2 + s^2)}$ kg. $\qquad\qquad\qquad$ (1)

Also $\qquad\qquad \tan \Psi = \dfrac{ws}{T_0} = \dfrac{ws}{wc} = \dfrac{s}{c},$

so that $\qquad\qquad s = c \cdot \tan \Psi$ m. $\qquad\qquad\qquad\qquad\qquad$ (2)

In the triangle shown in figure 7.7, ds m represents a very short portion of the conductor, in the region of P.

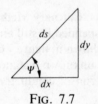

FIG. 7.7

Hence $\dfrac{dx}{ds} = \cos \Psi.$

However, $\dfrac{dx}{ds} = \cos \Psi = \dfrac{T_0}{T} = \dfrac{wc}{w \cdot \sqrt{(c^2 + s^2)}} = \dfrac{c}{\sqrt{(c^2 + s^2)}}.$

Integrating with respect to s gives

$$\int \frac{dx}{ds} \cdot ds = \int \frac{c}{\sqrt{(c^2 + s^2)}} \cdot ds.$$

Therefore $\qquad x = c \cdot \sinh^{-1} \dfrac{s}{c} + K,$

where K is the constant of integration. But when $x = 0$, $\Psi = 0$ and $\cos \Psi = 1$, so that

$$c = \sqrt{(c^2 + s^2)}, \quad s = 0, \quad \text{and} \quad \sinh^{-1} \frac{s}{c} = 0.$$

Therefore $\quad K = 0 \quad$ and $\quad x = c \cdot \sinh^{-1} \dfrac{s}{c},$

which gives $\dfrac{x}{c} = \sinh^{-1} \dfrac{s}{c},$

and $\qquad \dfrac{s}{c} = \sinh \dfrac{x}{c}.$ \hfill (3)

From equation (2) and figure 7.7,

$$\frac{s}{c} = \tan \Psi = \frac{dy}{dx}.$$

Substituting this into equation (3),

$$\frac{dy}{dx} = \sinh \frac{x}{c}.$$

Integrating both sides with respect to x:

$$y = \int \sinh \frac{x}{c} \cdot dx = c \cdot \cosh \frac{x}{c} + Q,$$

where Q is the constant of integration.

Now let $AO = c$ m, then when $x = 0$, $y = c = c \cdot \cosh 0 + Q$. Therefore

$$Q = 0 \quad \text{and} \quad y = c \cdot \cosh \frac{x}{c}. \hfill (4)$$

Now from equation (3), $\qquad s = c \cdot \sinh \dfrac{x}{c}$,

so that $\qquad\qquad\qquad s^2 = c^2 \cdot \sinh^2 \dfrac{x}{c}.$ $\qquad\qquad$ (5)

From equation (4), $\qquad y^2 = c^2 \cdot \cosh^2 \dfrac{x}{c}.$ $\qquad\qquad$ (6)

Subtracting (5) from (6) gives

$$y^2 - s^2 = c^2 \cdot \left[\cosh^2 \frac{x}{c} - \sinh^2 \frac{x}{c} \right] = c^2,$$

from which follows $\quad y = \sqrt{(c^2 + s^2)}.$ $\qquad\qquad$ (7)

Substituting equation (7) into equation (1) gives

$$T = wy.$$

Thus the tension at any point (x, y) in the conductor equals wy kg. The tension is therefore a minimum at midspan and a maximum at the supports.

In figure 7.8, the conductor sag is d m, the span l m, and the curved length of conductor $2s$ m.

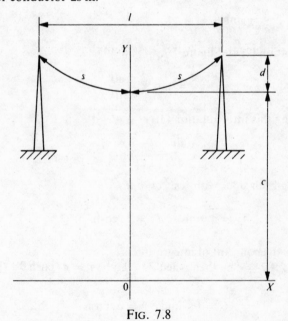

FIG. 7.8

T_{max} occurs at the supports where $y = c + d$ m. Substituting this into equation (7),

$$c + d = \sqrt{(c^2 + s^2)}.$$

Therefore $c^2 + 2cd + d^2 = c^2 + s^2$ and $c = \dfrac{s^2 - d^2}{2d}$

Hence we obtain

$$T_{max} = w \cdot (c + d) = w \cdot \left(\frac{s^2 - d^2}{2d} + d \right) = \frac{w \cdot (s^2 + d^2)}{2d} \text{ kg.}$$

T_{min} occurs at midspan where y equals c m, i.e.

$$T_{min} = wc = \frac{w \cdot (s^2 - d^2)}{2d} \text{ kg.}$$

Calculation of Line Tension—Parabolic Method

For most transmission lines, the sag is small compared with the span so that the curved length of conductor (l m) is approximately equal to the span length ($2s$ m). Thus $s \simeq l/2$.

Also, the mass of the half-span shown in figure 7.9 may be assumed to act at $l/4$ m from P. Let w = mass (kg) of conductor per metre run, T = tension (newtons), and d = sag (metres).

Taking moments about P, we have

moments clockwise = moments anticlockwise.

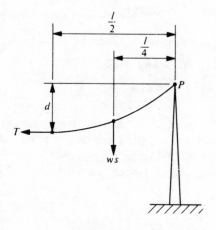

FIG. 7.9

This gives $\quad Td = 9{\cdot}81\,ws \cdot \dfrac{s}{2}$ newton . metres

i.e. $\qquad T = \dfrac{9{\cdot}81\,ws^2}{2d}$ newtons, where s = half the span.

This value is equal to the value of T_{min} obtained in the catenary method. Providing that d is small compared with s, the tension is almost constant throughout the conductor.

Example 7-1. A conductor hangs in the form of a catenary $y = c \cdot \cosh x/c$, where $c = 1{,}525$ m. If the span is 305 m and the conductor has a mass of 1·49 kg/m, calculate:

(a) The length of the conductor.

(b) The sag.

(c) The maximum and minimum values of tension using the catenary method.

(d) The approximate value of tension using the parabolic method.

(a) $y = 1{,}525 \cdot \cosh \dfrac{152{\cdot}5}{1{,}525} = 1{,}525 \cdot \cosh 0{\cdot}1$

$$= 1{,}525 \times 1{\cdot}005 = 1{,}532{\cdot}625 \text{ m.}$$

$$s = \sqrt{(y^2 - c^2)} = \sqrt{(1{,}532{\cdot}625^2 - 1{,}525^2)}$$

$$= \sqrt{(3{,}057{\cdot}625 \times 7{\cdot}625)} = \sqrt{23{,}314} = 152{\cdot}7 \text{ m.}$$

Therefore length of conductor = $2s$ = **305·4 m.**

(b) Sag = $d = y - c$ = **7·625 m.**

(c) $T_{max} = w \cdot (c + d) = wy = $ **2283·6 kg** = **22·4 kN.**

$T_{min} = wc = $ **2,272·3 kg** = **22·3 kN.**

(d) $T \simeq \dfrac{9{\cdot}81\,ws^2}{2d}\,\text{N} = \dfrac{9{\cdot}81 \times 1{\cdot}49 \times 152{\cdot}5^2}{2 \times 7{\cdot}625}\,\text{N} = $ **22·3 kN.**

Example 7-2. The maximum tension in a conductor suspended in still air from two towers at the same level is to be 2,000 kg. The conductor has a mass of 1·64 kg/m and is 300 m long.

Calculate the sag using, (a) the catenary method, and (b) the parabolic method.

(a) $T_{max} = \dfrac{w \cdot (s^2 + d^2)}{2d}\,\text{kg.}$

Substitution of the given values gives

$$4,000d = 1.64 . (150^2 + d^2) = 36,900 + 1.64d^2$$

from which

$$d = \frac{4,000 \pm \sqrt{(4,000^2 - 4 \times 1.64 \times 36,900)}}{2 \times 1.64}$$

$$= \frac{4,000 \pm \sqrt{15,760,000}}{3.28} = \frac{4,000 - 3,970}{3.28} = \mathbf{9.15\ m.}$$

(b) $T \simeq \dfrac{9.81\ ws^2}{2d}$ N. Thus $d \simeq \dfrac{9.81 \times 1.64 \times 150^2}{2 \times 9.81 \times 2,000} = \mathbf{9.23\ m.}$

It can be seen from examples 7-1 and 7-2 that the parabolic method is sufficiently accurate for practical purposes.

Calculation of Line Tension when the Supports are at Different Levels

In hilly country the supports may be at different levels. In still air, the conductor again takes the form of a catenary and the previously obtained expressions may be applied as shown in the following example.

Example 7-3. A conductor hangs in the form of a catenary $y = c . \cosh x/c$, where c is 1,525 m. The horizontal distance between the supports is 305 m and the conductor has a mass of 1.86 kg/m. If the horizontal distance between the lowest point in the catenary and the lower support is 54.9 m, calculate:

(a) The tension at each support.
(b) The minimum tension.
(c) The difference in levels of the supports.

(a) $y_1 = 1,525 . \cosh \dfrac{54.9}{1,525} = 1,525 . \cosh 0.036$

$$= 1,525 \times 1.00035 = 1,525.53\ m.$$

$$T_1 = wy_1 = 1.86 \times 1,525.53 = \mathbf{2,837.5\ kg.}$$

$$y_2 = 1,525 . \cosh \frac{250.1}{1,525} = 1,525 . \cosh 0.164$$

$$= 1,525 \times 1.01375 = 1,546\ m.$$

$$T_2 = wy_2 = 1.86 \times 1,546 = \mathbf{2,875.6\ kg.}$$

(b) $T_{\min} = wc = 1.86 \times 1,525 = 2,836\ kg = \mathbf{27.8\ kN.}$

(c) Difference in levels of the supports $= y_2 - y_1 = \mathbf{20.47\ m.}$

Calculation of Sag when the Supports are at Different Levels

Using the parabolic method and referring to figure 7.10:

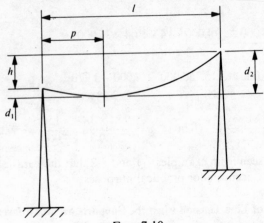

FIG. 7.10

$$d_2 \simeq \frac{9 \cdot 81w \cdot (l-p)^2}{2T} \quad \text{and} \quad d_1 \simeq \frac{9 \cdot 81wp^2}{2T}.$$

Hence $\quad h = d_2 - d_1 \simeq \dfrac{9 \cdot 81w}{2T} \cdot (l^2 - 2lp + p^2 - p^2) = \dfrac{9 \cdot 81wl}{2T} \cdot (l - 2p).$

Therefore $\quad l - 2p \simeq \dfrac{2Th}{9 \cdot 81wl} \quad \text{and} \quad p \simeq \dfrac{l}{2} - \dfrac{Th}{9 \cdot 81wl}.$

Example 7-4. An overhead line is supported in still air from two towers at levels of 30·5 m and 50·9 m above a horizontal datum line. The horizontal distance between the towers is 305 m. Calculate the sag if the conductor has a mass of 1·86 kg/m and the tension is to be 27·8 kN.

Referring to figure 7.10:

$$p \simeq \frac{l}{2} - \frac{Th}{9 \cdot 81wl} = 152 \cdot 5 - \frac{27,800 \times 20 \cdot 4}{9 \cdot 81 \times 1 \cdot 86 \times 305} = \mathbf{50 \cdot 5 \ m.}$$

$$d_1 \simeq \frac{9 \cdot 81wp^2}{2T} = \frac{9 \cdot 81 \times 1 \cdot 86 \times 50 \cdot 5^2}{2 \times 27,800} = \mathbf{0 \cdot 84 \ m.}$$

Or $\quad d_2 \simeq \dfrac{9 \cdot 81w \cdot (l-p)^2}{2T} = \dfrac{9 \cdot 81 \times 1 \cdot 86 \times 254 \cdot 5^2}{2 \times 27,800} = \mathbf{21 \cdot 24 \ m.}$

Comparing these figures with those in example 7-3, it can be seen that the discrepancies are small.

Effects of Ice and Wind Loading

Let the diameter of the conductor be d cm and the radial thickness of ice i cm. Then the cross-sectional area of the ice

$$= \frac{\pi}{4} \cdot [(d+2i)^2 - d^2]$$

$$= \frac{\pi}{4} \cdot (d^2 + 4id + 4i^2 - d^2)$$

$$= \pi i \cdot (d+i) \, \text{cm}^2.$$

Assume that the ice load is uniform throughout the length of the conductor, let the mass of ice be w_i kg/m, and take the density of ice as $912 \, \text{kg/m}^3$.

Then $\qquad w_i = \dfrac{\pi i \cdot (d+i) \cdot 912 \times 100}{10^6} = 0{\cdot}287 i \cdot (d+i) \, \text{kg/m}.$

It is usual to allow for the effect of wind by assuming it to blow uniformly and horizontally across the line.

Let the wind pressure exerted be $p \, \text{N/m}^2$ of projected area of ice covered line and let P kg/m be the resulting horizontal force exerted on the line.

Then $\qquad P = \dfrac{p \cdot (d+2i) \cdot 100}{10^4} \, \text{N/m} = \dfrac{p \cdot (d+2i)}{100} \, \text{N/m} = \dfrac{p \cdot (d+2i)}{981} \, \text{kg/m}.$

The effects of ice and wind may be combined with the mass of the conductor itself as shown in figure 7.11.

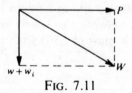

Fig. 7.11

Resultant force on line $= W = \sqrt{\{P^2 + (w + w_i)^2\}} \, \text{kg/m}.$

By replacing w by W in the previously derived expressions for tension and sag of a line in still air, these expressions may be applied to a wind- and ice-loaded line.

Safety Regulations

The regulations governing the erection of high voltage overhead lines in the United Kingdom specify that the tension must not be greater than half the breaking tension when a line is subjected to a horizontal wind pressure of 383 N/m² of total projected area of line covered with ice of radial thickness 0·953 cm at −5·5°C. (This wind pressure corresponds to a wind velocity of about 80 km/h perpendicular to the route.)

For voltages below 650 V d.c. and 325 V a.c., the same regulations apply except that the radial thickness of ice is taken as 0·477 cm.

It is not economical to design an overhead line to withstand the worst possible conditions, but experience has shown that the above regulations give a reasonable degree of safety and reliability.

The regulations also specify minimum ground clearances of the order of 6 to 7 m at 50°C. This is considered to be the highest temperature likely to occur in the United Kingdom in summer. The sag must therefore also be calculated at this temperature in order that the height of the towers may be determined.

Example 7-5. Using the parabolic method, calculate the approximate sag for a 305-m span of steel-cored aluminium conductor having a mass of 1·625 kg/m and having an overall diameter of 2·86 cm. Assume a radial thickness of ice of 0·953 cm and a wind pressure of 383 N/m² of total projected area. Take the breaking tension as 133·5 kN and use a safety factor of 2.

$$w_i = 0.287i \cdot (d+i) = 0.287 \times 0.953 \times 3.813 = 1.04 \text{ kg/m}.$$

$$P = \frac{p(d+2i)}{981} = \frac{383 \times 4.766}{981} = 1.86 \text{ kg/m}.$$

$$W = \sqrt{\{P^2 + (w+w_i)^2\}} = \sqrt{\{1.86^2 + (1.625 + 1.04)^2\}} = 3.25 \text{ kg/m}.$$

$$T = \frac{133,500}{2} = 66,750 \text{ N}.$$

$$\text{Sag} = d \simeq \frac{9.81 W s^2}{2T} = \frac{9.81 \times 3.25 \times 152.5^2}{2 \times 66,750} = \mathbf{5.55 \text{ m}.}$$

Example 7-6. Each phase of an overhead line consists of two steel-cored aluminium conductors spaced 30·5 cm apart. Each conductor has a mass of 2·01 kg/m, has an overall diameter of 3·18 cm and a steel core of cross-sectional area 0·684 cm². Add 2 per cent to the mass of each conductor for the mass of the spacers. The span is 366 m and the sag is 15·25 m when each conductor is coated with ice to a radial thickness of 0·953 cm and each is subjected to a wind pressure of 383 N/m² of total projected area.

For the above conditions, calculate the approximate value of stress in each steel core assuming that a negligible part of the mechanical load is supported by the aluminium.

Taking the ultimate tensile stress of the steel as 1,236 MN/m², calculate the safety factor.

Considering one conductor only, we have

$w = 2 \cdot 01 \times 1 \cdot 02 = 2 \cdot 05$ kg/m.

$w_i = 0 \cdot 287i \,.\, (d+i) = 0 \cdot 287 \times 0 \cdot 953 \times 4 \cdot 133 = 1 \cdot 13$ kg/m.

$P = \dfrac{p(d+2i)}{981} = \dfrac{383 \times 5 \cdot 086}{981} = 1 \cdot 985$ kg/m.

$W = \sqrt{\{P^2 + (w+w_i)^2\}} = \sqrt{\{1 \cdot 985^2 + (2 \cdot 05 + 1 \cdot 13)^2\}} = 3 \cdot 75$ kg/m.

$T \simeq \dfrac{9 \cdot 81 W s^2}{2d} = \dfrac{9 \cdot 81 \times 3 \cdot 75 \times 183^2}{2 \times 15 \cdot 25} = 40{,}400$ N.

$$\text{Stress} = \frac{0 \cdot 0404}{0 \cdot 684 \times 10^{-4}} \text{ MN/m}^2 = \mathbf{590\ MN/m^2}.$$

$\text{Safety factor} = \dfrac{1{,}236}{590} = \mathbf{2 \cdot 1}.$

Conditions during Erection

Overhead lines are not erected under the conditions of ice and wind loading specified in the safety regulations. The load during erection will be less than that laid down in the regulations so that the tension will be less. The resulting elastic contraction of the conductor slightly reduces the sag.

Also the temperature during erection will be higher than $-5 \cdot 5$°C. The resulting expansion of the conductor increases the sag.

The overall effect is for the sag to increase with temperature so that on hot summer days the sag may exceed the value calculated for the adverse regulation conditions.

In practice, the conductor is first suspended from the pulleys of snatch-blocks, pulled up to the correct sag or tension and then transferred to the insulators. It is not usual to measure the tension as the friction in the snatch-blocks makes accurate measurement difficult. Instead, a 2×5 cm white-painted batten is fixed horizontally to each of two adjacent towers. A man on one tower keeps his line of sight level with the battens and the conductor is raised until he signals that the sag is correct. In calculating this value of sag, due account is taken of the differences between the conditions during erection and those specified in the regulations.

Inductance of a Single-phase Overhead Line

Consider two parallel conductors in air, each of radius r metres and spaced d metres between centres.

Let the conductors carry the same current, I amperes, in opposite directions.

One of the conductors is shown in figure 7.12, all the dimensions being in metres.

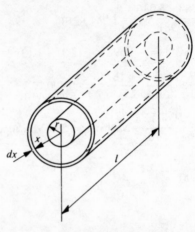

FIG. 7.12

Let the magnetic flux set up in the elementary cylinder by the current in this conductor be $d\Phi$ weber.

The length of the magnetic path in the elementary cylinder is $2\pi x$ metre and the cross-sectional area of this path is $dx . l$ m^2.

Let the flux density at radius $x = B$ Wb/m^2, where

$$B = \frac{d\Phi}{dx . l} \text{ Wb/m}^2.$$

Let the magnetizing force at radius x be H A.t/m,

then
$$H = \frac{I \times 1}{2\pi x} \text{A.t/m}.$$

But $B = \mu_0 H$, so that

$$\frac{d\Phi}{dx . l} = \frac{4\pi}{10^7} \times \frac{I}{2\pi x},$$

and
$$\frac{d\Phi}{dx} = \frac{2Il}{10^7} \times \frac{1}{x}.$$

Both conductors are shown in figure 7.13.

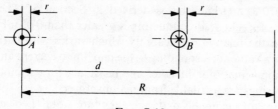

Fig. 7.13

In this figure, R metres is some very large radius at which the flux is zero.

Consider only the flux which links with conductor B:

Flux set up by $+I$ amperes flowing in conductor B

$$= \frac{2Il}{10^7} \cdot \int_r^R \frac{1}{x} \cdot dx$$

$$= \frac{2Il}{10^7} \cdot \log_e \frac{R}{r} \text{ Wb.}$$

Flux set up by $-I$ amperes flowing in conductor A

$$= \frac{-2Il}{10^7} \cdot \int_d^R \frac{1}{x} \cdot dx$$

$$= \frac{-2Il}{10^7} \cdot \log_e \frac{R}{d} \text{ Wb.}$$

Thus, total flux linking with conductor B

$$= \frac{2Il}{10^7} \cdot \left(\log_e \frac{R}{r} - \log_e \frac{R}{d} \right)$$

$$= \frac{2Il}{10^7} \cdot \log_e \frac{d}{r} \text{ Wb.}$$

But inductance (L henrys) = flux linkages per ampere, hence

$$L \text{ of conductor } B \text{ only} = \frac{2l}{10^7} \cdot \log_e \frac{d}{r} \text{ H.}$$

or

$$L = 0.2 \log_e \frac{d}{r} \text{ mH/km.}$$

To this must be added the internal inductance of the conductor. The internal inductance of a conductor composed of non-magnetic material is 0·05 mH/km (this is derived in Section 5). The internal inductance of steel-cored conductors is greater than 0·05 mH/km and depends on the relative permeability which varies with current. It is usual to use a value corresponding to the maximum current anticipated. Tables giving values of inductance and resistance for various sizes and current densities are available from manufacturers.

Assuming non-magnetic material, therefore, total L of conductor B only = $0·05 + 0·2 \log_e (d/r)$ mH/km.

This is also the inductance of conductor A.

Since the two conductors are in series, the total inductance of the line = $0·1 + 0·4 \log_e (d/r)$ mH/route km.

Inductance of a Three-phase, Three-wire Overhead Line

(a) Symmetrically Spaced Conductors

The three conductors are said to be symmetrically spaced when their centres lie on the corners of an equilateral triangle.

Let each side of the triangle be d metres long and the radius of each conductor be r metres.

Let the three instantaneous values of current be i_A, i_B, and i_C amperes. Then $i_A + i_B + i_C = 0$, so that $i_B + i_C = -i_A$.

This is true for every instant.

Using a similar method to that used in deriving the inductance of a single-phase line:

Let R metres be some very large radius at which the flux is zero.

Consider only the flux which links with conductor A:

Flux set up by i_A amperes flowing in conductor A

$$= \frac{2i_A l}{10^7} \cdot \log_e \frac{R}{r} \text{ Wb.}$$

Flux set up by i_B amperes flowing in conductor B

$$= \frac{2i_B l}{10^7} \cdot \log_e \frac{R}{d} \text{ Wb.}$$

Flux set up by i_C amperes flowing in conductor C

$$= \frac{2i_C l}{10^7} \cdot \log_e \frac{R}{d} \text{ Wb.}$$

Hence the total flux linking with conductor A

$$= \frac{2l}{10^7} \cdot \left(i_A \cdot \log_e \frac{R}{r} + i_B \cdot \log_e \frac{R}{d} + i_C \cdot \log_e \frac{R}{d} \right)$$

$$= \frac{2l}{10^7} \cdot \left[i_A \cdot \log_e \frac{R}{r} + (i_B + i_C) \cdot \log_e \frac{R}{d} \right]$$

$$= \frac{2l}{10^7} \cdot \left(i_A \cdot \log_e \frac{R}{r} - i_A \cdot \log_e \frac{R}{d} \right)$$

$$= \frac{2i_A l}{10^7} \cdot \log_e \frac{d}{r} \text{ Wb.}$$

Therefore the inductance of conductor A only

$$= \frac{2l}{10^7} \cdot \log_e \frac{d}{r} \text{ H}$$

$$= 0 \cdot 2 \log_e \frac{d}{r} \text{ mH/km.}$$

Assuming non-magnetic material and adding the internal inductance, gives for the total inductance of conductor A,

$$0 \cdot 05 + 0 \cdot 2 \log_e (d/r) \text{ mH/km.}$$

This is also the inductance of each of the other conductors.
Thus this expression gives the phase value of inductance.

(b) Asymmetrically Spaced Conductors
Let the conductors be spaced as shown in figure 7.14, all the dimensions being in metres.

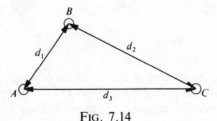

FIG. 7.14

Since the conductors are no longer equidistant, the inductance is no longer the same for each phase. In practice the difference may be averaged out by transposing the conductors as shown in figure 7.15.

Each conductor then occupies each position for one third of the length of the line.

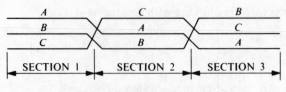

FIG. 7.15

Assuming that the conductors are transposed in this way, average inductance per phase

$$= \frac{2l}{10^7} \cdot \left(\frac{1}{3} \cdot \log_e \frac{d_1}{r} + \frac{1}{3} \cdot \log_e \frac{d_2}{r} + \frac{1}{3} \cdot \log_e \frac{d_3}{r} \right)$$

$$= \frac{2l}{10^7} \cdot \left(\frac{1}{3} \cdot \log_e \frac{d_1 \cdot d_2 \cdot d_3}{r^3} \right) = \frac{2l}{10^7} \cdot \log_e \frac{\sqrt[3]{(d_1 \cdot d_2 \cdot d_3)}}{r} \text{ H.}$$

Hence the average total inductance per phase

$$0.05 + 0.2 \log_e \frac{d_e}{r} \text{ mH/km.}$$

where $d_e = \text{'effective spacing'} = \sqrt[3]{(d_1 \cdot d_2 \cdot d_3)}.$

(c) Flat Regular Spacing

The conductors may be spaced as shown in figure 7.16.

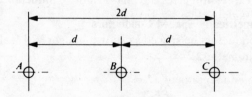

FIG. 7.16

Then the effective spacing $= d_e = \sqrt[3]{(d \cdot d \cdot 2d)} = \sqrt[3]{(2)} \cdot d = 1.26d.$

The majority of overhead conductors are transposed as shown in figure 7.15 in order to equalize the phase voltage drops due to the inductive and capacitive reactances and to minimize electromagnetic interference with neighbouring communication circuits.

Capacitance of a Single-phase Overhead Line

Consider two parallel conductors in air, each of radius r metres and spaced d metres between centres, as shown in figure 7.17.

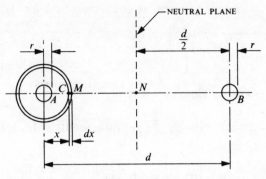

Fig. 7.17

Let the potential difference between the conductors be V volts and let the corresponding charge be q coulombs.

The number of lines of electric flux between the conductors is q.

Let the electric flux density at point C due to conductor A be D_A and that due to conductor B be D_B.

Considering one metre length of line, then

$$D_A = \frac{q}{2\pi x \times 1} \text{ coulombs/m}^2$$

and

$$D_B = \frac{q}{2\pi . (d-x) \times 1} \text{ coulombs/m}^2.$$

Let D be total flux density at C, then

$$D = \frac{q}{2\pi x} + \frac{q}{2\pi . (d-x)} \text{ coulombs/m}^2.$$

Let the potential gradient across $CM = dV/dx$, then

$$\frac{dV}{dx} = \frac{D}{\varepsilon} = \frac{q}{2\pi x \varepsilon} + \frac{q}{2\pi . (d-x) . \varepsilon}.$$

Therefore

$$V = \frac{q}{2\pi\varepsilon} . \int_r^{d-r} \left(\frac{1}{x} + \frac{1}{d-x} \right) . dx = \frac{q}{2\pi\varepsilon} . [\log_e x - \log_e (d-x)]_r^{d-r}$$

$$= \frac{q}{2\pi\varepsilon} . [\log_e (d-r) - \log_e r - \log_e r + \log_e (d-r)]$$

$$= \frac{q}{2\pi\varepsilon} . 2 . \log_e \left(\frac{d-r}{r} \right) = \frac{q . \log_e [(d-r)/r]}{\pi\varepsilon}.$$

Let the capacitance between the conductors be C farads; then

$$C = \frac{q}{V} \text{ F/m},$$

and hence

$$C = \frac{\pi\varepsilon}{\log_e [(d-r)/r]} \text{ F/m, line to line.}$$

But $\varepsilon = \varepsilon_0 \cdot \varepsilon_r$ where $\varepsilon_0 = \dfrac{1}{36\pi \times 10^9}$ and ε_r for air $\simeq 1$, so that

$$C = \frac{1}{36 \times 10^9 \times \log_e [(d-r)/r]} \text{F/m, line to line.}$$

or

$$C = \frac{1}{36 \cdot \log_e [(d-r)/r]} \mu\text{F/km, line to line.}$$

Let C_N be the capacitance between each conductor and the neutral plane, as shown in figure 7.18.

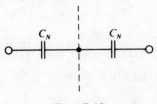

$$C_N \qquad\qquad C_N$$

FIG. 7.18

Then C_N must equal $2C$ so that the total capacitance between the conductors

$$= \frac{C_N \times C_N}{C_N + C_N} = \frac{C_N}{2} = C, \text{ as before. Hence}$$

$$C_N = 2C = \frac{1}{18 \cdot \log_e [(d-r)/r]} \mu\text{F/km, line to neutral plane.}$$

In deriving this expression, the capacitance between each conductor and earth $(=C_e)$ has been neglected. C_e is very small compared with C_N, however, so that C_e is usually neglected in the calculation of line voltage drops and regulation.

Capacitance of a Three-phase, Three-wire Overhead Line

(a) Symmetrically Spaced Conductors

In figure 7.19, the conductors are each of radius r metres and spaced d metres between centres.

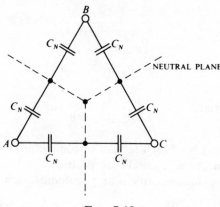

FIG. 7.19

Also
$$C_N = \frac{1}{18 \cdot \log_e [(d-r)/r]} \ \mu\text{F/km}.$$

The capacitance between each conductor and the neutral plane consists of two capacitors in parallel. Hence the total charging current between any conductor and the neutral plane is the phasor sum of two equal charging currents 120 degrees apart.

As shown in figure 7.20, the resultant has the same magnitude as each of the component currents.

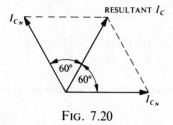

FIG. 7.20

Hence the total equivalent capacitance C_N between any conductor and the neutral plane is

$$\frac{1}{18 \cdot \log_e [(d-r)/r]} \ \mu\text{F/km}.$$

(b) Asymmetrically Spaced Conductors

Let the conductors be spaced and transposed as shown in figures 7.14 and 7.15.

Consider conductor A only:

Capacitance of Section 1 to neutral plane

$$= \frac{1}{18 \cdot \log_e [(d_1 - r)/r]} \; \mu F/km,$$

that of Section 2 $\qquad = \dfrac{1}{18 \cdot \log_e [(d_2 - r)/r]} \; \mu F/km$

and that of Section 3 $\quad = \dfrac{1}{18 \cdot \log_e [(d_3 - r)/r]} \; \mu F/km.$

Let the potentials of each section of conductor A, with respect to the neutral plane, be v_1, v_2, and v_3 respectively.

Let the charge on conductor A be q coulombs, then

$$v_1 = 18q \cdot \log_e [(d_1 - r)/r], \qquad v_2 = 18q \cdot \log_e [(d_2 - r)/r]$$

and $\quad v_3 = 18q \cdot \log_e [(d_3 - r)/r].$

Let the average potential of conductor A, with respect to the neutral plane, be v_A, then

$$v_A = \frac{18}{3} \cdot \left[q \cdot \log_e \left(\frac{d_1 - r}{r} \right) + q \cdot \log_e \left(\frac{d_2 - r}{r} \right) + q \cdot \log_e \left(\frac{d_3 - r}{r} \right) \right]$$

$$= \frac{18q}{3} \cdot \log_e \left(\frac{d_1 - r}{r} \right)\left(\frac{d_2 - r}{r} \right)\left(\frac{d_3 - r}{r} \right)$$

$$= 18q \cdot \log_e \sqrt[3]{\left[\left(\frac{d_1 - r}{r} \right)\left(\frac{d_2 - r}{r} \right)\left(\frac{d_3 - r}{r} \right) \right]}.$$

Hence average capacitance between conductor A and the neutral plane

$$= \frac{q}{v_A} = \frac{1}{18 \cdot \log_e \sqrt[3]{\left[\left(\dfrac{d_1 - r}{r} \right)\left(\dfrac{d_2 - r}{r} \right)\left(\dfrac{d_3 - r}{r} \right) \right]}} \; \mu F/km.$$

This is also the average capacitance between each of the other conductors and the neutral plane.

For overhead lines, r is small compared with d so that $d - r \simeq d$. Then the average capacitance per phase

$$\simeq \frac{1}{18 \cdot \log_e \dfrac{\sqrt[3]{(d_1 \cdot d_2 \cdot d_3)}}{r}} \; \mu\text{F/km}.$$

Hence the average capacitance per phase

$$\simeq \frac{1}{18 \cdot \log_e (d_e/r)} \; \mu\text{F/km}.$$

where d_e = 'effective spacing' $= \sqrt[3]{(d_1 \cdot d_2 \cdot d_3)}$.

Provided that d is of the order of $90r$ or more, the error in the above approximation is negligible.

(c) Flat Regular Spacing

When the conductors are spaced as shown in figure 7.16, an effective spacing of $d_e = 1{\cdot}26d$ may be used, bearing in mind the above proviso.

Example 7-7. Calculate the total resistance, inductance and capacitance of 13 km of single-phase overhead line having solid copper conductors of diameter 1 cm and spaced 60 cm between centres. Take ρ as $1{\cdot}71$ microhm cm and ignore the skin effect.

$$\text{Total } R = \frac{\rho l}{a} = \frac{1{\cdot}71 \times 26 \times 10^5}{10^6 \times \pi \times 0{\cdot}5^2} = \textbf{5·65}\,\boldsymbol{\Omega}.$$

$$\text{Total } L = 26[(0{\cdot}05 + 0{\cdot}2 \cdot \log_e (d/r)] = 1{\cdot}3 + 5{\cdot}2 \cdot \log_e 120$$

$$= 1{\cdot}3 + 5{\cdot}2 \times 4{\cdot}7875 = \textbf{26·2 mH}.$$

$$\text{Total } C = \frac{13}{36 \cdot \log_e [(d-r)/r]} = \frac{13}{36 \cdot \log_e 119}$$

$$= \frac{13}{36 \times 4{\cdot}7792} = \textbf{0·0756}\,\boldsymbol{\mu}\textbf{F, line to line}.$$

Example 7-8. Calculate the inductance and capacitance per phase of 13 km of three-phase overhead line having solid copper conductors of diameter 1 cm and

(a) symmetrically spaced 60 cm between centres,

(b) spaced 60 cm between adjacent centres in flat regular spacing,

(c) spaced on the corners of a triangle having sides of length 60 cm, 90 cm and 120 cm.

(a) $L = 13\left(0.05 + 0.2 \cdot \log_e \dfrac{d}{r}\right) = 0.65 + 2.6 \cdot \log_e 120$

$= 0.65 + 2.6 \times 4.7875 = \textbf{13.1 mH per phase.}$

$C = \dfrac{13}{18 \cdot \log_e [(d-r)/r]} = \dfrac{13}{18 \cdot \log_e 119}$

$= \dfrac{13}{18 \times 4.7792} = \textbf{0.1514 } \boldsymbol{\mu}\textbf{F per phase.}$

(b) $L = 13\left(0.05 + 0.2 \cdot \log_e \dfrac{d_e}{r}\right) = 0.65 + 2.6 \cdot \log_e (1.26 \times 120)$

$= 0.65 + 2.6 \times 5.0186 = \textbf{13.7 mH per phase.}$

$C \simeq \dfrac{13}{18 \cdot \log_e (d_e/r)} = \dfrac{13}{18 \times 5.0186} = \textbf{0.144 } \boldsymbol{\mu}\textbf{F per phase.}$

(c) $d_e = \sqrt[3]{(60 \times 90 \times 120)} = \sqrt[3]{648{,}000} = 86.5$ cm.

$L = 13(0.05 + 0.2 \cdot \log_e 173) = 0.65 + 2.6 \times 5.1533$

$= \textbf{14.05 mH per phase.}$

$C \simeq \dfrac{13}{18 \times 5.1533} = \textbf{0.14 } \boldsymbol{\mu}\textbf{F per phase.}$

Long Transmission Lines

In Section 1, a short line was described as a line for which the effect of capacitance currents could be neglected.

For lines greater than about 16 km in length, it is usually necessary to consider the effect of such currents. The line is then described as a long line.

The values of 'send end' voltage, current and power factor for known 'receive end' conditions can be obtained very accurately by assuming the capacitance to be lumped at intervals along the line, as shown in figure 7.21.

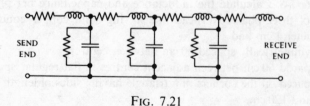

Fig. 7.21

The resistors shunting the capacitances represent the leakage currents which flow through the air between the conductors. The shorter the intervals between the capacitances, the more accurate will be the result.

In practice, however, it is usual to use either of the following methods, in which the leakage resistance currents are ignored. These methods are less rigorous but are sufficiently accurate for most purposes.

(i) Nominal π Method

In this method, one half of the total capacitance is assumed to be lumped at either end of the line, as shown in figure 7.22.

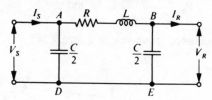

FIG. 7.22

(ii) Nominal T Method

In this method, the total capacitance is assumed to be lumped at the centre of the line, as shown in figure 7.23.

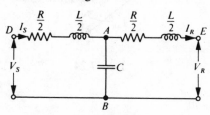

FIG. 7.23

Example 7-9. A three-phase, 50-Hz overhead line is 100 km long. The phase values of resistance, inductance and capacitance per km are $0.15\,\Omega$, 1.2 mH and $0.0087\,\mu\text{F}$.

Calculate, using the nominal π method, the 'send end' voltage, current and power factor when the line supplies a load of 70 MW at 0.8 power factor lagging and 132 kV line.

Referring to figure 7.22:

$R = 0.15 \times 100 = 15\,\Omega.$

$X_L = 314 \times 0.0012 \times 100 = 37.7\,\Omega.$

Total $C = 0.0087 \times 100 = 0.87 \mu\text{F}$.

$C_{AD} = C_{BE} = 0.435 \mu\text{F}$.

$X_{AD} = X_{BE} = \dfrac{3,183}{0.435} = 7,320 \ \Omega$.

Assuming a star-connected, balanced load:

$$I_R = \frac{70 \times 10^6}{\sqrt{3} \times 132 \times 10^3 \times 0.8} = 383 \ \text{A}.$$

$$V_R = \frac{132,000}{\sqrt{3}} = 76,200 \ \text{V}.$$

Taking V_R as reference, as shown in figure 7.24:

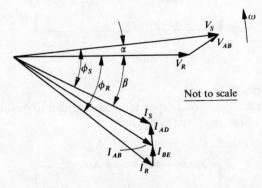

Fig. 7.24

$\bar{V}_R = 76,200 + j0$.

$\bar{I}_R = 383(0.8 - j0.6) = 306 - j230$.

$\bar{I}_{BE} = \dfrac{76,200}{-j7,320} = +j10.4$.

$\bar{I}_{AB} = 306 - j230 + j10.4 = 306 - j220$.

Voltage drop $A \rightarrow B = (306 - j220)(15 + j37.7) = 12,880 + j8,240$.

$\bar{V}_S = 76,200 + 12,880 + j8,240 = 89,080 + j8,240$.

$\bar{I}_{AD} = \dfrac{89,080 + j8,240}{-j7,320} = j12.2 - 1.1$.

$\bar{I}_S = 306 - j220 + j12.2 - 1.1 = 305 - j208$.

$V_S = \sqrt{(89 \cdot 08^2 + 8 \cdot 24^2)}$ kV phase $= 89 \cdot 5$ kV phase $=$ **155 kV line**.

$I_S = \sqrt{(305^2 + 208^2)} =$ **369 A**.

Referring to figure 7.24:

$\text{Tan } \alpha = \dfrac{8{,}240}{89{,}080} = 0 \cdot 0925$, and $\quad \alpha = 5° \ 17'$

$\text{Tan } \beta = \dfrac{208}{305} = 0 \cdot 6821$, and $\quad \beta = 34° \ 18'$

therefore $\hspace{4cm} \phi_S = 39° \ 35'$

and $\hspace{4cm} \cos \phi_S =$ **0·77 lagging**.

Example 7-10. Repeat example 7-9 using the nominal *T* method.

Referring to figure 7.23:

$\dfrac{R}{2} = 7 \cdot 5 \ \Omega. \hspace{2cm} \dfrac{X_L}{2} = 18 \cdot 85 \ \Omega.$

$C = 0 \cdot 87 \ \mu\text{F}. \hspace{1cm} X_{AB} = \dfrac{3{,}183}{0 \cdot 87} = 3{,}660 \ \Omega.$

Taking V_R as reference, as shown in figure 7.25:

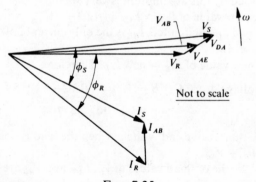

FIG. 7.25

$\overline{V}_R = 76{,}200 + j0.$

$\overline{I}_R = 306 - j230.$

Voltage drop $A \to E = (306 - j230)(7 \cdot 5 + j18 \cdot 85) = 6{,}630 + j4{,}040.$

$\overline{V}_{AB} = 76{,}200 + 6{,}630 + j4{,}040 = 82{,}830 + j4{,}040.$

$$\bar{I}_{AB} = \frac{82,830 + j4,040}{-j3,660} = j22 \cdot 6 - 1 \cdot 1.$$

$$\bar{I}_S = 306 - j230 + j22 \cdot 6 - 1 \cdot 1 = 305 - j207.$$

Voltage drop $D \rightarrow A = (305 - j207)(7 \cdot 5 + j18 \cdot 85) = 6,190 + j4,200.$

$$\bar{V}_S = 82,830 + j4,040 + 6,190 + j4,200 = 89,020 + j8,240.$$

Hence $V_S = \mathbf{155\ kV\ line}$, $I_S = \mathbf{369\ A}$, and $\cos \phi_S = \mathbf{0 \cdot 77\ lagging}$, as before.

Ferranti Effect

When a load supplied by a long transmission line is switched off, the voltage at the 'receive end' rises to a value exceeding that at the 'send end'. This phenomenon is due to the voltage drop caused by the capacitance current and is called the Ferranti Effect.

Example 7-11. Calculate, (a) accurately and (b) approximately, the 'receive end' voltage when the load connected to the transmission line in example 7-9 is switched off. Assume that the 'send end' voltage remains constant.

(a) Using the nominal π method and referring to figure 7.22 :

The value of I_{BE} when the load is open-circuited is determined by assuming that $\bar{V}_{BE} = \bar{V}_S$. (In fact, $\bar{V}_{BE}$ is slightly greater than $\bar{V}_S$ but the error caused by this assumption is very small.)

Hence the new value of $\bar{I}_{BE} \simeq \bar{I}_{AD} = j12 \cdot 2 - 1 \cdot 1.$

With the load open-circuited, $\bar{I}_{BE}$ is the only current flowing through the impedance AB.

Thus the new value of $\bar{I}_{AB} = $ new $\bar{I}_{BE}$. Therefore,

$$\text{new voltage drop } A \rightarrow B = \bar{V}_{AB} = (j12 \cdot 2 - 1 \cdot 1)(15 + j37 \cdot 7)$$

$$= j142 - 477.$$

Let V_{R_0} be the 'receive end' voltage when the load is open-circuited, then $\bar{V}_S = \bar{V}_{R_0} + \bar{V}_{AB}.$

In figure 7.26, the on-load values of V_R, I_{AB}, and V_{AB} are represented by dotted phasors and the open-circuit values by full phasors.

It can be seen that, on open-circuit, I_{AB} is much smaller and has advanced through angle θ. So has the voltage drop V_{AB}, making V_{R_0} greater than V_S.

$$\bar{V}_{R_0} = \bar{V}_S - \bar{V}_{AB} = 89,080 + j8,240 - j142 + 477 = 89,557 - j8,098.$$

$$V_{R_0} = \sqrt{(89 \cdot 56^2 + 8 \cdot 098^2)}\ \text{kV phase} = 89 \cdot 9\ \text{kV phase} = \mathbf{156\ kV\ line}.$$

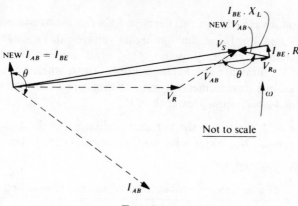

Fɪɢ. 7.26

Alternatively, using the nominal T method and referring to figure 7.23:

$$\text{New } \bar{I}_{AB} = \frac{89{,}020 + j8{,}240}{-j3{,}660} = j24{\cdot}3 - 2{\cdot}25.$$

New voltage drop $D \rightarrow A = (j24{\cdot}3 - 2{\cdot}25)(7{\cdot}5 + j18{\cdot}85) = j140 - 475.$

So $\bar{V}_{R_0} = 89{,}020 + j8{,}240 - j140 + 475 = 89{,}495 + j8{,}100,$

and $V_{R_0} = 89{\cdot}9$ kV phase = **156 kV line**, as before.

(b) Using the nominal π method and referring to figure 7.22, the voltage drop $A \rightarrow B$ is the phasor sum of $I_{BE} \cdot R$ and $I_{BE} \cdot X_L$. Of these two components, it is clear from figure 7.26 that $I_{BE} \cdot X_L$ causes most of the difference between the lengths of the phasors representing V_S and V_{R_0}; $I_{BE} \cdot R$ causes a negligible amount of this difference. Moreover, V_S and V_{R_0} are so nearly in phase that negligible error will result from assuming that V_{R_0} is the arithmetic sum of V_S and $I_{BE} \cdot X_L$, thus

$I_{BE} = \sqrt{(12{\cdot}2^2 + 1{\cdot}1^2)} = 12{\cdot}25$ A.

$I_{BE} \cdot X_L = 12{\cdot}25 \times 37{\cdot}7 = 462$ V.

$V_{R_0} = 89{\cdot}46 + 0{\cdot}462 = 89{\cdot}9$ kV phase = **156 kV line**, as before.

Alternatively, using the nominal T method and referring to figure 7.23,

$$I_{AB} = \sqrt{(24{\cdot}3^2 + 2{\cdot}25^2)} = 24{\cdot}4 \text{ A.}$$

$$I_{AB} \cdot \frac{X_L}{2} = 24{\cdot}4 \times 18{\cdot}85 = 460 \text{ V.}$$

Hence $V_{R_0} = $ **156 kV line**, as before.

The voltage rise due to the Ferranti Effect in the above example is only 1 kV line. For longer lines at higher voltages, this voltage rise will be considerably greater. On the other hand, quite a small load is sufficient to eliminate the Ferranti Effect. Thus, when a long line is terminated in a transformer, the magnetizing current is often sufficient to prevent V_R becoming greater than V_S.

Example 7-12. Calculate the per unit regulation of the transmission line in example 7-9, (a) ignoring and (b) including the Ferranti Effect.

Per unit regulation

$$= \frac{\text{rise in 'receive end' voltage when load is switched off}}{\text{rated on-load 'receive end' voltage}}$$

(a) Per unit regulation $= \dfrac{V_S - V_R}{V_R} = \dfrac{155 - 132}{132} = \textbf{0·174}$

(b) Per unit regulation $= \dfrac{V_{R_0} - V_R}{V_R} = \dfrac{156 - 132}{132} = \textbf{0·182.}$

Example 7-13. Calculate the efficiency of the transmission line in example 7-9.

Using the nominal π method and referring to figure 7.22:

$\bar{I}_{AB} = 306 - j220.$ $I_{AB} = \sqrt{(306^2 + 220^2)} = 377 \, \text{A}.$

Power loss per phase $= I_{AB}^2 \cdot R = 377^2 \times 15 \text{ watts} = 2 \cdot 13 \text{ MW}.$

Total power loss $= 3 \times 2 \cdot 13 = 6 \cdot 39 \text{ MW}.$

Efficiency $= 1 - \dfrac{\text{losses}}{\text{output} + \text{losses}}$

$= 1 - \dfrac{6 \cdot 39}{76 \cdot 39} = 1 - 0 \cdot 084 = \textbf{0·916.}$

Synchronous Phase Modifier

The voltage (V_R) at the 'receive end' of a transmission line can be controlled by connecting a synchronous motor in parallel with the load. The excitation of the motor can be adjusted, automatically if desired, in such a way as to maintain V_R constant on varying load. When used for this purpose, the synchronous motor is called a 'synchronous phase modifier'.

No mechanical load is connected to the modifier and the power losses in a large machine are only of the order of 3 or 4 per cent of the kVA rating. It may therefore be assumed that the modifier intake is kVAr only.

Example 7-14. Calculate the required kVAr input to a synchronous phase modifier, connected in parallel with the load supplied by the transmission line in example 7-9, so that the voltage at each end of the line shall be 132 kV.

Using the nominal π method and referring to figure 7.22:
$\bar{I}_{AB} = 306 - j220$, as in example 7-9.
Let the active and reactive components of $\bar{I}_{AB}$ be I_a and I_r, respectively, as shown in figure 7.27.

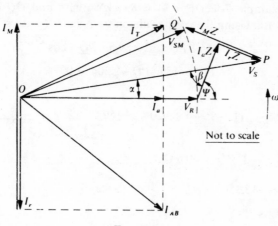

Fig. 7.27

Then $\bar{I}_a = 306$ A and $\bar{I}_r = -j220$ A. Let the impedance between A and $B = Z\,\Omega$, then $\bar{Z} = 15 + j37\cdot7$.

$$\bar{I}_a . \bar{Z} = 306(15 + j37\cdot7) = 4{,}590 + j11{,}540.$$

$$\bar{I}_r . \bar{Z} = -j220(15 + j37\cdot7) = -j3{,}300 + 8{,}290.$$

Hence the 'send end' voltage if no synchronous phase modifier were used $= \bar{V}_S = 89{,}080 + j8{,}240$, as in example 7-9. Let V_{SM} be the 'send end' voltage with the modifier connected.

Then the end of the V_{SM} phasor must lie on an arc of radius OV_R and centre O.

The addition of the modifier does not appreciably alter I_a. Therefore $\bar{I}_a . \bar{Z}$ may be assumed constant.

The end of the V_{SM} phasor must therefore also lie on the line $I_a . Z$ produced.

It can thus be seen that the synchronous phase modifier must be over-excited to a value which causes it to take a leading reactive current I_M, of such a magnitude that it causes a voltage drop $= I_M . Z = PQ$. The current flowing through Z will then be modified from I_{AB} to I_T.

$$\alpha = 5° \ 17', \text{ as in example 7-9.}$$

$$\text{Tan } \Psi = \frac{11,540}{4,590} = 2\cdot514. \qquad \text{Thus } \Psi = 68° \ 18'.$$

$$\beta = \Psi - \alpha = 63° \ 1'.$$

$$\angle OPQ = 90° - 63° \ 1' = 26° \ 59'.$$

From example 7-9, $OP = V_S = 89\cdot5 \ \text{kV}$ phase and $OQ = OV_R = 76\cdot2 \ \text{kV}$ phase. Using the cosine rule on triangle OPQ, gives

$$76\cdot2^2 = 89\cdot5^2 + PQ^2 - 2 \times 89\cdot5 \times PQ \times \cos 26° \ 59',$$

so that $$PQ^2 - 159\cdot5PQ + 2,204 = 0,$$

and

$$PQ = \frac{159\cdot5 \pm \sqrt{(159\cdot5^2 - 4 \times 2,204)}}{2} = \frac{159\cdot5 - 128\cdot8}{2} = 15\cdot35 \ \text{kV phase.}$$

$$Z = \sqrt{(15^2 + 37\cdot7^2)} = 40\cdot6 \ \Omega.$$

$$I_M = \frac{PQ}{Z} = \frac{15,350}{40\cdot6} = 378 \ \text{A.}$$

kVAr input to synchronous phase modifier $= 3 \times 378 \times 76\cdot2 = \mathbf{86,400}$.

Corona

Consider two parallel overhead conductors in air. If an alternating potential difference between the conductors is gradually increased, a point is reached at which the air at the surface of the conductors becomes ionized. The potential difference between the conductors at this point is known as the 'disruptive critical voltage' (V_0) and the cylinder of ionized air surrounding each conductor is called 'corona'.

If the potential difference is further increased, a second point is reached at which a faint luminous glow of violet colour can be seen to surround each conductor. The potential difference at this point is known as the 'visual critical voltage' (V_v) and the luminous glow is called 'visible corona'.

If the potential difference were further raised until the two cylinders of luminous glow touch, then flashover would occur. For conductors spaced less than 15 conductor diameters apart, flashover occurs before visible corona.

The current (I_0) flowing through the air between the conductors is sinusoidal until corona occurs. Also, I_0 is almost entirely capacitive since the leakage resistance current between the conductors is very small. When V_0 is exceeded, however, the waveform of I_0 is as shown in figure 7.28.

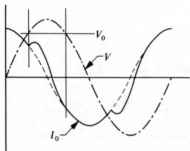

FIG. 7.28

The increase in I_0 is due to the reduction in insulation resistance between the conductors caused by the ionization of some of the air. This increase commences at the point in the voltage cycle at which V_0 is exceeded and I_0 returns to its sinusoidal waveform when the voltage falls below V_0. There is also an increase in the power loss since additional energy is used in ionizing the air. The distortion of the waveform of I_0 is mainly third harmonic.

The fundamental magnetic and electrostatic fields associated with a three-phase overhead line each sum to zero but the third harmonic fields are in phase and give a resultant which causes interference with neighbouring telephone, radio and television circuits. A 150-Hz hissing noise can be heard by the human ear when visible corona occurs.

Electric Stress between Two Parallel Overhead Conductors in Air

Referring to figure 7.17 and the derivation of the expression for the capacitance of a single-phase overhead line, the potential gradient across $CM = \dfrac{q}{2\pi x \varepsilon} + \dfrac{q}{2\pi \varepsilon (d-x)}$.

This expression has a maximum value when $x = r$. Hence

$$E_{\max} = \frac{q}{2\pi r \varepsilon} + \frac{q}{2\pi \varepsilon (d-r)}.$$

If d is large compared with r, $\frac{q}{2\pi\varepsilon(d-r)}$ is negligible, and

$$E_{max} \simeq \frac{q}{2\pi r \varepsilon}. \tag{1}$$

But

$$V = \frac{q \cdot \log_e [(d-r)/r]}{\pi\varepsilon}.$$

Therefore

$$q = \frac{V\pi\varepsilon}{\log_e [(d-r)/r]}. \tag{2}$$

Substituting equation (2) in (1) gives

$$E_{max} = \frac{V}{2r \cdot \log_e[(d-r)/r]}.$$

Let V_N be the potential difference between each conductor and the neutral plane, then $V_N = \frac{1}{2}V$ and

$$E_{max} = \frac{V_N}{r \cdot \log_e[(d-r)/r]}.$$

Electric Stress between Any Pair of Parallel Conductors of a Three-phase Overhead Line

As for the single-phase line,

$$E_{max} = \frac{V_N}{r \cdot \log_e[(d-r)/r]},$$

but V_N is now the phase voltage.

This expression may be applied to asymmetrically spaced conductors by using the effective spacing d_e.

Calculation of Disruptive Critical Voltage for a Three-phase Overhead Line

$$E_0 = \frac{V_0}{r \cdot \log_e[(d-r)/r]},$$

where E_0 = value of stress at which disruption commences (kV peak/cm),

V_0 = phase value of disruptive critical voltage (kV peak),

r = radius of conductors (cm),

d = distance between centres of conductors (cm).

The breakdown strength of air ($= E_0$) is 30 kV peak/cm when the atmospheric pressure is 76 cm of mercury and the temperature is

25°C. E_0 is directly proportional to the density of the air which is directly proportional to atmospheric pressure and inversely proportional to absolute temperature.

Let the atmospheric pressure be p cm of mercury,

the temperature above 0°C be t°C, and

the ratio $\dfrac{\text{density of air at } p \text{ cm mercury and } t°C}{\text{density of air at 76 cm mercury and 25°C}} = \delta$.

Then $E_0 = 30\delta$ kV peak/cm, where

$$\delta = \frac{p}{76} \times \frac{273 + 25}{273 + t} = \frac{3 \cdot 92 p}{273 + t}.$$

Hence $\qquad\qquad V_0 = 30 \delta r . \log_e\left(\frac{d - r}{r}\right) \text{ kV peak.}$

The surface of a stranded conductor consists of a series of small arcs which increase the electric stress at the conductor surface. During service, conductors become weathered and dirt is deposited on them so that the irregularity of the surfaces and hence the stress are increased. The above value of V_0 must therefore be reduced by multiplying it by an irregularity factor, m_0.

For a smooth, polished, cylindrical conductor, $m_0 = 1$.

For a weathered, cylindrical conductor, $m_0 = 0 \cdot 93$ to $0 \cdot 98$.

For a weathered conductor having more than 7 strands, $m_0 = 0 \cdot 87$ to $0 \cdot 93$.

For a weathered conductor having up to 7 strands, $m_0 = 0 \cdot 8$ to $0 \cdot 87$.

Converting to r.m.s. values gives

$$V_0 = 21 \cdot 2 \delta r m_0 . \log_e\left(\frac{d - r}{r}\right) \text{ kV r.m.s. phase.}$$

Other factors which reduce the breakdown strength of air are rain, mist, fog, snow, and pollution. The breakdown strength is also reduced during thunder storms when free electrons present in the air make ionization easier. These conditions may reduce the disruptive critical voltage to about 80 per cent of the above value.

Calculation of Visual Critical Voltage for a Three-phase Overhead Line

Before ionization can become visible, the electrons must be moving with such velocity as to release sufficient energy during collisions to sustain a luminous glow. Peek found that the required velocity is not attained until the air has been ionized to a radius of $r + 0.3\sqrt{(\delta r)}$ cm from the centre of each conductor. The phase voltage required for this

$$= V_v = \left[1 + \frac{0.3}{\sqrt{(\delta r)}}\right] V_0.$$

In addition to developing this empirical formula, Peek found that V_v is reduced by irregularities such as stranding and dirt. Taking m_v as the irregularity factor for visible corona, he found that the following values were typical.

For a smooth, polished, cylindrical conductor, $m_v = 1$.

For continuous, visible corona along a weathered, stranded conductor, $m_v = 0.8$ to 0.85.

For patchy, visible corona along a weathered, stranded conductor, $m_v = 0.7$ to 0.75.

Hence $V_v = 30\delta r m_v \left[1 + \dfrac{0.3}{\sqrt{(\delta r)}}\right] . \log_e\left(\dfrac{d-r}{r}\right)$ kV peak, where r is in

cm. Converting to r.m.s. values gives

$$V_v = 21.2\delta r m_v \left[1 + \frac{0.3}{\sqrt{(\delta r)}}\right] . \log_e\left(\frac{d-r}{r}\right) \text{ kV r.m.s. phase.}$$

The visual critical voltage may be reduced to about 80 per cent of the above value in the adverse atmospheric conditions previously mentioned.

Example 7-15. A three-phase overhead transmission line comprises three conductors, each of overall diameter 3.05 cm, symmetrically spaced 3.66 m between centres. The barometric pressure is 75 cm of mercury and the temperature is $7°C$.

Taking the irregularity factor as 0.8 in each case, calculate the r.m.s. line voltages at which, (a) disruption, and (b) visible corona would commence.

$$\delta = \frac{3.92p}{273+t} = \frac{3.92 \times 75}{273+7} = 1.05.$$

(a) $V_0 = 21.2\delta r m_0 . \log_e\left(\dfrac{d-r}{r}\right) = 21.2 \times 1.05 \times 1.525 \times 0.8 \times \log_e 239$

$$= 149 \text{ kV phase} = \textbf{257 kV line.}$$

(b) $V_v = 21 \cdot 2 \delta r m_v \left[1 + \dfrac{0 \cdot 3}{\sqrt{(\delta r)}} \right] . \log_e \left(\dfrac{d - r}{r} \right)$

$= 21 \cdot 2 \times 1 \cdot 05 \times 1 \cdot 525 \times 0 \cdot 8 \left[1 + \dfrac{0 \cdot 3}{\sqrt{(1 \cdot 05 \times 1 \cdot 525)}} \right] . \log_e 239$

$= 21 \cdot 2 \times 1 \cdot 05 \times 1 \cdot 525 \times 0 \cdot 8 \times 1 \cdot 239 \times 5 \cdot 477 = 184 \text{ kV phase}$

$= \textbf{319 kV line.}$

Corona Power Loss

Peek developed the following empirical formula for corona power loss:

$$P_0 = \frac{242}{\delta} \times (f + 25) \times \sqrt{\left(\frac{r}{d} \right)} \times (V_{ph} - V_0)^2 \times 10^{-5} \text{ kW/km/phase.}$$

Example 7-16. Calculate the total corona power loss for the line in example 7-15, assuming that it operates at 275 kV line, 50 Hz, and is 129 km long.

$V_{ph} = \dfrac{275}{\sqrt{3}} = 159 \text{ kV.}$

$P_0 = \dfrac{242}{1 \cdot 05} \times (50 + 25) \times \sqrt{\left(\dfrac{1 \cdot 525}{366} \right)} \times (159 - 149)^2 \times 10^{-5} \times 129$

$= \dfrac{242}{1 \cdot 05} \times 75 \times 0 \cdot 06455 \times 0 \cdot 129 = 144 \text{ kW/phase} = \textbf{432 kW total.}$

Factors affecting Corona

(i) The breakdown strength of air which varies with atmospheric conditions.

(ii) The irregularity of the conductor surfaces.

(iii) The conductor radius. The greater the radius, the less likelihood of corona. The use of a steel core increases the radius and the use of bundle conductors increases the effective radius by reducing the electric stress at the conductor surfaces.

(iv) The distance between the conductors. The greater the distance, the less likelihood of corona. It is not usually economically possible to design an overhead line so that corona will never occur, since increasing the spacing increases the cost of the towers. Lines are therefore usually designed to operate just below the disruptive critical voltage in fair weather so that corona only occurs during adverse atmospheric conditions.

Effects of Corona

(i) Interference with communications. Power lines should be kept as far away as possible from communication lines. Parallel runs should be avoided wherever possible and intersections made at right angles. Where parallel runs are unavoidable, the interference can be reduced by transposing the conductors of both lines.

(ii) Non-sinusoidal charging current which causes a non-sinusoidal line voltage drop.

(iii) Corona power loss caused by the ionization of some of the air between the conductors.

(iv) Corona helps to attenuate high voltage surges caused by lightning or switching. The energy associated with such surges is partly dissipated in corona power loss.

EXAMPLES 7

1. A conductor hangs in the form of a catenary $y = c \cdot \cosh(x/c)$, where $c = 1{,}220$ m. If the span is 293 m and the conductor has a mass of 1·64 kg/m, calculate:

(a) The length of the conductor.

(b) The sag.

(c) The maximum and minimum values of tension using the catenary method.

(d) The approximate tension using the parabolic method.

(Answers (a) **293 m**, (b) **8·78 m**, (c) **19·7 kN, 19·6 kN**, (d) **19·65 kN**.)

2. A conductor hangs from supports at different levels and takes the form of a catenary $y = c \cdot \cosh(x/c)$, where $c = 1{,}220$ m. The horizontal distance between the supports is 317·2 m and the conductor has a mass of 1·49 kg/m. If the horizontal distance between the lowest point in the catenary and the lower support is 73·2 m, calculate:

(a) The tension at each support.

(b) The minimum tension.

(c) The difference in levels of the supports.

(Answers (a) **17·85 kN, 18·15 kN**, (b) **17·8 kN**, (c) **22·3 m**.)

3. List the various materials available for overhead conductors and briefly outline the conditions for which each is suitable. Give, with reasons, the advantages of 'bundle conductors'.

Each phase of a three-phase overhead line has a single steel-cored aluminium conductor with a span length of 366 m. The sag is not to exceed 7·625 m under a wind pressure of 383 N/m² of total projected area with an ice covering of radial thickness 1·27 cm; use a safety factor of 2.

Calculate whether either of the following conductors will comply with the above conditions:

Conductor	Outside diameter	Mass per m	Breaking strength
A	3·02 cm	1·82 kg	145·5 kN
B	3·15 cm	2·21 kg	194 kN

Take the density of ice as 912 kg/m^3.

Explain how the above two conductors can be designed to have the same resistance per metre. State with reasons which conductor has the higher disruptive critical voltage.

(Answers **Sag for A = 9·05 m, sag for B = 7·5 m, therefore B complies.**)

4. Each conductor of a twin conductor overhead line has a diameter of 3·05 cm, has a mass of 1·64 kg/m and has a breaking strength of 133·7 kN.

Calculate the approximate maximum sag if the span is 335 m and the line is to operate with a safety factor of 2 under the following conditions:

1·27 cm radial thickness of ice and a wind pressure of 383 N/m^2 of total projected area. Density of ice = 912 kg/m^3.

Deduce any formula used.

Discuss fully the reasons for the choice of twin conductors.

State why the stress and sag must be adjusted during erection to give the above sag under the given conditions.

(Answer **8·01 m**.)

5. Each conductor of a twin conductor overhead line has a diameter of 2·86 cm, has a mass of 1·64 kg/m and has a breaking strength of 129 kN. The sag is not to exceed 7·625 m under the following conditions:

1·27 cm radial thickness of ice and a wind pressure of 383 N/m^2 of total projected area. Density of ice = 912 kg/m^3.

Estimate the maximum permissible span, using a safety factor of 2.

(Answer **326 m**.)

6. An overhead line is supported in still air from two towers at levels of 30·5 and 61 m above a horizontal datum line. The horizontal distance between the towers is 305 m.

Calculate the sag if the conductor has a mass of 1·86 kg/m and the tension is to be 17·8 kN.

(Answers **32·2 or 1·54 m**.)

7. Calculate the resistance, inductance, and capacitance per phase of 32·2 km of three-phase overhead line having solid copper conductors of diameter 1·91 cm and

(a) symmetrically spaced with 1·22 m between centres,

(b) spaced with 1·22 m between adjacent centres in flat regular spacing.

(c) spaced on the corners of a triangle having sides of length 1·22 m, 1·525 m and 1·83 m.

Take the resistivity of copper as 1·7 microhm.cm and ignore the skin effect.

(Answers $R = 1·92\,\Omega$, (a) **32·8 mH, 0·368 μF**, (b) **34·3 mH, 0·352 μF**, (c) **34·2 mH, 0·353 μF**.)

8. A long transmission line delivers 40 MW at 0·8 power factor lagging at 132 kV, three-phase, 50 Hz. Each conductor has a resistance of 18 ohms, an inductance of 0·15 H and a capacitance to neutral of 1·2 μF.

Calculate, using the nominal π method, the voltage, current, and power factor at the sending end. Draw the phasor diagram and determine the efficiency of transmission.

(Answers **147 kV line, 200 A, 0·83 lag, 0·944**.)

9. Calculate, using the nominal π method, the sending end voltage and current for a long line supplying a load of 60 MVA, three-phase at 0·8 power factor lagging at 132 kV, 50 Hz. Each conductor has a resistance of 25 ohms, an inductance of 0·2 H and a capacitance to neutral of 1·5 μF.

Explain, with the aid of a phasor diagram, how a synchronous phase modifier, connected at the load end, may be used to make the line regulation zero.

(Answers **157 kV line, 237 A**.)

10. A three-phase transmission line is 80 km long and supplies a load of 45 MW at 0·8 power factor lagging at 132 kV, 50 Hz. The phase values of inductance and capacitance per km are 1·25 mH and 0·009375 μF. The total power loss in the line is 5 per cent of the delivered power.

Calculate, using the nominal T method, the sending end voltage and current.

(Answers **144 kV line, 234 A**.)

11. Calculate, using the nominal π method, the voltage at the sending end of a 110-kV, three-phase, 50 Hz, overhead transmission line which delivers 30 MW at 0·8 power factor lagging. Each conductor has a resistance of 20 Ω, an inductive reactance of 46 Ω and a capacitive reactance to neutral of 2,650 Ω. Draw the phasor diagram.

If the sending end voltage remains constant, estimate the approximate rise in voltage at the receiving end when the load is switched off. With the aid of a phasor diagram, explain the method employed for this estimation, stating the approximations made.

Calculate the per unit voltage regulation of the line.

(Answers **124 kV line, 15·1 kV line, 0·137 p.u.**)

12. Calculate, using the nominal π method, the voltage, current and power factor at the sending end of an 80-kV, three-phase, 50-Hz, overhead transmission line which delivers 12 MW at 0·85 power factor lagging. Each conductor has a resistance of 0·275 Ω/km, an inductive reactance of 0·5625 Ω/km and a capacitance to neutral of 0·008625 μF/km. The line is 160 km long.

If the sending end voltage remains constant, estimate the approximate rise in voltage at the receiving end when the load is switched off. Hence calculate the per unit voltage regulation of the line.

(Answers **94 kV line, 91·3 A, 0·89 lag, 15·6 kV line, 0·195 p.u.**)

13. Calculate the required kVAr input to a synchronous phase modifier, connected in parallel with the load supplied by the transmission line in example 12 above, so that the voltage at each end of the line shall be 80 kV.

(Answer **13,700 kVAr.**)

14. Derive a formula, in terms of line voltage to neutral, for the stress at the surface of a three-phase, symmetrically-spaced overhead transmission line.

Explain what is meant by disruptive critical voltage and visual critical voltage.

Sketch the wave-shapes of applied voltage and current between conductors when corona occurs and explain why corona causes interference with communications.

A three-phase overhead line comprises three conductors symmetrically spaced with 1·83 m between centres. Each conductor has a diameter of 2·54 cm. The atmospheric pressure is 73·7 cm of mercury and the temperature is 15·6°C. Calculate the disruptive critical voltage assuming an irregularity factor of 0·8.

(Answer **186 kV r.m.s. line**.)

15. A three-phase, overhead transmission line comprises three conductors, each of overall diameter 3·91 cm, symmetrically spaced with 3·81 m between centres. The barometric pressure is 73·5 cm of mercury and the temperature is 15°C.

Calculate the r.m.s. line voltages at which, (a) disruption, and (b) visible corona would commence. Assume an irregularity factor of 0·8 for (a) and 0·7 for (b).

Also calculate the total corona power loss if the line is 113 km long and operates at 315 kV line, 50 Hz.

(Answers (a) **303 kV**, (b) **323 kV, 216 kW**.)

8

Economics of Power Supply

Most Economical c.s.a. of a Conductor

The c.s.a. (cross-sectional area) of a distributor is generally determined by the maximum voltage drop which can be tolerated.

In the case of feeders and transmission lines, however, voltage drop is less important than the cost of energy loss and the initial cost. The larger the c.s.a., the lower the energy loss but the higher the initial cost.

The capital required when an overhead line is to be erected is nearly always borrowed and an annual interest payment is usually made. In addition, a sum is paid annually into a sinking fund to cover depreciation, maintenance, and replacement of conductors, insulators and towers.

The most economical design is that for which the sum of these annual payments plus the annual cost of the energy loss is a minimum.

The initial expenditure on a complete line comprises:

(i) The cost of the conductor itself. This cost is directly proportional to the c.s.a. of the conductor.

(ii) The cost of towers, insulators, and erection of an overhead line. Or, in the case of an underground cable, the cost of insulation, laying, and jointing. These costs depend to some extent on the conductor c.s.a. but are considered constant in deriving Kelvin's Law.

Kelvin's Law

Let the total annual interest and depreciation charges be $£C_1$, the annual cost of energy losses be $£C_2$ and the total annual cost of operating the line be $£C$, then

$$C = C_1 + C_2.$$

Let the most economical c.s.a. of conductor be A cm^2, then $C_1 = PA + Q$ where P is a constant which depends on the cost per unit volume of the conductor material used, and Q is a constant which depends on the cost of towers, insulators, and erection. Both these constants also depend on the rate of the interest and depreciation charges.

Ignoring corona, leakage resistance and dielectric losses, the annual cost of the energy loss is directly proportional to $I^2 Rt$ where I is the load current, R the resistance of the conductor, and t the time for which the current flows.

Since R is inversely proportional to A,

$$C_2 = \frac{K}{A},$$

where K is a constant which depends on the cost of energy;

therefore
$$C = PA + Q + \frac{K}{A}.$$

For C to be a minimum, $\dfrac{dC}{dA} = 0$. Hence

$$P - \frac{K}{A^2} = 0, \quad \text{and} \quad PA = \frac{K}{A}.$$

This relationship is known as Kelvin's Law and can be stated as follows:

The most economical c.s.a. of a conductor is that which makes the annual cost of the energy losses equal to the annual interest and depreciation charges on the initial cost of the conductor material only.

The variation of annual costs with conductor c.s.a. is illustrated in figure 8.1.

Example 8-1. A three-phase, 33-kV, overhead line is to be designed to transmit a balanced load of 5 MVA over a distance of 32 km for 3,000 hours per annum, there being no load for the remainder of the year. The conductors are to be of copper costing 39·4 p/kg and having a density of $0·886 \times 10^4$ kg/m³. The interest and depreciation charges total 10 per cent per annum and energy costs 0·313 p per kWh. The resistance of one km of copper conductor of cross-sectional area 1 cm² is 0·177 Ω.

Calculate the most economical conductor c.s.a. and the corresponding value of current density.

Considering 1 km of single conductor:

$$\text{Line current} = \frac{5 \times 10^6}{\sqrt{3} \times 33 \times 10^3} = 87·5 \, \text{A}.$$

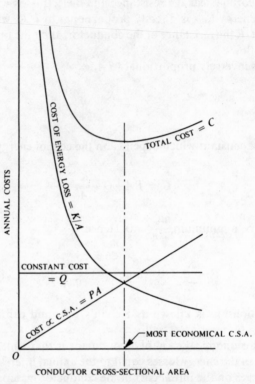

FIG. 8.1

Let the most economical c.s.a. be A cm^2, then

$$\text{Volume of copper} = 10^5 \times A \text{ cm}^3.$$

$$\text{Mass of copper} = \frac{10^5 \times A \times 0.886 \times 10^4}{10^6} = 886A \text{ kg}.$$

$$\text{Annual charges on the initial cost of copper} = £0.394 \times 0.1 \times 886A$$
$$= £34.9A.$$

$$\text{Resistance} = \frac{0.177}{A} \Omega.$$

$$\text{Annual energy loss} = 87.5^2 \times \frac{0.177}{A} \times 3,000 \times 10^{-3} \text{ kWh.}$$

In the figure, labels read:

COST OF ENERGY LOSS = K/A

TOTAL COST = C

ANNUAL COSTS

CONSTANT COST = Q

COST ∝ C.S.A. = PA

MOST ECONOMICAL C.S.A.

CONDUCTOR CROSS-SECTIONAL AREA

Annual cost of energy loss $= £87.5^2 \times \dfrac{0.177}{A} \times 3 \times 0.00313$

$$= £\,\frac{12.7}{A}.$$

Using Kelvin's Law, $\qquad 34.9A = \dfrac{12.7}{A}.$

Hence $\qquad\qquad\qquad A = \mathbf{0.604\ cm^2}.$

$$\text{Current Density} = \frac{87.5}{0.604} = \mathbf{145\ A/cm^2}.$$

Current Density

Typical values of working current density for oil-filled, buried, paper-insulated cables are as follows.

$$0.387\ cm^2 - 465\ A/cm^2$$

$$4.52\ \ cm^2 - 155\ A/cm^2$$

$$6.45\ \ cm^2 - 124\ A/cm^2.$$

Typical values for dry, impregnated paper-insulated cables are somewhat lower than those above. Working current densities for overhead lines are higher than those above.

The following table gives a comparison between various sizes of cylindrical conductor made from copper of resistivity 1.7 microhm.cm. The values are calculated for a length of one km and a current density of 100 A/cm².

Cross-sectional area (cm²)	Resistance (Ω)	Current (A)	Copper loss (kW)	Surface area (m²)	Cooling rate (W/m²)
7	0.02429	700	11.9	93.8	127
6	0.02833	600	10.2	86.8	118
5	0.03400	500	8.5	79.3	107
4	0.04250	400	6.8	70.9	96
3	0.05667	300	5.1	61.4	83
2	0.08500	200	3.4	50.1	68
1	0.17000	100	1.7	35.5	48

It is obvious from the above table that the smaller the conductor c.s.a., the greater can be the current density for the same temperature rise. For example, the 1 cm² conductor could be worked at a current density of 515 A/cm² and yet still have the same cooling rate as the 7 cm² conductor.

Form and Load Factors

In most cases, the load is not constant for the whole year. The demand for electrical energy is greatest during winter and the load variation throughout the year is roughly the same for many transmission lines.

The r.m.s. and average values of the annual load curve can be found in the usual way (see example 8-2) and should not be confused with those associated with the sinusoidal waveshape of the load current.

Let the form factor of the annual load curve be k_f,

then $$k_f = \frac{\text{r.m.s. value of annual load curve}}{\text{average value of annual load curve}}.$$

The ratio $\dfrac{\text{average value of load per annum}}{\text{maximum value of load per annum}}$ is called the load factor

(k_l).

When using Kelvin's Law to find the most economical c.s.a. of a transmission line, the r.m.s. value of the annual load curve must be used. This can be found by multiplying the maximum value of load current per annum by $k_f \times k_l$, since $I_{max} \times \dfrac{I_{r.m.s.}}{I_{av}} \times \dfrac{I_{av}}{I_{max}} = I_{r.m.s.}$.

The following table gives the corresponding values of k_l and k_f for annual load curves typical of the United Kingdom:

k_1	0·1	0·2	0·3	0·4	0·5	0·6	0·7	0·8	0·9	1·0
k_f	2·2	1·7	1·45	1·3	1·2	1·12	1·08	1·04	1·02	1·0

Example 8-2. Find the most economical conductor c.s.a. to transmit a three-phase balanced load which varies throughout the year as follows:

1,800 kVA for 1,500 hours,

800 kVA for 1,600 hours,

No load for the remaining 5,660 hours.

The transmission voltage is 33 kV line. The annual interest and depreciation charges total 10 per cent. Energy costs 0·417 p per kWh. The conductors are to be of copper costing 34·5 p/kg and having a density of $0·886 \times 10^4$ kg/m^3. The resistance of 1 km of single conductor of c.s.a. 1 cm^2 is 0·177 Ω.

Also calculate the conductor diameter, the maximum current density and the load and form factors.

Considering 1 km of single conductor:
Let the most economical c.s.a. be A cm^2.

When the load is 1,800 kVA, $I = \dfrac{1,800}{\sqrt{3 \times 33}} = 31.5$ A.

Hence $\quad$ energy loss $= 31.5^2 \times \dfrac{0.177}{A} \times 1,500 \times 10^{-3}$

$$= \frac{264}{A} \text{ kWh.}$$

When the load is 800 kVA, $I = \dfrac{800}{\sqrt{3 \times 33}} = 14$ A.

Hence $\quad$ energy loss $= 14^2 \times \dfrac{0.177}{A} \times 1,600 \times 10^{-3}$

$$= \frac{55.5}{A} \text{ kWh.}$$

Therefore annual cost of energy loss $= £\,\dfrac{264 + 55.5}{A} \times 0.00417$

$$= £\,\frac{1.33}{A}.$$

Mass of copper $= \dfrac{10^5 \times A \times 0.886 \times 10^4}{10^6} = 886A$ kg.

Annual charges on the initial cost of copper $= £0.345 \times 0.1 \times 886A$

$$= £30.6A.$$

Using Kelvin's Law, $\qquad 30.6A = \dfrac{1.33}{A},$

so that $\qquad\qquad\qquad A = 0.208$ cm^2.

Conductor diameter $= \sqrt{\left(\dfrac{0.208 \times 4}{\pi}\right)} = 0.515$ cm.

Maximum current density $= \dfrac{31.5}{0.208} = 151.5$ A/cm^2.

Average value of load per annum

$$= \frac{(31 \cdot 5 \times 1{,}500) + (14 \times 1{,}600) + (0 \times 5{,}660)}{8{,}760}$$

$$= 7 \cdot 95 \, \text{A}.$$

Hence $\quad k_l = \dfrac{7 \cdot 95}{31 \cdot 5} = \mathbf{0 \cdot 252}.$

r.m.s. value of load per annum

$$= \sqrt{\left(\frac{(31 \cdot 5^2 \times 1{,}500) + (14^2 \times 1{,}600) + (0^2 \times 5{,}660)}{8{,}760} \right)}$$

$$= \sqrt{\left(\frac{1{,}801{,}500}{8{,}760} \right)}$$

$$= 14 \cdot 34 \, \text{A}.$$

Hence $\quad k_f = \dfrac{14 \cdot 35}{7 \cdot 95} = \mathbf{1 \cdot 8}.$

The total annual energy loss could have been found by using the r.m.s. value of load per annum as follows:

As before, total annual energy loss is

$$14 \cdot 34^2 \times \frac{0 \cdot 177}{A} \times 8{,}760 \times 10^{-3} = \frac{319 \cdot 5}{A} \, \text{kWh}.$$

Example 8-3. A 1,000-kVA transformer, supplying a rural area is fed by an 11,000-V, three-phase, overhead transmission line.

Estimate the most economical cross-sectional area of conductor using Kelvin's Law and the following data:

Load factor 0·6. Form factor 1·15.

Conductors are of hard drawn copper costing £2,020/m³ and of resistance 0·177 Ω/km of 1 cm² c.s.a.

Interest and depreciation 8 per cent.

Cost of energy 0·292 p per kWh.

Considering 1 km of single conductor:

$$\text{Maximum load current} = \frac{1{,}000}{\sqrt{3} \cdot 11} = 52 \cdot 5 \, \text{A}.$$

R.m.s. value of load per annum $= 52 \cdot 5 \times 0 \cdot 6 \times 1 \cdot 15 = 36 \cdot 2 \, \text{A}.$

Let the most economical c.s.a. be A cm^2.

$$\text{Annual energy loss} = 36 \cdot 2^2 \times \frac{0 \cdot 177}{A} \times 8{,}760 \times 10^{-3} = \frac{2{,}030}{A}$$

$$\text{Annual cost of energy loss} = \pounds \frac{2{,}030}{A} \times 0 \cdot 00292$$

$$= \pounds \frac{5 \cdot 93}{A}.$$

Annual charges on the initial cost of copper

$$= \pounds 2{,}020 \times \frac{10^5 \cdot A}{10^6} \times 0 \cdot 08 = \pounds 16 \cdot 16 A.$$

But $$16 \cdot 16 A = \frac{5 \cdot 93}{A},$$

therefore $$A = \mathbf{0 \cdot 606 \ cm^2}.$$

Limitations to the Application of Kelvin's Law

(i) Kelvin's Law is derived on the assumption that the cost of towers, insulators and erection are independent of conductor c.s.a. In practice, the cost of these items increases with conductor c.s.a.

(ii) In the case of very high voltage, steel-cored aluminium overhead lines, the cost of the conductor material is not a major part of the initial cost.

(iii) In deriving Kelvin's Law, only the copper losses are considered. At the higher voltages corona losses may be comparable with the copper losses.

(iv) When applying the law to underground cables, the c.s.a. obtained may be too small because dielectric losses are ignored and heat dissipation is more difficult.

(v) The correct value of load current is difficult to estimate in advance.

(vi) The c.s.a. obtained using the law is based on financial considerations and must be checked for current density, voltage drop, corona and mechanical strength. During the past twenty years, the cost of conductor materials has risen at a much faster rate than that of electrical energy and this trend leads to smaller c.s.a.'s being obtained from the law.

In general, Kelvin's Law is most useful up to 33 kV line. The concept of economic current density is sometimes worth considering for higher voltages, however. The curve of total cost against conductor c.s.a. is usually very flat near the minimum point, as shown in figure 8.1. An error of the order of 20 per cent either way does not, therefore, usually make much difference to total annual operating costs.

For an important line, the only satisfactory method is to take at least two standard conductor sizes on either side of the most economical c.s.a. and to calculate the total annual costs for each, including towers, insulators, and erection.

Transmission Voltage

It was shown in Section 3 that as the transmission voltage is raised the amount of conductor material required is reduced. However, the cost of transformers, switchgear, and other equipment increases with voltage so that there is an optimum voltage of transmission.

The most economical transmission voltage increases with the length of the line and the size of the load.

The only satisfactory method of arriving at the most economical voltage is to take at least two probable standard voltages and to calculate the total annual costs for each.

The voltage of generation, the length of the line, and the size of the load are first decided upon. The costs of transformers at both ends, of switchgear, of overvoltage surge diverters, of insulators, and of towers are then considered for each voltage.

The costs of these items increase with voltage at different rates as shown in the following table:

Plant	6·6 kV	33 kV	66 kV	110 kV	275 kV
Transformers	100	115	150	200	300
Switchgear	100	110	155	420	600
Surge diverters	100	300	600	1,900	5,000
Insulators and towers	100	650	3,500	6,500	12,000

The most economical conductor c.s.a. is calculated for each voltage using Kelvin's Law and hence the annual costs of the conductor material and the energy losses are found.

Generating Costs

The annual cost of running a steam power station may be conveniently divided into three parts:

(i) A fixed cost which is independent of the maximum power and annual energy outputs. This cost comprises part of the cost of the central administrative organization and the capital cost of the station site.

(ii) A cost which is directly proportional to the maximum possible power output but is independent of the annual energy output. This cost comprises the salaries of charge engineers and maintenance staff and the cost of buildings, plant, and spares.

(iii) A cost which is directly proportional to the annual energy output. This cost is mainly that of fuel and water.

Since costs (i) and (ii) are independent of the number of kWh generated per annum, these costs are called the 'standing charges' and (iii) is called the 'running charge'.

It is difficult to separate these charges precisely since, for example, the cost of maintenance does partly depend on the kWh generated per annum. It is obvious, however, that the greater the load factor, the lower the cost of each kWh since the standing charges will be distributed over more units. The following table shows how the cost per kWh varies with load factor for a typical steam station:

k_l	0·2	0·3	0·4	0·5	0·6	0·8	1
Standing charge per kWh	93	61	46	37	31	23	18
Running charge per kWh	82	82	82	82	82	82	82
Total cost per kWh	175	143	128	119	113	105	100

In the case of a hydro-electric station, the capital costs are very high and the running costs are very low. Thus, in order to keep down the cost per kWh, it is even more important to maintain a high load factor than it is for a steam station.

Maximum Demand

The maximum demand to be made on a generating station determines the size and cost of the installation. If the maximum demand is high compared with the average load, that is if the load factor is low, then the cost per kWh will be high.

The maximum demand on a station may be reduced in two ways:

(i) Encouragement to diversify the load

The maximum demands of a number of consumers are unlikely to occur all at the same time, so that the maximum demand on the generating station is always much less than the sum of the maximum demands of the separate consumers.

The diversity factor is the ratio

$$\frac{\text{sum of maximum demands of separate consumers}}{\text{maximum demand on station}}.$$

This ratio is always greater than 1 and should be as high as possible.

The diversity factor can be increased by offering tariff inducements to consumers using energy during the night or at week-ends. An example of the former is the special tariff available for 'off-peak' storage heaters used for central heating.

(ii) Encouragement of Power Factor Correction

The full-load output of an alternator is determined by the voltage at which it is designed to generate and the current which can be carried by the stator windings without overheating. Thus an alternator which is capable of generating 60 MVA will have a full-load output of 60 MW at unity power factor, 48 MW at 0·8, 36 MW at 0·6, and so on. The same argument also applies to other equipment such as transformers, feeders, and switchgear. Thus, if the overall power factor of a supply system is 0·8 lagging, the amount of plant required is 1·25 times greater than would be necessary had the overall power factor been unity.

In order to encourage consumers to correct lagging power factors by fitting static capacitors or synchronous condensers, industrial tariffs include a maximum demand charge as well as a kWh charge. The maximum demand charge is usually based on the greatest kVAh supplied during any thirty consecutive minutes during the account month.

Loss Factor

The ratio of $\dfrac{\text{average power losses per annum}}{\text{maximum power losses per annum}}$ for a transmission system is called the loss factor.

The loss factor differs from the load factor because the copper losses vary as the square of the load current. The loss factor of copper losses only is therefore always less than the load factor.

In addition to the copper losses, however, there are losses which are independent of load current such as iron losses in transformers and dielectric losses in cables. If such plant is permanently energized, these losses alone have a loss factor of 1. They therefore raise the value of overall loss factor when combined with the copper losses.

Since the loss factor differs from the load factor, the cost of transmitting each kWh varies with load in a different way from the cost of generating each kWh.

Efficiency of Transformers

Most transformers used in supply systems are continuously energized throughout the year but do not continuously deliver full-load output. It is therefore important to keep the iron losses as low as possible by using high grade magnetic materials such as cold-rolled, grain-oriented steel. The use of such materials increases the initial cost of the transformer, however, so that for given load conditions there is an optimum design for which the sum of the annual interest and depreciation charges on the initial cost plus the annual cost of the energy losses is a minimum.

Thus the full-load efficiency calculated in terms of power input and output is not the only criterion. The 'all-day' efficiency, 'all-year' efficiency, and initial cost are also important.

$$\text{Full-load efficiency} = 1 - \frac{\text{power losses}}{\text{output power} + \text{power losses}}.$$

$$\text{'All-day' efficiency} = 1 - \frac{\text{daily energy loss}}{\text{daily output energy} + \text{daily energy loss}}.$$

$$\text{'All-year' efficiency} = 1 - \frac{\text{annual energy loss}}{\text{annual output energy} + \text{annual energy loss}}.$$

Example 8-4. A certain load varies as follows for 250 days per year:

250 kVA at 0·8 p.f. lagging for 8 hours per day;

100 kVA at 0·8 p.f. lagging for 8 hours per day;

50 kVA at unity p.f. for 8 hours per day.

For the remaining 115 days, the load varies thus:

50 kVA at unity p.f. for 8 hours per day;

10 kVA at unity p.f. for 8 hours per day;

No load for 8 hours per day.

(a) Calculate the annual load and form factors.

(b) Calculate the efficiency, at full load, 0·8 p.f. lagging, the two 'all-day' efficiencies and the 'all-year' efficiency for each of the following 250 kVA transformers:

Transformer	Initial cost	Iron loss	Full load copper loss
X	£1,600	1 kW	4 kW
Y	£1,540	2 kW	3·5 kW

(c) Calculate the total annual running cost of each transformer, allowing 10 per cent for annual interest and depreciation and assuming the cost of energy to be 0·417p per kWh.

(d) Calculate the annual loss factor for each transformer.

(a) Average value of load per annum is

$$\frac{(250 \times 2,000) + (100 \times 2,000) + (50 \times 2,920) + (10 \times 920)}{8,760}$$

$$= \frac{855,200}{8,760} = 97 \cdot 6 \, \text{kVA}.$$

$$\text{Load factor} = k_l \equiv \frac{97 \cdot 6}{250} = \mathbf{0 \cdot 39}.$$

R.m.s. value of load per annum is

$$\sqrt{\left\{ \frac{(250^2 \times 2,000) + (100^2 \times 2,000) + (50^2 \times 2,920) + (10^2 \times 920)}{8,760} \right\}}$$

$$= \sqrt{\left(\frac{1 \cdot 524 \times 10^8}{8,760} \right)} = 131 \cdot 9 \, \text{kVA}.$$

$$\text{Form factor} = k_f = \frac{131 \cdot 9}{97 \cdot 6} = \mathbf{1 \cdot 35}.$$

(b) For transformer X:

$$\text{Full load efficiency} = 1 - \frac{5}{200 + 5}$$

$$= 1 - 0 \cdot 0244 = 0 \cdot 9756.$$

For transformer Y:

$$\text{Full load efficiency} = 1 - \frac{5 \cdot 5}{200 + 5 \cdot 5}$$

$$= 1 - 0 \cdot 0268 = 0 \cdot 9732.$$

For each of 250 days per annum:

	Transformer X	Transformer Y
Iron loss	$1 \times 24 = 24 \, \text{kWh}$	$2 \times 24 = 48 \, \text{kWh}$
Copper loss at 250 kVA	$4 \times 8 = 32 \, \text{kWh}$	$3 \cdot 5 \times 8 = 28 \, \text{kWh}$
Copper loss at 100 kVA	$\left[\frac{100}{250}\right]^2 \times 4 \times 8 = 5 \cdot 1 \, \text{kWh}$	$\left[\frac{100}{250}\right]^2 \times 3 \cdot 5 \times 8 = 4 \cdot 5 \, \text{kWh}$
Copper loss at 50 kVA	$\left[\frac{50}{250}\right]^2 \times 4 \times 8 = 1 \cdot 3 \, \text{kWh}$	$\left[\frac{50}{250}\right]^2 \times 3 \cdot 5 \times 8 = 1 \cdot 1 \, \text{kWh}$
Total daily copper loss	$38 \cdot 4 \, \text{kWh}$	$33 \cdot 6 \, \text{kWh}$
Total daily losses	$62 \cdot 4 \, \text{kWh}$	$81 \cdot 6 \, \text{kWh}$

Daily output $= (250 \times 0.8 \times 8) + (100 \times 0.8 \times 8) + (50 \times 1.0 \times 8)$

$\qquad\qquad\quad = 1,600 + 640 + 400$

$\qquad\qquad\quad = 2,640 \text{ kWh.}$

All-day efficiency of transformer $X = 1 - \dfrac{62.4}{2,702}$

$\qquad\qquad\qquad\qquad\qquad\qquad\quad = 1 - 0.0231$

$\qquad\qquad\qquad\qquad\qquad\qquad\quad = 0.9769.$

All-day efficiency of transformer $Y = 1 - \dfrac{81.6}{2,722}$

$\qquad\qquad\qquad\qquad\qquad\qquad\quad = 1 - 0.03$

$\qquad\qquad\qquad\qquad\qquad\qquad\quad = 0.9700.$

For each of 115 days per annum:

	Transformer X	Transformer Y
Iron loss	$1 \times 24 = 24 \text{ kWh}$	$2 \times 24 = 48 \text{ kWh}$
Copper loss at 50 kVA	$\left[\dfrac{50}{250}\right]^2 \times 4 \times 8 = 1.28 \text{ kWh}$	$\left[\dfrac{50}{250}\right]^2 \times 3.5 \times 8 = 1.12 \text{ kWh}$
Copper loss at 10 kVA	$\left[\dfrac{10}{250}\right]^2 \times 4 \times 8 = 0.05 \text{ kWh}$	$\left[\dfrac{10}{250}\right]^2 \times 3.5 \times 8 = 0.05 \text{ kWh}$
Total daily copper loss	1.33 kWh	1.17 kWh
Total daily losses	25.3 kWh	49.2 kWh

Daily output $= (50 \times 1.0 \times 8) + (10 \times 1.0 \times 8)$

$\qquad\qquad\quad = 400 + 80 = 480 \text{ kWh.}$

All-day efficiency of transformer $X = 1 - \dfrac{25.3}{505.3}$

$\qquad\qquad\qquad\qquad\qquad\qquad\quad = 1 - 0.0501$

$\qquad\qquad\qquad\qquad\qquad\qquad\quad = 0.9499.$

All-day efficiency of transformer $Y = 1 - \dfrac{49.2}{529.2}$

$\qquad\qquad\qquad\qquad\qquad\qquad\quad = 1 - 0.0930$

$\qquad\qquad\qquad\qquad\qquad\qquad\quad = 0.9070.$

	Transformer X	Transformer Y
Total annual losses	$(62{\cdot}4 \times 250) + (25{\cdot}3 \times 115)$	$(81{\cdot}6 \times 250) + (49{\cdot}2 \times 115)$
	$= 15{,}600 + 2{,}910$	$= 20{,}400 + 5{,}660$
	$= 18{,}510$ kWh	$= 26{,}060$ kWh
Annual output	$(2{,}640 \times 250) + (480 \times 115) = 660{,}000 + 55{,}200 = 715{,}200$ kWh	
All-year efficiency	$1 - \dfrac{18{,}510}{733{,}700}$	$1 - \dfrac{26{,}060}{741{,}300}$
	$= 1 - 0{\cdot}0252$	$= 1 - 0{\cdot}0352$
	$= 0{\cdot}9748$	$= 0{\cdot}9648$

(c)

	Transformer X	Transformer Y
Annual cost of losses	£18,510 × 0·00417 = £77·1	£26,060 × 0·00417 = £108·6
Annual interest and depreciation charges	£1,600 × 0·1 = £160	£1,540 × 0·1 = £154
Total annual cost	£237·1	£262·6

(d) For transformer X:

Average copper loss per annum is

$$\frac{(4 \times 2{,}000) + (0{\cdot}64 \times 2{,}000) + (0{\cdot}16 \times 2{,}920) + (0{\cdot}0064 \times 920)}{8{,}760}$$

$$= \frac{8{,}000 + 1{,}280 + 467 + 6}{8{,}760} = \frac{9{,}753}{8{,}760} = 1{\cdot}114 \text{ kW}.$$

Loss factor of copper losses only $= \dfrac{1{\cdot}114}{4} = 0{\cdot}278.$

Average iron and copper losses per annum

$$= \frac{9{,}753 + (1 \times 8{,}760)}{8{,}760} = 2{\cdot}114 \text{ kW}.$$

Overall loss factor $= \dfrac{2{\cdot}114}{5} = 0{\cdot}423.$

For transformer Y:

Average copper loss per annum is

$$\frac{(3 \cdot 5 \times 2,000) + (0 \cdot 56 \times 2,000) + (0 \cdot 14 \times 2,920) + (0 \cdot 0056 \times 920)}{8,760}$$

$$= \frac{7,000 + 1,120 + 409 + 5}{8,760}$$

$$= \frac{8,534}{8,760} = 0 \cdot 974 \, \text{kW}.$$

Loss factor of copper losses only $= \dfrac{0 \cdot 974}{3 \cdot 5} = 0 \cdot 278$, as for trans-

former X.

Average iron and copper losses per annum $= \dfrac{8,534 + (2 \times 8,760)}{8,760}$

$$= 2 \cdot 974 \, \text{kW}.$$

Overall loss factor $= \dfrac{2 \cdot 974}{5 \cdot 5} = 0 \cdot 541$.

Tariffs

Tariffs may be divided into the following groups:

(a) Domestic premises   (b) Off-peak
(c) Combined premises   (d) Commercial
(e) Agricultural   (f) Industrial

Other tariffs are designed for some special circumstances.

(a) applies to electrical energy used for domestic purposes in a private residence. This tariff usually consists of a kWh charge plus a fixed quarterly charge based on the number of rooms and/or the floor area.

(b) applies to electrical energy supplied to any premises usually between 10 p.m. and 7.30 a.m., and 1 p.m. and 4 p.m. This tariff consists of a kWh charge lower than that of (a) plus a similar fixed quarterly charge.

(c) applies to electrical energy used for trade, business, or professional purposes as well as for domestic purposes. For example, a shop with house or flat combined or a doctor's surgery. This tariff does not apply to premises in which items are manufactured or grown for sale. This tariff is usually similar to (a) but the fixed quarterly charge is higher.

(d) applies to electrical energy supplied to premises used solely for commercial purposes, but not to premises in which items are manu-factured or grown for sale. This tariff is similar to (a) except that there is an additional fixed quarterly charge based on the maximum kVA required.

(e) applies to electrical energy supplied to a farm, market garden, or other agricultural holding. This tariff is similar to (d).

(f) applies to electrical energy supplied to industrial premises. This tariff is a monthly maximum demand tariff.

Maximum demand is defined as twice the number of kVAh supplied during any thirty consecutive minutes during the account month. This maximum demand is divided into blocks of units and a decreasing scale of charges is applied to successive blocks.

In addition a kWh charge is made. The energy supplied during the account month is divided into blocks of kWh and a decreasing scale of charges is applied to successive blocks. These blocks are linked to the kVA of maximum demand. The overall effect of this tariff is that the lower the power factor, the greater the average cost to the consumer of each kWh. For loads exceeding 100 kVA, consumers are encouraged to take their supply at 11 kV or above. The substation is then the property and responsibility of the consumer, the supply being metered on the HV side. Otherwise an additional charge per kWh is made to cover the interest and depreciation charges on the initial cost of the substation and the cost of the transformer losses.

Example 8-5. An industrial consumer has a constant load of 1,500 kW at 0·8 p.f. lagging for 8 hours per day for 20 days per month. For the remaining hours in a month of 30 days there is a constant unity power factor load of 100 kW.

(a) Calculate the monthly cost on the following tariff:

Maximum Demand Charge each month:

Each kVA of the first 200 kVA of maximum demand	£1.20
Each kVA of the next 300 kVA of maximum demand	£1.10
Each kVA of the next 500 kVA of maximum demand	£1.00
Each additional kVA of maximum demand	£0.90

Kilowatt-hour (Unit) Charge each month:

Each of the first 180 kilowatt-hours per kVA of maximum demand made in the month	0.7p
Each of the next 180 kilowatt-hours per kVA of maximum demand made in the month	0.6p
Each additional kilowatt-hour supplied	0.5p

(b) If the consumer corrects the power factor of the main load from 0·8 to 0·95 lagging by means of loss-free static capacitors costing £100 per month, calculate the monthly saving.

(a) kVA of maximum demand $= \dfrac{1,500}{0.8} = 1,875.$

Maximum demand charge

$$= £(200 \times 1.2) + (300 \times 1.1) + (500 \times 1) + (875 \times 0.9)$$
$$= £240 + 330 + 500 + 788$$
$$= £1,858.$$

kWh used in one month

$$= (1,500 \times 160) + (100 \times 560) = 240,000 + 56,000$$
$$= 296,000.$$

The first block of kWh $= 180 \times 1,875 = 337,500.$

Thus every kWh costs 0·7p.

$$\text{and kWh charge} = £296,000 \times 0.007 = £2,072.$$
$$\text{Total cost} = £1,858 + 2,072 = £3,930.$$

(Average cost per kWh = 1·33p).

(b) kVA of maximum demand $= \dfrac{1,500}{0.95} = 1,579.$

Maximum demand charge

$$= £(200 \times 1.2) + (300 \times 1.1) + (500 \times 1) + (579 \times 0.9)$$
$$= £240 + 330 + 500 + 521$$
$$= £1,591.$$

kWh used in one month $= 296,000$ as before.

The first block of kWh $= 180 \times 1,579 = 284,220.$

Therefore the first block of kWh costs $£284,220 \times 0.007$

$$= £1,990.$$

Remaining kWh $= 296,000 - 284,220 = 11,780.$

Cost of these units $= £11,780 \times 0.006$

$\qquad\qquad\qquad\quad = £71.$

Total cost of supply $= £1,591$

$\qquad\qquad\qquad\quad\;\; 1,990$

$\qquad\qquad\qquad\qquad\;\; 71$

$\qquad\qquad\qquad\quad\; \overline{£3,652}$

(Average cost per kWh $= 1.23$ p).

Total cost including capacitors $= £3,752$

Monthly saving $\qquad\qquad\quad = \quad £3,930$

$\qquad\qquad\qquad\qquad\qquad\quad -£3,752$

$\qquad\qquad\qquad\qquad\qquad\quad \overline{\;\;£178.}$

Power Factor Correction

The capital required for purchasing power factor correction equipment is usually borrowed and interest payments have to be made. In addition, a depreciation charge is also made, even though this may not be strictly necessary with modern static capacitors.

It can be seen from example 8-5 that the use of power factor correction equipment results in a monthly tariff saving. This saving, less the interest and depreciation charges, should repay the borrowed capital in a reasonable time.

During this time there are technical advantages to the consumer such as less heat loss, more efficient loading of plant, smaller distribution cable sizes and switchgear, and better voltage regulation.

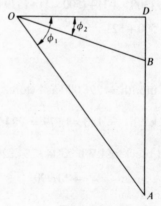

FIG. 8.2

After the capital has been repaid, the technical advantages continue and the consumer is saving money through the more favourable tariff charges.

Obviously the annual interest and depreciation charges must not exceed the annual tariff saving. There is therefore an optimum value of power factor beyond which it does not pay the consumer to correct.

Constant kW Correction

If loss-free, static capacitors are used to correct a power factor from $\cos \phi_1$ to $\cos \phi_2$, the kVA diagram is as in figure 8.2.

$$OA = \text{kVA of load before correction.}$$

$$OD = \text{kW of load.}$$

$$DA = \text{kVAr lagging before correction.}$$

$$OB = \text{kVA of load after correction.}$$

$$DB = \text{kVAr lagging after correction.}$$

The required leading kVAr $= AB$

$$= DA - DB = OD(\tan\phi_1 - \tan\phi_2).$$

Constant kVA Correction

In figure 8.3, the kVA before correction ($= OA$) is numerically equal to the kVA after correction ($= OF$).

$$OD = \text{kW before correction.}$$

$$DA = \text{kVAr lagging before correction.}$$

$$OE = \text{kW after correction.}$$

$$EF = \text{kVAr lagging after correction.}$$

If correction is by means of an over-excited synchronous motor,

$$AF = \text{kVA input to motor.}$$

$$GF = \text{kVAr leading input to motor.}$$

$$AG = \text{kW input to motor.}$$

The kW losses in the motor are usually less than AG so that the remainder represents the mechanical load which can be driven by the motor.

If correction is by means of low-loss or loss-free static capacitors, then GF is equal to their leading kVAr rating and AG equals the increase in kW made available.

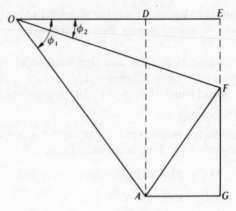

FIG. 8.3

Example 8-6. A sub-station transformer is supplying 360 kW at 0·6 power factor lagging.

Calculate:

(a) The kVAr rating of the loss-free static capacitors required for constant kW correction to 0·95 lagging.

(b) The kVA rating of the synchronous motor required for constant kVA correction to 0·95 lagging.

(a) Referring to figure 8.2:

$$\phi_1 = \cos^{-1} 0·6 = 53° \, 8'. \quad \phi_2 = \cos^{-1} 0·95 = 18° \, 12'.$$

Leading kVAr required $= AB = 360 \,(\tan 53° \, 8' - \tan 18° \, 12')$

$$= 360 \,(1·3335 - 0·3288)$$

$$= 360 \times 1·0047 = \mathbf{362}.$$

(b) Referring to figure 8.3:

$$\phi_1 = 53° \, 8' \quad \text{and} \quad \phi_2 = 18° \, 12'.$$

kVA before correction $= OA = \dfrac{360}{0·6} = 600.$

kW after correction $= OE = 600 \times 0·95$

$$= 570.$$

Hence, kW input to synchronous motor $= AG = 570 - 360$

$$= 210.$$

kVAr lagging before correction = DA = 600 sin 53° 8′

$$= 600 \times 0·8$$

$$= 480.$$

kVAr lagging after correction = EF = 600 sin 18° 12′

$$= 600 \times 0·3123$$

$$= 187.$$

Hence, kVAr leading input to synchronous motor = $480 - 187$ = 293.

kVA input to synchronous motor = $\sqrt{(210^2 + 293^2)} = \mathbf{361}$.

Most Economical Power Factor to which a Constant kW Load may be Corrected by means of Loss-free Static Capacitors

As seen in example 8-5, the calculation of energy costs is laborious. The maximum demand tariff will therefore be simplified to an annual tariff in which each kVA of maximum demand costs £A and each kWh costs b pence.

Let the annual interest and depreciation charges on the initial cost of the required capacitors be £C per kVAr and let the most economical phase angle be θ.

The value of θ must be such that the sum of the annual tariff charge and the annual interest and depreciation charges on the required capacitors is a minimum.

Since constant kW correction is being considered, then on the simplified tariff specified above, the kWh charge will be the same before and after correction.

Thus only the kVA of maximum demand charge need be considered. The kVA diagram is as in figure 8.4.

$$OD = \text{kW of load.}$$

$$OE = \text{kVA before correction.}$$

$$OB = \text{kVA after correction.}$$

Annual cost of kVA m.d. = £$\dfrac{AW}{\cos \theta}$, where $W = OD$ kW.

Annual cost of capacitors = £$CW (\tan \phi - \tan \theta)$.

Let total annual cost = £T,

then
$$T = \frac{AW}{\cos \theta} + CW \tan \phi - CW \left[\frac{\sin \theta}{\cos \theta} \right].$$

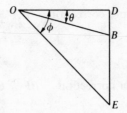

FIG. 8.4

For T to be a minimum, $(dT/d\theta)$ must be zero. This gives

$$\frac{dT}{d\theta} = \frac{(\cos\theta \times 0) - AW(-\sin\theta)}{\cos^2\theta} + 0 - CW\left[\frac{\cos\theta \cdot \cos\theta - \sin\theta(-\sin\theta)}{\cos^2\theta}\right]$$

$$= \frac{AW\sin\theta}{\cos^2\theta} - \frac{CW}{\cos^2\theta} = 0.$$

Hence $$A\sin\theta = C$$

or $$\sin\theta = \frac{C}{A}.$$

Note that the most economical angle is independent of ϕ. If the power factor is corrected to $\cos\theta$, then the annual tariff saving is

$$\pounds A\left[\frac{W}{\cos\phi} - \frac{W}{\cos\theta}\right]$$

and the annual net saving is $\pounds A\left[\dfrac{W}{\cos\phi} - \dfrac{W}{\cos\theta}\right] - \pounds CW(\tan\phi - \tan\theta)$.

Example 8-7. A load of 700 kVA m.d. at 0·7 power factor lagging is to be corrected to the most economical power factor, $\cos\theta$. The annual tariff may be taken as £6 per kVA m.d. and the initial cost of static, loss-free capacitors as £10 per kVAr. The annual interest and depreciation charges total 15 per cent.

Calculate:

(a) Cos θ.

(b) The kVAr rating of the capacitors required.

(c) The annual net saving.

(d) The time taken to save the initial cost of the capacitors.

(a) $C = £10 \times 0·15 = £1·5$

                               $A = £6.$

$$\sin \theta = \frac{C}{A} = \frac{1 \cdot 5}{6} = 0 \cdot 25.$$

$$\theta = 14° \ 29'.$$

$$\cos \theta = 0 \cdot 97 \ \text{lagging}.$$

(b) kVAr rating of capacitors $\quad = 490 \ (\tan 45° \ 35' - \tan 14° \ 29')$

$$= 490 \ (1 \cdot 0206 - 0 \cdot 2584)$$

$$= 490 \times 0 \cdot 7622 = 374.$$

(c) kVA m.d. before correction = 700.

kVA m.d. after correction $\quad = \dfrac{490}{0 \cdot 97} = 506.$

Reduction in kVA m.d. $\quad = 194.$

Annual tariff saving $\quad = £194 \times 6 = £1,164.$

Annual cost of capacitors $\quad = £10 \times 0 \cdot 15 \times 374$

$$= £561.$$

Annual net saving $\quad = £1,164 - 561 = £603.$

(d) Time taken to save the initial cost of the capacitors is

$$\frac{3,740}{603} = 6 \cdot 2 \ \text{years}.$$

Example 8-8. A load of 700 kVA m.d. at 0·7 power factor lagging is to be corrected by connecting a 370 kVAr static capacitor in parallel. The capacitor losses are 5 watts per kVAr.

Calculate:

(a) the kVA m.d. after correction.

(b) the annual net saving taking the annual tariff as £6 per kVA m.d. and the annual interest and depreciation charge on the initial cost of the capacitor as £555.

Assume that the capacitor is permanently connected to the supply and that energy costs 0·833 pence per kWh.

(a) Referring to figure 8.5:

Capacitor losses $BF = 370 \times 0 \cdot 005 = 1 \cdot 85 \ \text{kW}.$

Phase angle before correction $= \phi_1 = 45° \ 35'.$

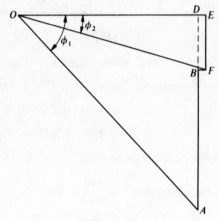

Fig. 8.5

kW before correction $OD = 490$ kW.

kVAr lagging before correction $= 490 \cdot \tan \phi_1$

$$= 490 \times 1 \cdot 0206$$

$$= 500 \cdot 1.$$

kVAr lagging after correction $= DB = EF$

$$= 500 \cdot 1 - 370 = 130 \cdot 1.$$

kW after correction $OE = 490 + 1 \cdot 85 = 491 \cdot 9.$

kVA m.d. after correction $OF = \sqrt{(491 \cdot 9^2 + 130 \cdot 1^2)}$

$$= 509.$$

(b) Reduction in kVA m.d. $= 700 - 509 = 191.$

Corresponding tariff saving $= £191 \times 6 = £1,146.$

Increase in kWh charge $= £1 \cdot 85 \times 8,760 \times 0 \cdot 00833 = £135.$

Annual net saving $= £1,146 - 135 - 555$

$$= £456.$$

Example 8-9. An additional motor load of 20 kW (including losses) is to be added to an existing load of 100 kVA at 0·707 power factor lagging. The new load may be: (a) an induction motor costing £200 which is to be fitted with loss-free capacitors costing £5 per kVAr to improve its power factor from 0·8 to 0·95 lagging; or (b) a synchronous-induction motor costing £10 per kVA which can be excited so that the overall total load kVA remains the same as before the extension of load.

Calculate the total annual cost of each scheme if the tariff is £4 per kVA m.d. plus 0·312 pence per kWh and the annual interest and depreciation charge for (a) is 8 per cent and for (b) 12 per cent. Assume the loads to be constant for 3,000 hours per annum and zero for the remainder of the year.

(a) The kVA diagram for this scheme is as shown in figure 8.6.

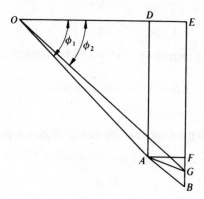

Fɪɢ. 8.6

ϕ_1 = phase angle of existing load = $\cos^{-1} 0.707$ = 45°.

OD = kW of existing load = 70·7.

OA = kVA of existing load = 100.

AF = kW input to induction motor = 20.

$\angle FAB$ = $\cos^{-1} 0.8$ = 36° 52′.

    FB = kVAr lagging input to induction motor before correction = 20 . tan 36° 52′ = 20 × 0·75 = 15.

$\angle FAG$ = $\cos^{-1} 0.95$ = 18° 12′.

    FG = kVAr lagging input to induction motor after correction = 20 . tan 18° 12′ = 20 × 0·3288 = 6·58.

    BG = required leading kVAr of capacitors = 15 − 6·58 = 8·42.

Initial cost of capacitors = £8·42 × 5 = £42·1.

Annual interest and depreciation on induction motor and capacitors = £242·1 × 0·08 = £19·4.

EG = total kVAr lagging after load extension

$$= EF + FG = 70·7 + 6·58 = 77·28.$$

OE = total kW after load extension = $OD + DE$

$$= 70·7 + 20 = 90·7.$$

OG = kVA m.d. after load extension

$$= \sqrt{(90·7^2 + 77·28^2)} = 119·2.$$

Annual kVA m.d. charge = £4 × 119·2 = £476·8.

Annual kWh charge = £90·7 × 3,000 × 0·00312 = £850·4.

Total annual cost = £19·4 + 476·8 + 850·4.

$$= £1,347.$$

(b) The kVA diagram for this scheme is as shown in figure 8.3.

ϕ_1 = phase angle of existing load = 45°.

OD = kW of existing load = 70·7.

$EG = DA$ = kVAr lagging of existing load.

OA = kVA of existing load = 100.

AG = kW input to synchronous motor.

OE = total kW after load extension = 90·7.

OF = kVA m.d. after load extension = 100.

EF = total kVAr lagging after load extension

$$= \sqrt{(100^2 - 90·7^2)} = 42·1.$$

GF = leading kVAr input to s.m. = $EG - EF = 70·7 - 42·1$
$$= 28·6.$$

AF = kVA input to s.m. = $\sqrt{(20^2 + 28·6^2)} = 34·9.$

Annual interest and depreciation on s.m. = £34·9 × 10 × 0·12
= £41·9.

Annual kVA m.d. charge = £4 × 100 = £400.

Annual kWh charge = £850·4, as for scheme (a).

Total annual cost = £41·9 + 400 + 850·4

= £1,292.

Example 8-10. A remote, balanced three-phase load of 200 kW at 0·72 power factor lagging is supplied at 400 volts for 2,000 hours per year. The load is connected to the supply point through a three-core cable of resistance 0·05 ohm/core.

Calculate:

(a) The power factor at the supply point.

(b) The annual cost taking the tariff as £4 per kVA m.d. plus 0·208 pence per kWh.

Static capacitors of negligible loss and costing £5 per kVAr are now connected at the load end to improve the load end power factor to 0·95 lagging. Find the new total annual cost allowing 10 per cent for interest and depreciation. Hence find the time taken to save the initial cost of the capacitors.

(a) Line current = $\dfrac{200 \times 1,000}{\sqrt{3} \times 400 \times 0·72}$ = 401 A.

Total I^2R loss in cable = $3 \times 401^2 \times 0·05$ W

= 24·1 kW.

This is represented by AB in figure 8.7.

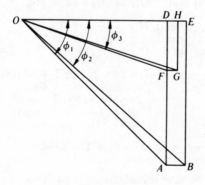

FIG. 8.7

kW at the supply end = OE = 200 + 24 = 224.

kVA at the load end = OA = $\dfrac{200}{0·72}$ = 278.

$\cos\phi_1 = 0·72$. $\phi_1 = 43° 57'$. $\sin\phi_1 = 0·694$.

kVAr lagging $= EB = 278 \times 0.694 = 193$.

kVA at the supply end, $OB = \sqrt{(224^2 + 193^2)} = 296$.

Power factor at supply point $\cos \phi_2 = \dfrac{224}{296} = 0.76$ lagging.

(b) Annual cost $= £4 \times 296 + £\dfrac{224 \times 2,000 \times 0.5}{240}$

$\qquad = £1,184 + £933$

$\qquad = £2,117$.

$\qquad \cos \phi_3 = 0.95. \quad \phi_3 = 18° \, 12'$.

Leading kVAr required $= AF = 200 \, (\tan 43° \, 57' - \tan 18° \, 12')$

$\qquad\qquad = 200 \, (0.964 - 0.3288)$

$\qquad\qquad = 200 \times 0.6352 = 127$.

Annual cost of capacitors $= £5 \times 127 \times 0.1 = £63 \; 10s. \; 0d$.

New line current $= \dfrac{200 \times 1,000}{\sqrt{3} \times 400 \times 0.95} = 304 \, \text{A}$.

New total I^2R loss in cable $= FG = 3 \times 304^2 \times 0.05 = 13.9 \, \text{kW}$.

kW at supply end, $\quad OH = 200 + 14 = 214$.

kVAr at supply end, $HG = 193 - 127 = 66$.

kVA at supply end, $OG = \sqrt{(214^2 + 66^2)} = 224$.

New total an. cost $= £4 \times 224 + £214 \times 2,000 \times 0.00208 + £63.5$

$\qquad\qquad = £896 + £891.7 + £63.5$

$\qquad\qquad = £1,851$.

Annual saving $= £2,117 - £1,851 = £266$.

Time taken to save initial cost of capacitors is $\dfrac{635}{266} = 2.39$ years.

EXAMPLES 8

1. A factory is to be supplied at 6·6 kV, three-phase by a three-conductor cable, the anticipated daily load being 800 kVA for 8 hours,

300 kVA for 8 hours, and 100 kVA for 8 hours, for 250 days per year. Take the cost of wasted energy as 0·417p per kWh and the cost of copper as 29·6 p/kg. One km of copper conductor of cross-sectional area 1 cm^2 has a resistance of 0.177Ω and has a mass of 886 kg. Allowing 12 per cent for interest and depreciation, calculate the most economical cross-sectional area of each core.

Also calculate the greatest working current density and the load and form factors. (Answers **0·517 cm^2, 135 A r.m.s./cm^2, 0·343, 1·5.**)

2. The cost per km of a three-conductor, overhead line is £72·2A + B per conductor where A is the cross-sectional area of each conductor (cm^2) and B is a constant. Interest and depreciation is 10 per cent per annum and energy costs 0·208 pence per kWh. Take the load factor as 0·5 and the form factor as 1·2. One km of conductor of cross-sectional area 1 cm^2 has a resistance of 0·177 Ω.

Calculate the greatest working current density.
(Answer **79 A r.m.s./cm^2.**)

3. State the fundamental principle upon which the economic design of a piece of electrical plant should be based and hence derive Kelvin's Law. Show how the problem may be represented graphically. Explain why the principle cannot be readily applied to high voltage lines and transformers.

The loading on a 750-kVA transformer varies as follows:

> Full load for 3,000 hours.
> Half full-load for 3,000 hours.
> No load for the remainder of the year.

Calculate the load factor.

Determine the total annual running costs for each of the following transformers allowing 10 per cent for interest and depreciation and taking the cost of energy as 0·541 pence per kWh.

Transformer	Core material	Initial cost	Iron loss	F/L copper loss
A	Hot rolled silicon iron	£1,250	2·5 kW	8 kW
B	Cold rolled grain oriented iron	£1,500	1·6 kW	6 kW

State why the iron and copper losses of transformer B are lower than those of A. (Answers **0·51, £406 for A, £348 for B.**)

4. The load to be supplied by a 500 kVA distribution transformer varies as follows:

> 500 kVA at 0·8 power factor lagging for 2,000 hours.

250 kVA at 0·8 power factor lagging for 2,000 hours.

100 kVA at unity power factor for the remainder of the year.

Calculate:

(a) The annual load and form factors.

(b) The efficiency at full load, 0·8 power factor lagging and the 'all-year' efficiency if the transformer iron loss is 2 kW and the full-load copper loss is 6 kW.

(c) The total annual running cost allowing 10 per cent for interest and depreciation and taking the cost of energy as 0·5 pence per kWh and the initial cost of the transformer as £1,200.

(d) The annual loss factor.

(Answers (a) **0·451, 1·23**, (b) **0·9804, 0·9803**, (c) **£288**, (d) **0·48**.)

5. A certain daily load varies as follows:

250 kVA at 0·8 p.f. lagging for 8 hours.

100 kVA at 0·8 p.f. lagging for 8 hours.

50 kVA at unity p.f. for 8 hours.

Determine the 'all-day' efficiency of each of the following 250 kVA supply transformers:

Transformer	Iron loss	Full load copper loss
A	1 kW	4 kW
B	2 kW	3·5 kW

What would be the tariff saving effected in 10 weeks (7 days per week) with the more economical transformer if the charge for electrical energy is 0·417 p per kWh?

(Answers **0·9769 for A, 0·9700 for B, £5·60**.)

6. An industrial consumer has a constant load of 2,000 kW at 0·8 p.f. lagging for 10 hours per day for 25 days per month. For the remaining hours in a month of 30 days there is a constant unity power factor load of 200 kW.

(a) Calculate the monthly cost on the following tariff:

Maximum demand charge each month:

Each kVA of the first 200 kVA of maximum demand   68·75p

Each kVA of the next 300 kVA of maximum demand   66·25p

Each kVA of the next 500 kVA of maximum demand   63·75p

Each additional kVA of maximum demand   61·25p

Kilowatt-hour (unit) charge each month:

Each of the first 180 kilowatt-hours per kVA of maximum demand   0·396p

Each of the next 180 kilowatt-hours per kVA of maximum demand   0·342p

Each additional kilowatt-hour supplied   0·313p

(b) Express this consumer's *annual* costs in the form £A per kVA m.d. + b pence per kWh.

(c) Calculate the load factor and form factor.

(Answers (a) **£3,847**, (b) **£7·56 per kVA m.d. + 0·383 p per kWh**, (c) **0·399, 1·49**.)

7. A load of 700 kVA m.d. at 0·7 power factor lagging is to be corrected to the most economical power factor, cos θ.

The annual tariff charge may be taken as £5 per kVA m.d. and the initial cost of static, loss-free capacitors, including that of the necessary control gear, is £7 per kVAr. The annual interest and depreciation charges total 15 per cent.

Calculate:

(a) Cos θ.

(b) The kVAr rating of the capacitors required.

(c) The annual net saving.

(d) The time taken to save the initial cost of the capacitors.

(Answers (a) **0·98 lagging**, (b) **395 kVAr**, (c) **£580**, (d) **4·77 years**.)

8. An industrial load of 500 kW at a power factor of 0·76 lagging is corrected to the most economical power factor by means of a loss-free capacitor having a rating of 300 kVAr. The annual tariff charge may be taken as £5 per kVA m.d. and annual interest and depreciation charges total 20 per cent.

If the capacitor alone costs £1,100, find the maximum amount which may be initially spent on the associated control gear.

(Answer **£754**.)

9. A consumer's supply transformer is rated at 500 kVA and the present load is 350 kW at 0·7 power factor lagging. It is required to add a further load of 110 kW at the same power factor.

This increase may be achieved by either (a) installing an additional transformer and its associated switchgear at a total cost of £4 per kVA, or (b) raising the power factor of the new total load so that its kVA does not exceed the rating of the existing transformer. The cost of suitable loss-free capacitors is £6 per kVAr. The interest and depreciation charges for either scheme total 12 per cent and the annual tariff charge may be taken as £4 per kVA m.d.

Calculate the total annual running cost of each scheme.

(Answers (a) **£2,703**, (b) **£2,197**.)

10. The power factor of a 200 kW, three-phase, balanced load is to be improved from 0·707 to 0·9 lagging by connecting loss-free capacitors in delta across the 3·3 kV supply.

The cost of suitable capacitors and control gear is £20 per μF, the annual tariff charge is £6·50 per kVA m.d. and the interest and depreciation charges total 12 per cent.

Calculate:

(a) The total kVAr rating of the capacitors.

(b) The required value of capacitance in μF/phase.

(c) The net annual saving.

(d) The time taken to save the initial cost of the capacitors and control gear.

(Answers (a) **103·5 kVAr**, (b) **10·1 μF/ph**, (c) **£317·50**, (d) **1·91 years**.)

11. An existing load of 400 kVA at 0·65 power factor lagging is to be extended by the addition of a mechanical drive requiring 100 h.p. A 150 kVA synchronous motor, full load efficiency 0·92, is available for this purpose.

Calculate the leading kVAr made available by operating this motor at full load kVA, and the resulting overall power factor. Draw a kVA diagram, roughly to scale, to illustrate your answer.

(Answers **126 kVAr, 0·89 lagging**.)

12. A remote, balanced three-phase load of 300 kW at 0·673 power factor lagging is supplied at 415 volts for 2,000 hours per year. The load is connected to the supply point through a three-core cable of resistance 0·026 Ω/core.

Calculate:

(a) The power factor at the supply point.

(b) The annual cost taking the tariff as £6·50 per kVA m.d. plus 0·292 pence per kWh.

Static capacitors of negligible loss and costing £10 per kVAr are now connected at the load end to improve the load end power factor to 0·95 lagging. Find the new total annual cost allowing 10 per cent for interest and depreciation. Hence find the time taken to save the initial cost of the capacitors.

(Answers (a) **0·71 lagging**, (b) **£4,955, £4,210, 3·08 years**.)

9

High Frequency Transients

Voltage Surges

A voltage surge is initiated by a sudden change in voltage at a point in a system. Since a transmission system is equivalent to a large number of shunt capacitors interconnected with series inductors and resistors, there is a time delay before the change reaches other parts of the system. This delay is due to the time required for changes in electrostatic and electromagnetic fields to take place. The velocity at which the change (or surge) travels to other parts of the system depends on the medium in which the surge is travelling.

Typical Voltage Surge Waveform

The waveform shown in figure 9.1 is in fact a graph of the build up of voltage with respect to time at a particular point in a system.

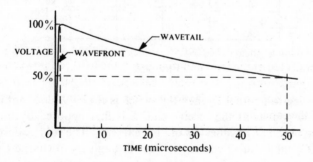

FIG. 9.1

The waveform shown is known as a 1/50 surge. That is, a surge in which the peak is reached in 1 microsecond and the tail falls to half the peak value in 50 microseconds. In practice, the steepness of the wavefront is of great importance since it indicates the rate of rise of voltage at any point in the system. The breakdown voltage of insulation varies with rate of rise voltage. In most cases the time taken to reach the voltage peak is of the order of 1 to 5 microseconds.

235

Current Surges

A voltage surge is always accompanied by a current surge which travels at the same velocity. The associated current surge consists of charging or discharging capacitance current caused by the change in voltages across the shunt capacitances of the transmission system.

Causes of High Voltage Surges

(i) A direct lightning stroke on overhead conductors.

This may initiate a surge having an amplitude of the order of 10 million volts. The most severe surges are due to direct strokes but these are rare.

(ii) A cloud to cloud or cloud to earth lightning discharge in the vicinity of overhead conductors.

A positively charged cloud electrostatically induces a corresponding negative charge on an overhead line in the vicinity. When such a cloud discharges to earth or to another cloud, the negative charge on the line is isolated resulting in a high negative voltage surge. Such surges are less severe but more common than those due to a direct stroke.

(iii) Switching on an open-circuited line.

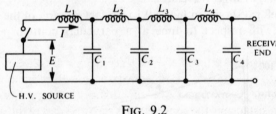

FIG. 9.2

Referring to figure 9.2, when the switch is closed, E does not instantaneously appear at the receive end. E is first opposed by the back e.m.f. induced in L_1 by the flow of I to charge C_1. The voltage developed across C_1 then causes current to flow through L_2 to charge C_2, and so on. The continuous interchange of electromagnetic and electrostatic energy along the line causes a time delay before E appears at the receive end.

(iv) Short-circuiting a transmission line.

At the fault the voltage is suddenly reduced to zero, causing a sudden redistribution of electromagnetic and electrostatic energy.

(v) An arcing ground fault.

This is an earth fault on one phase of an insulated neutral system. The faulted phase will have its potential lowered to such an extent that the arc will be extinguished. At this instant the potentials of the healthy phases are so suddenly raised that voltage surges are initiated. The extinction of the arc on the faulted phase restores its potential and the arc is thereby restruck to earth. Intermittent arcing continues for the duration of the fault and a succession of voltage surges is generated. This type of fault is dealt with more fully later in this section.

(vi) Interruption of load or fault current by switching.

This causes a sudden redistribution of electromagnetic and electro-static energy. The severity of the resulting surges depends on the rate at which the arc is extinguished in the circuit breaker (see Section 4).

Surge Velocity

In the following theory, voltage surges will be assumed to have the waveform shown in figure 9.3 instead of the typical waveform shown in figure 9.1.

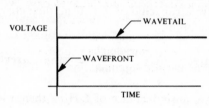

FIG. 9.3

The very steep wavefront of an actual surge will be assumed to be vertical and the long tail of an actual surge will be assumed to be infinitely long. It will also be assumed that the system is loss-free, that is, the resistance of the conductors is zero and that of the insulation infinite.

These assumptions greatly simplify the theory and in any case give a 'pessimistic' result. The actual surge is less severe than the theoretical one as the resistance losses in the actual system will reduce both the magnitude and wavefront gradient of the surge.

The initiation of a voltage surge may be represented by closing the switch in figure 9.4.

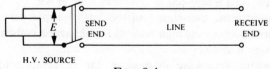

FIG. 9.4

Assuming that the line is uniform, the vertical wavefront of E will travel from left to right at a uniform velocity. Let this velocity be

x metres/second. The voltage surge and its associated current surge I are shown in figure 9.5.

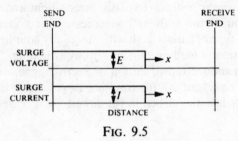

FIG. 9.5

The line will be charged to a potential of E volts at the rate of x metres/second.

In any second, the length of line charged is x metres.

Let the line have a capacitance of C F/m, then charge required per second is ECx coulombs.

$$\text{Rate of charge} = ECx \frac{\textbf{coulombs}}{\textbf{second}} = \textbf{surge current} = I\,\text{A} \qquad (1)$$

Let the line have an inductance of L H/m, then a length of line of x metres has an inductance of Lx H.

The current in such a length is changed from zero to I amperes in 1 second.

The voltage required to overcome the back e.m.f. is inductance × rate of change of current $= Lx \times I$ V.

$$\text{Since resistance is being ignored,} \quad LxI = E \qquad (2)$$

Substituting equation (2) into (1):

$$I = LxICx,$$

hence
$$x = \frac{1}{\sqrt{(LC)}} \text{ m/sec.} \qquad (3)$$

Surge Velocity in a Single-phase Overhead Line in Air

In considering the inductance of the line, the internal inductance can be ignored because the high velocity of the surge has the same 'skin' effect as a high frequency.

Therefore the following expression for inductance (derived in Section 7) may be used:

$$L = 4 \times 10^{-7} \times \log_e \frac{d}{r} \text{ H/m.}$$

In considering the capacitance of the line, the spacing will be such that $d - r \simeq d$. Also $\varepsilon_r = 1$.

Therefore the following expression for capacitance (derived in Section 7) may be used:

$$C = \frac{1}{36 \times 10^9 \times \log_e \dfrac{d}{r}} \text{ F/m.}$$

Substituting for L and C in equation (3) gives

$$x = \frac{1}{\sqrt{\left(\dfrac{1}{9 \times 10^{16}}\right)}} = \sqrt{(9 \times 10^{16})} = 3 \times 10^8 \text{ m/sec.}$$

Thus the surge velocity is equal to the speed of light.

Surge Velocity in a Three-phase Overhead Line in Air

The following expressions (derived in Section 7) are applicable when the conductors are symmetrically spaced:

$$L = 2 \times 10^{-7} \times \log_e (d/r) \text{ H/m,}$$

$$C = \frac{1}{18 \times 10^9 \times \log_e \dfrac{d}{r}} \text{ F/m.}$$

Substituting for L and C in equation (3) gives $x = 3 \times 10^8$ m/sec, as for a single-phase line.

The surge velocity is in fact independent of the size and spacing of the conductors. The same value of x holds for all configurations of loss-free conductors in air.

Surge Velocity in a Single-phase Concentric Cable

The following expressions (derived in Section 5) are applicable:

$$L = 2 \times 10^{-7} \times \log_e \frac{R}{r} \text{ H/m.}$$

$$C = \frac{10^{-9} \cdot \varepsilon_r}{18 \cdot \log_e \dfrac{R}{r}} \text{ F/m.}$$

Substituting for L and C in equation (3) gives

$$x = \frac{3 \times 10^8}{\sqrt{\varepsilon_r}} \text{ m/sec.}$$

Thus for a cable with a dielectric having $\varepsilon_r = 4$, the surge velocity is half that for an overhead line in air.

In 0·001 second, a surge would travel 300 km in the overhead line and 150 km in the cable.

On a 50-Hz system, this time is equal to one-twentieth of a cycle and the voltage of the source will not have changed appreciably. Therefore, if a 50-Hz source is suddenly connected to a line, the amplitude of the surge may be taken as the instantaneous voltage when the switch is closed. The same theory as for high-voltage surges may then be applied.

Surge Impedance

Dividing equation (2) by (1) gives

$$\frac{E}{I} = \frac{LxI}{Ecx},$$

or

$$\frac{E}{I} = \sqrt{\left(\frac{L}{C}\right)}.$$

This quantity is called the *surge impedance* (Z_0) or the *characteristic impedance*.

Since L is the inductance per metre and C the capacitance per metre Z_0 is independent of the length of line or cable. Z_0 does, however depend on the conductor spacing and on the relative permittivity of the dielectric between them.

The inductance per metre increases with increased spacing and the capacitance per metre decreases. Hence Z_0 increases with increased spacing.

For increasing values of ε_r, the capacitance per metre increases and the surge impedance falls.

Both these factors make the surge impedance of an overhead transmission line greater than that of a power cable.

Typical values of Z_0 are 300 Ω for an overhead line and 50 Ω for a cable.

Surge Power Input and Energy Storage

When the switch in figure 9.2 is closed, the potential E volts sends the surge current I amperes along the line at a velocity of x m/sec

hence   surge power input to line = EI W.

Since the far end of the line is open-circuited and assumed loss-free energy input per second equals energy stored per second. Hence

$$EI = \tfrac{1}{2}CxE^2 = \tfrac{1}{2}LxI^2 \text{ W}.$$

But

$$\frac{1}{2}CxE^2 = \frac{1}{2}\left[\frac{C}{\sqrt{(LC)}}\right]E^2 = \frac{1}{2}\left[\frac{E}{\sqrt{(L/C)}}\right]E = \frac{1}{2}EI \text{ W.}$$

and

$$\frac{1}{2}LxI^2 = \frac{1}{2}\left[\frac{L}{\sqrt{(LC)}}\right]I^2 = \tfrac{1}{2}[I \cdot \sqrt{(L/C)}]I = \tfrac{1}{2}EI \text{ W.}$$

Thus the electrostatic and electromagnetic stored energies are equal.

Terminations

When the voltage and current surges reach the far end of a transmission line, they are said to 'impinge' on the termination and are called the incident surges E_i and I_i.

Thus
$$Z_0 = \frac{E_i}{I_i}.$$

The power conveyed to the termination by these surges is $E_i \cdot I_i$ W.

First suppose that the far end of the line is connected to a pure resistor of value $Z_0 \, \Omega$.

When the surges arrive at the termination, the current in this resistor $= E_i/Z_0$ A.

The power absorbed by the resistor equals

$$E_i \times \frac{E_i}{Z_0}$$

$$= E_i I_i$$

which is the power transmitted by the surge.

In this case the surge power is exactly absorbed by the termination and no further changes take place. The line continues to carry a current of I_i amperes and the potential remains constant at E_i V.

Now suppose that the termination is a pure resistor of value $R \, \Omega$ which is greater than Z_0. When the surges arrive at the termination, the current in the resistor $= E_i/R$ A and will be less than the surge current $= I_i = E_i/Z_0$ A.

Thus the incident current I_i is greater than that which can be absorbed by the terminating resistor when it has E_i volts across it. Moreover, the incident current is prevented from instantaneously decreasing by the inductance of the line. The excess current therefore charges the capacitance at the end of the line and raises the potential at the termination to a value higher than the incident voltage E_i.

Let the potential at the termination rise to E_T V, and hence the current through the terminating resistor will be

$$\frac{E_T}{R} = I_T \, \text{A}.$$

Excess voltage appearing at the termination $= E_T - E_i$ V.

Excess current appearing at the termination $= I_T - I_i$ A.

The whole length of the line is now charged to a potential of E_i V, and there is an excess potential of $E_T - E_i$ V at the termination. The sudden build up of this excess potential causes reflected surges to travel from the termination back towards the sending end of the line.

Reflected surge voltage $= E_r = E_T - E_i$ V.

Reflected surge current $= I_r = I_T - I_i$ A.

Thus
$$E_T = E_r + E_i \tag{4}$$

and
$$I_T = I_r + I_i. \tag{5}$$

Now
$$I_i = \frac{E_i}{Z_0}, \quad I_T = \frac{E_T}{R}, \quad \text{and} \quad I_r = -\frac{E_r}{Z_0},$$

the negative sign indicating that I_r is travelling in the opposite direction to I_i. Substituting these values into equation (5):

$$\frac{E_T}{R} = \frac{E_i}{Z_0} - \frac{E_r}{Z_0} \, \text{A}.$$

Substituting the value of E_T given in equation (4) gives

$$\frac{E_r + E_i}{R} = \frac{E_i - E_r}{Z_0} \, \text{A}.$$

Hence
$$Z_0 E_r + Z_0 E_i = RE_i - RE_r,$$

from which
$$E_r(R + Z_0) = E_i(R - Z_0),$$

or
$$E_r = \frac{R - Z_0}{R + Z_0} \cdot E_i \, \text{V}. \tag{6}$$

Substituting equation (6) into (4), we obtain

$$E_T = \frac{R - Z_0}{R + Z_0} \cdot E_i + E_i,$$

$$E_T = \left[\frac{R - Z_0 + R + Z_0}{R + Z_0} \right] E_i,$$

and finally
$$E_T = \frac{2R}{R+Z_0} \cdot E_i \quad \text{V.} \tag{7}$$

Reflection Factor or Coefficient (ρ)

The quantity $\frac{R-Z_0}{R+Z_0}$ in equation (6) is known as the reflection factor ρ.

Now
$$-\frac{E_r}{Z_0} = I_r \quad \text{and} \quad \frac{E_i}{Z_0} = I_i.$$

Hence
$$E_r = -Z_0 \cdot I_r \quad \text{and} \quad E_i = Z_0 \cdot I_i.$$

Substituting these values into equation (6) gives
$$-Z_0 \cdot I_r = \rho \cdot Z_0 \cdot I_i$$

and hence
$$I_r = -\rho \cdot I_i. \tag{8}$$

Transmission Factor or Coefficient (τ)

The quantity $\frac{2R}{R+Z_0}$ in equation (7) is known as the transmission factor τ.

Now
$$\frac{E_T}{R} = I_T \quad \text{and} \quad \frac{E_i}{Z_0} = I_i.$$

Hence
$$E_T = R \cdot I_T \quad \text{and} \quad E_i = Z_0 \cdot I_i.$$

Substituting these values into equation (7) gives
$$R \cdot I_T = \tau \cdot Z_0 \cdot I_i$$

and hence
$$I_T = \tau \cdot \frac{Z_0}{R} \cdot I_i.$$

Note that
$$\tau = \rho + 1 = \frac{R-Z_0}{R+Z_0} + 1 = \frac{R-Z_0+R+Z_0}{R+Z_0} = \frac{2R}{R+Z_0}.$$

Voltage and Current Surges when R is greater than Z_0

Graphs of voltage and current distribution along the line are shown in figure 9.6.

From these graphs it can be seen that for this condition the reflected surges consist of increased voltage and reduced current.

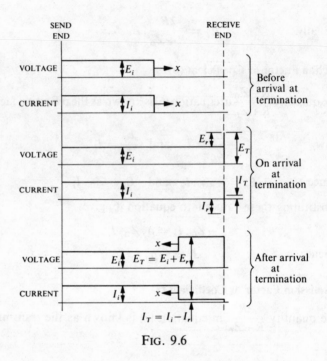

FIG. 9.6

Voltage and Current Surges when R is less than Z_0

When the surges arrive at the termination, the current in the resistor is (E_i/R) amperes as before, but this is now greater than the surge current I_i, (E_i/Z_0) amperes. The incident current is prevented from instantaneously increasing by the inductance of the line. The current deficit is therefore derived from the discharge of the line capacitance at the termination, thus reducing the potential at the termination.

Graphs of voltage and current distribution along the line are shown in figure 9.7.

From these graphs it can be seen that for this condition the reflected surges consist of reduced voltage and increased current. The previously derived equations (4), (5), (6), and (7) apply without alteration.

Termination of an Overhead Line by a Transformer

The high velocity of a surge has a similar effect to high frequency. At high frequencies, the capacitance currents between the transformer windings, between each winding and the earthed iron core and between the turns of each winding are large enough to alter the distribution of voltage across each winding. It can be seen from figure 9.8 that the

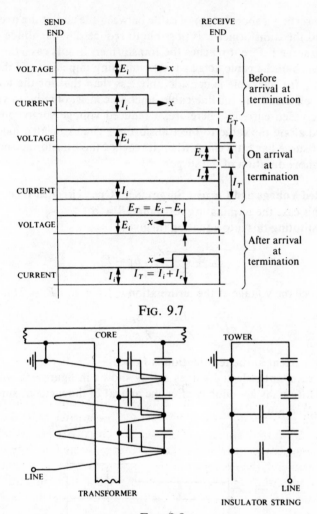

Fig. 9.7

Fig. 9.8

capacitance network is similar to that formed by a string of suspension insulators suspended from an earthed tower.

It was seen in Section 6 that the effect of such a network is to increase the electric stress on the line end insulator. Similarly, in a transformer under surge conditions, the line end turns experience the greatest electric stress.

For this reason, graded insulation is used on star-connected transformers for use in earthed neutral systems, the line end turns on each phase being more heavily insulated.

By inserting a short length of cable between the end of the overhead line and the transformer it is possible to reduce the magnitude of the voltage surge before it reaches the transformer. In this case, the surge impedance of the cable acts as the terminating impedance of the line. Since Z_0 for the cable is considerably less than that for the line, the surges reflected from the line/cable junction consist of reduced voltage and increased current. Therefore, a reduced voltage surge continues forward along the cable to the transformer. The associated increased current surge has little effect when it reaches the transformer because of the short duration of the surge.

Reflected Voltage and Current Surges in an Open-circuited Line

In this case the terminating resistance $R = \infty$.

Substituting this into equation (6) gives

$$E_r = \frac{\infty - Z_0}{\infty + Z_0} \cdot E_i = E_i,$$

and hence the voltage at the termination is $E_T = E_i + E_r = 2E_i$.

Also
$$I_r = \frac{-E_r}{Z_0} = \frac{-E_i}{Z_0} = -I_i,$$

and the current at the termination is $I_T = I_i + I_r = 0$.

The resultant reflected surges are as shown in figure 9.9, which is drawn for an instant shortly after the arrival of the incident surges at the termination.

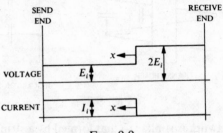

FIG. 9.9

Reflected Voltage and Current Surges in a Short-circuited Line

In this case the terminating resistance $R = 0$. Substituting this into equation (6) gives

$$E_r = \frac{0 - Z_0}{0 + Z_0} \cdot E_i = -E_i,$$

so that the voltage at the termination is $E_T = E_i + E_r = 0$.

Also $$I_r = \frac{-E_r}{Z_0} = \frac{-(-E_i)}{Z_0} = I_i,$$

and the current at the termination is $I_T = I_i + I_r = 2I_i$.

The resultant reflected surges are as shown in figure 9.10, which is drawn for an instant shortly after the arrival of the incident surges at the termination.

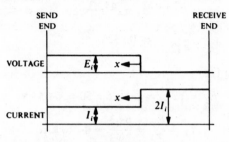

FIG. 9.10

Example 9-1. An overhead line having an inductance of 1·38 mH/km and a capacitance of 0·00808 μF/km is connected in series with an underground cable having an inductance of 0·187 mH/km and a capacitance of 0·217 μF/km.

Calculate the values of the transmitted and reflected waves of voltage and current at the line/cable junction caused by a voltage surge of 50 kV travelling towards the junction, (a) from the line end, and (b) from the cable end.

Let the surge impedance of the line be $Z_L \; \Omega$ and that of the cable $Z_C \; \Omega$.

Then $$Z_L = \sqrt{\left(\frac{0·00138}{0·00808 \times 10^{-6}}\right)} = 413 \; \Omega$$

and $$Z_C = \sqrt{\left(\frac{0·000187}{0·217 \times 10^{-6}}\right)} = 29·3 \; \Omega.$$

(a) $E_i = 50 \; \text{kV}$ (given). $I_i = \dfrac{E_i}{Z_L} = \dfrac{50}{413} = 0·121 \; \text{kA}.$

In this case, the terminating impedance of the line is the surge impedance of the cable so that in equations (6) and (7) R becomes Z_C and Z_0 becomes Z_L.

Also E_T is the surge voltage transmitted forward into cable,
$\quad I_T$ is the surge current transmitted forward into cable,
$\quad E_r$ is the surge voltage reflected back along line, and
$\quad I_r$ is the surge current reflected back along line.

Hence ρ becomes $\dfrac{Z_C - Z_L}{Z_C + Z_L}$,

and τ becomes $\dfrac{2Z_C}{Z_C + Z_L}$.

Thus $\qquad \rho = \dfrac{29 \cdot 3 - 413}{29 \cdot 3 + 413} = \dfrac{-383 \cdot 7}{442 \cdot 3} = -0 \cdot 8674,$

and $\qquad \tau = \dfrac{2 \times 29 \cdot 3}{442 \cdot 3} = 0 \cdot 1326.$

From equation (7)

$$E_T = \tau \,.\, E_i = 0 \cdot 1326 \times 50 = \mathbf{6 \cdot 63 \, kV}.$$

Also $\qquad\qquad I_T = \dfrac{E_T}{Z_C} = \dfrac{6 \cdot 63}{29 \cdot 3} = \mathbf{0 \cdot 226 \, kA}.$

From equation (6)

$$E_r = \rho \,.\, E_i = -0 \cdot 8674 \times 50 = \mathbf{-43 \cdot 4 \, kV}.$$

From equation (8)

$$I_r = -\rho \,.\, I_i = 0 \cdot 8674 \times 0 \cdot 121 = \mathbf{+0 \cdot 105 \, kA}.$$

Graphs of these voltage and current surges, drawn for an instant shortly after arrival at the line/cable junction, are shown in figure 9.11.

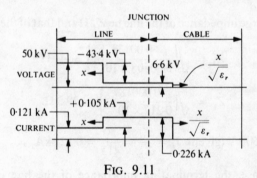

FIG. 9.11

(b) $E_i = 50 \, \text{kV}$ (given). $I_i = \dfrac{E_i}{Z_C} = \dfrac{50}{29 \cdot 3} = 1 \cdot 71 \, \text{kA}.$

In this case, the terminating impedance of the cable is the surge impedance of the line so that in equations (6) and (7) R becomes Z_L and Z_0 becomes Z_C.

Also E_T is the surge voltage transmitted forward into line,

  I_T is the surge current transmitted forward into line,

  E_r is the surge voltage reflected back along cable, and

  I_r is the surge current reflected back along cable.

Hence ρ becomes $\dfrac{Z_L - Z_C}{Z_L + Z_C},$

and τ becomes $\dfrac{2Z_L}{Z_L + Z_C}.$

Thus $\rho = \dfrac{413 - 29 \cdot 3}{413 + 29 \cdot 3} = \dfrac{383 \cdot 7}{442 \cdot 3} = 0 \cdot 8674,$

and $\tau = \dfrac{2 \times 413}{442 \cdot 3} = 1 \cdot 867.$

From equation (7)

$$E_T = \tau \, . \, E_i = 1 \cdot 867 \times 50 = \textbf{93·4 kV.}$$

Also $I_T = \dfrac{E_T}{Z_L} = \dfrac{93 \cdot 4}{413} = \textbf{0·226 kA.}$

From Equation (6)

$$E_r = \rho \, . \, E_i = 0 \cdot 8674 \times 50 = \textbf{43·4 kV.}$$

From equation (8)

$$I_r = -\rho \, . \, I_i = -0 \cdot 8674 \times 1 \cdot 71 = \textbf{-1·48 kA.}$$

Graphs of these voltage and current surges, drawn for an instant shortly after arrival at the cable/line junction, are shown in figure 9.12.

Example 9-2. Calculate the velocities of the surges in example 9-1 and the relative permittivity of the dielectric of the cable. Also find the time taken for the surges to travel 161 km (a) in the line, (b) in the cable.

Surge velocity in the line

$$= \frac{1}{\sqrt{(LC)}} = \frac{1}{\sqrt{(0 \cdot 00138 \times 0 \cdot 00808 \times 10^{-6})}}$$

$$= \frac{10^6}{\sqrt{(1 \cdot 38 \times 8 \cdot 08)}} = \frac{10^6}{\sqrt{11 \cdot 11}} = \frac{10^6}{3 \cdot 333}$$

$$= \textbf{3} \times \textbf{10}^5 \textbf{ km/sec.}$$

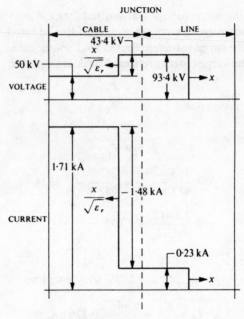

FIG. 9.12

Surge velocity in the cable

$$= \frac{1}{\sqrt{(LC)}}$$

$$= \frac{1}{\sqrt{(0.000187 \times 0.217 \times 10^{-6})}}$$

$$= \frac{10^6}{\sqrt{(1.87 \times 21.7)}} = \frac{10^6}{\sqrt{40.6}} = \frac{10^6}{6.37}$$

$$= \mathbf{1.57 \times 10^5 \text{ km/sec.}}$$

Now surge velocity in cable

$$= \frac{1}{\sqrt{\varepsilon_r}} \times \text{surge velocity in line.}$$

Therefore $\qquad 1.57 \times 10^5 = \dfrac{1}{\sqrt{\varepsilon_r}} \times 3 \times 10^5,$

and $\qquad \varepsilon_r = \left[\dfrac{3}{1.57}\right]^2 = \mathbf{3.64}.$

(a) Time $= \dfrac{161}{3 \times 10^5}$ second $=$ **0·537 millisecond.**

(b) Time $= \dfrac{161}{1 \cdot 57 \times 10^5}$ second $=$ **1·025 millisecond.**

Over-voltage Protection

The insulation of a transmission system is usually designed to withstand voltages of the order of twice normal operating voltage. Under normal circumstances, switching surges rarely exceed this magnitude but over-voltage surges caused by lightning or fault conditions may be many times the normal operating voltage.

There are many different types of protective devices which may be used to protect a system against severe overvoltages but those most commonly used are:

(1) Overhead earth wire.
(2) Horn gap.
(3) Non-linear surge diverter.
(4) Petersen coil.

Use of Overhead Earth Wire

The wire is usually of steel and is suspended from the towers above the main conductors and earthed at regular intervals. The earth wire reduces the possibility of a direct lightning stroke reaching the main conductors and also partly shields them from electrostatically induced charges caused by charged clouds in the vicinity of the line. An array of earth wires would be much more effective for both these purposes but is too expensive. For this reason, the number of earth wires even on important double-circuit lines, rarely exceeds two. (See figures 7.2, 7.3, and 7.4, Section 7.)

Use of Horn Gap

The type of horn gap used on a vertical string of suspension insulators is shown in figure 6.5. A gap between two horns is usually used on almost horizontal tension insulator strings and the type shown in figure 9.13 is commonly used on plant such as transformers.

In each case, the horn gaps are connected between line and earth. Under normal circumstances there is only operating phase voltage across each gap and this is insufficient to cause spark-over. When a high-voltage surge reaches a horn gap, however, spark-over occurs and the surge energy is diverted to earth. In order to protect a piece of equipment successfully, the horn gap must be situated as near as

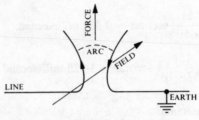

FIG. 9.13

possible to the equipment. Otherwise a surge may be initiated between the horn gap and the equipment.

Electrical breakdown between any pair of conductors at different potentials never occurs instantaneously when an overvoltage is applied. The time delay depends on the following factors.

(i) The insulating material between the conductors. In the case of a solid insulator, time is taken in rearranging the molecular structure to allow sufficient current to flow to cause complete breakdown. In the case of an air gap, time is required in which to ionize the air.

(ii) The shape and spacing of the conductors. A sphere gap in which the spacing is small compared with the diameter of the spheres breaks down almost instantaneously. A needle gap, on the other hand, takes an appreciable time to break down because before it does so, a spherical corona discharge has to form around each conductor.

(iii) The amplitude of the over-voltage. The greater the over-voltage, the shorter is the breakdown time, as shown in figure 9.14.

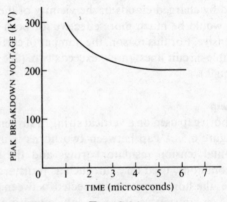

FIG. 9.14

Because of the above three factors, the breakdown of various parts of a transmission system will occur at different levels of over-voltage and will also depend on the duration of the surge.

The ratio, $\dfrac{\text{breakdown voltage at surge frequency}}{\text{breakdown voltage at normal system frequency}}$, is known as the impulse ratio.

A sphere gap with relatively small spacing has an impulse ratio of unity whilst that of a needle gap is between 1·5 and 2·3.

For insulators the ratio is of the order 1·2 to 1·6 for suspension types and 1·3 to 2·3 for pin types. The behaviour of a horn gap is similar to that of a sphere gap when the distance between the horns is small and similar to a needle gap when the distance is large. Thus the horn gap setting is critical and should be so designed that its impulse ratio is less than that of the insulators or plant being protected. Also the breakdown of the gap must occur almost instantaneously as a short delay would allow the surge to pass further into the system instead of being diverted to earth. Thus the sphere gap would give ideal protection if it were not for the fact that once the arc is struck it continues after the over-voltage has passed. The shape of the horn gap forces the arc upwards by magnetic and thermal effects and the arc is self-extinguishing. The shape of the horns should therefore be such as to obtain self-extinction whilst retaining an impulse ratio as near to unity as possible.

Use of Non-linear Surge Diverter

A vertical stack of silicon-carbide discs is housed within a hollow glazed porcelain insulator. The discs have the non-linear characteristic shown in figure 9.15.

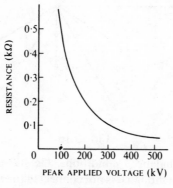

Fig. 9.15

A stack of discs is connected between each line and earth close to the transformer or other plant to be protected. The small current which would pass to earth under normal operating conditions is prevented from doing so by means of a small series spark-gap. When an over-voltage occurs, this gap breaks down and the resistance of the stack is very low allowing a high surge current to be diverted to earth. The breakdown time on over-voltages equal to twice normal system voltage is less than 1 microsecond. The impulse ratio is practically unity and the resistance of the stack returns to its high value once the over-voltage has passed.

Insulated Neutral System

An alternator stator winding or transformer secondary winding with unearthed star-point is shown in figure 9.16.

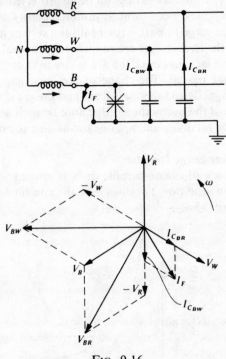

FIG. 9.16

Under healthy, balanced conditions, the star-point (N) will be at earth potential even though it is not connected to earth. When an arcing ground fault occurs on one line, as shown, the fault current is limited by the line to earth capacitances, one of which is shorted out by the arc itself. Thus the fault current (I_F) is the phasor sum of $I_{C_{BW}}$ and $I_{C_{BR}}$. These currents lead their respective line voltages V_{BW} and V_{BR} by 90°, as shown, and I_F leads V_B by 90°.

At the instant of arc extinction (i.e. when I_F waveform passes through zero), the point B is therefore either at $+$max. phase voltage to earth or at $-$max. phase voltage to earth. Taking the instant when B is at $+$max. V_{PH} to earth, then N is at earth potential, and R and W will each be at 0.5 max. V_{PH} to earth.

Since the potential of B to earth is a maximum, the arc will be immediately restruck. This instantaneously earths B, so that N is then at $-$max. V_{PH} to earth and R and W are each at -1.5 max. V_{PH} to earth. Thus, at the instant of restrike, R and W have their potentials with respect to earth suddenly changed from -0.5 max. V_{PH} to -1.5 max. V_{PH}. This happens each time the I_F waveform passes through zero and causes a succession of voltage surges to be generated into the system. Furthermore, all line insulation must be capable of withstanding 1.5 max. V_{PH} instead of max. V_{PH} to earth.

Advantages of Earthing the Neutral

(i) The star-point is always at earth potential so that when an earth fault occurs on one line, the potential difference between the healthy lines and earth cannot exceed max. V_{PH}. Also graded insulation can be used on the line end turns of transformers (see figure 9.8).

(ii) Simple protective systems based on the detection of earth leakage currents can be used.

(iii) An arcing ground fault cannot occur.

Disadvantages of Earthing the Neutral

(i) The earth fault current is very much heavier than in an insulated neutral system because in the latter the fault current is limited by the line to earth capacitances.

(ii) Earth connections must be made at all vulnerable points in the system. This is at grid substations and consumer substations as well as at generating stations and consumers' premises.

(iii) In an earthed neutral system, an earth fault must be isolated immediately because of the heavy fault current. In an insulated neutral system immediate isolation is not essential although it is desirable, since the voltage surges generated by arcing ground faults may be three or four times normal voltage.

Above 33 kV line, the cost of transformer insulation is an important part of the total cost of a system. Therefore significant economies can be made by earthing the neutral, so that graded insulation may be used. Also, above 33 kV, the line impedance is usually high enough to limit earth fault currents to a reasonable value without using a resistance or reactor in the earth connection.

In general, therefore, high voltage transmission systems have their star-points solidly earthed and systems up to about 33 kV line are earthed through a resistor or tuned reactor.

Methods of Earthing

(i) Solid copper connection to buried earth electrode.

(ii) Connection to earth through a resistor of a few ohms.

(iii) Connection to earth through an untuned reactor.

(iv) Connection to earth through a tuned reactor (called an arc suppression coil or Petersen coil).

(v) If the supply system has no star-point, an artificial one can be created by means of the special earthing transformer shown in figure 9.17.

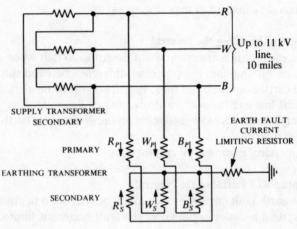

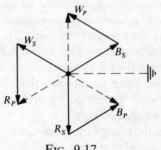

FIG. 9.17

Petersen Coil

Suppose that an arcing ground fault occurs on one line, as shown in figure 9.18.

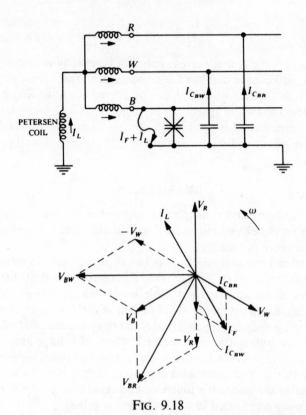

FIG. 9.18

The fault connects the Petersen coil across the blue phase winding causing a current I_L to flow through the coil. Assuming that the coil has negligible resistance, I_L must lag V_B by 90° as shown. If I_L is made numerically equal to I_F by tuning the reactor appropriately, then the arcing current is the phasor sum of I_F and I_L and is zero at all instants.

Let the appropriate inductance of the Petersen coil be L H, then

$$I_L = \frac{V_{\text{LINE}}}{\sqrt{3}} \bigg/ \omega L \text{ A}.$$

Now

$$I_F = \sqrt{3} . I_{C_{BW}} \quad \text{or} \quad \sqrt{3} . I_{C_{BR}} \text{ A}.$$

But

$$I_{C_{BR}} = V_{\text{LINE}} \bigg/ \frac{1}{\omega C} = V_{\text{LINE}} . \omega C \text{ A}.$$

Therefore

$$I_F = \sqrt{3} . V_{\text{LINE}} . \omega C = \frac{V_{\text{LINE}}}{\sqrt{3} . \omega L} \text{ A},$$

and
$$L = \frac{1}{3\omega^2 C} \text{ H} \quad \text{or} \quad X_L = \frac{X_c}{3} \, \Omega.$$

In practice, the arcing current may not be exactly zero due to the fact that the Petersen coil has a little resistance. Also, tappings will be necessary, so that the value of L can be altered when the length of the line is altered by switching sections in or out. It has been found however, that the Petersen coil is completely effective in preventing damage by arcing grounds providing that L is within ± 10 per cent of the theoretical value.

EXAMPLES 9

1. Derive from first principles an expression for the velocity of a surge in a loss-free overhead transmission line in terms of its inductance and capacitance per metre.

An overhead line of length 193 km has an inductance of 1·49 mH/km and a capacitance of 0·00745 μF/km. The receiving end of the line is terminated in an underground cable having an inductance of 0·187 mH/km and a capacitance of 0·217 μF/km. A 100-kV surge originates at the sending end and travels towards the receiving end. Calculate the values of the transmitted and reflected waves of voltage and current at the line/cable junction. Illustrate your answers by sketching graphs of the surge voltage and current for an instant shortly after the arrival of the surges at the line/cable junction, and state briefly why overhead lines are often terminated in a short length of cable.
(Answers $E_T = 12\cdot3$ kV, $I_T = 0\cdot42$ kA, $E_r = -87\cdot7$ kV, $I_r = 0\cdot196$ kA.)

2. Calculate the velocities of the surges in example 1 above and the relative permittivity of the dielectric of the cable. Also calculate the time taken for the surges to travel 80·5 km (a) in the line, (b) in the cable.
(Answers 3×10^5 km/sec, $1\cdot57 \times 10^5$ km/sec, 3·64, (a) 0·269 millisec, (b) 0·512 millisec.)

3. An overhead line of surge impedance 400 Ω terminates in a transformer of surge impedance 3,600 Ω. Calculate the amplitudes of the current and voltage surges transmitted to the transformer due to an incident voltage of 40 kV.
(Answer 20 A, 72 kV.)

4. An overhead line of surge impedance 350 Ω has a steady voltage of 132 kV suddenly applied to the sending end. Calculate the values of the voltage and current surges reflected from the receiving end (a) when it is open-circuited, (b) when it is short-circuited.
(Answers (a) $+132$ kV, $-0\cdot377$ kA, (b) -132 kV, $+0\cdot377$ kA.)

5. Give reasons why the neutral of a high voltage system is usually

solidly connected to earth, while the neutral of a medium voltage system may be connected to earth through a resistor or tuned reactor.

Briefly, describe with circuit and phasor diagrams, the action of a Petersen coil in minimizing the effects of arcing grounds. Each conductor of a 33-kV, three-phase, 50-Hz overhead line has a capacitance to earth of 0·4 microfarad. Neglecting the power loss in the coil, calculate the inductance and kVA rating of a correctly tuned Petersen coil.

(Answers **8·44 H, 137 kVA.**)

10

Protection

General Requirements

Any system of protection must,

(i) be sufficiently sensitive to detect a fault in its early stages,

(ii) be absolutely reliable in operation—the simpler and more robust the design the better,

(iii) discriminate between currents fed to faults within the section being protected and current passing through to a fault in another section.

Figure 10.1 shows a system consisting of three series sections, each protected separately and capable of isolation by a circuit breaker at the feeding end.

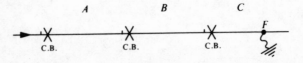

Fig. 10.1

The fault at F is a *section fault* relative to section C but a through fault relative to sections A and B. Thus the protective devices on sections A and B should not trip their respective circuit breakers whilst the protection on section C should open its circuit breaker.

Systems of protection may be divided into two types:

(a) Pilot or unit systems in which pilot wires are run between current transformers at either end of each section. This greatly facilitates discrimination between through and section faults but is expensive on long runs.

(b) Pilotless or non-unit systems in which either no attempt is made to obtain discrimination or it is achieved without the use of pilot wires.

Simple Electromagnetic Relay

The relay shown in figure 10.2 may be used for overcurrent protection and operates almost instantaneously.

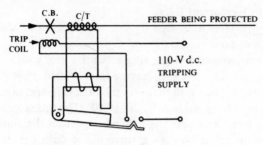

FIG. 10.2

The relay may be used to protect any size of feeder by choosing an appropriate C/T ratio.

The relay operating current can be altered either by adjusting the air gap or by having tappings on the relay coil. When the latter method is used, a special tapping plug bridge is incorporated in the relay which prevents the C/T secondary being open-circuited whilst the tapping is changed. Otherwise the uncancelled primary flux generated by the feeder current may cause such a high flux density and secondary induced e.m.f. as to seriously damage the C/T.

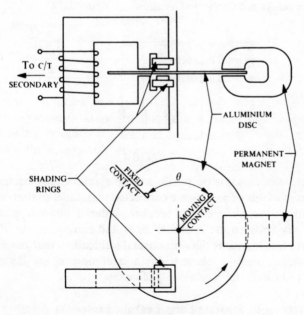

FIG. 10.3

Shaded Pole Overcurrent Relay

In the relay shown in figure 10.3, closed copper shading rings embrace half of each pole.

The current induced in each ring sets up a flux which opposes the flux entering the ring. The flux leaving this 'shaded' pole is the phasor sum of the original flux and that set up by the ring and usually lags the flux leaving the unshaded pole by 20° to 40°. The fluxes leaving the two poles form a two-phase rotating field which causes the aluminium disc to rotate in the same way as a three-phase field causes the short-circuited rotor of an induction motor to rotate. The torque developed is not as great as in some other types of relay as the two fluxes have to be in quadrature for maximum torque. Nevertheless, the torque developed is sufficient to close the contacts by turning the disc through angle θ against controlling hair springs. A permanent magnet is often used to reduce the speed of the disc by inducing eddy currents in it. The field due to these is such as to oppose the motion. The operating time can be altered by re-positioning the fixed or moving contacts to vary angle θ. The operating current can be adjusted by altering the number of operating coil turns by means of a tapping plug bridge.

Combined Overcurrent and Earth Leakage Protection

Three relays are connected as shown in figure 10.4.

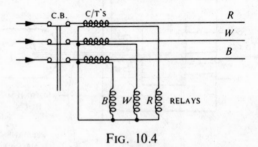

Fig. 10.4

Simple electromagnetic or shaded pole relays may be used. The three pairs of relay contacts are connected in parallel so that closure of any pair will trip the circuit breaker. When a phase-to-phase fault occurs, say between the R and W lines, the currents in the R and W C/T's are much greater than on normal full load so that the R and W relays close. When a phase-to-earth fault occurs, say between the R line and earth, the R relay only closes.

Overcurrent with Separate Earth Leakage Protection

The three relays are now connected as shown in figure 10.5.

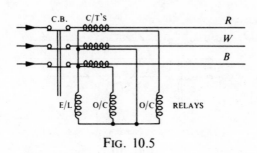

FIG. 10.5

The *R* and *B* relays still give complete protection against phase-to-phase faults.

The phasor sum of the three line currents in any three-wire system is zero, even when the load is unbalanced or when there is a phase-to-phase fault. Thus there can only be current flowing in the *E/L* relay when there is an earth fault. This relay can therefore be given a much more sensitive setting than the two overcurrent relays since these must be set to operate only when normal full load current is exceeded. This is an important advantage over combined *O/C* and *E/L* protection because many phase-to-phase faults begin as earth faults and these can be detected at an early stage.

Electrical Core Balance Protection

A single electromagnetic or shaded pole relay is connected as shown in figure 10.6.

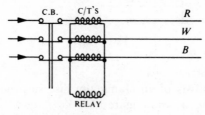

FIG. 10.6

The phasor sum of the three C/T secondary currents is zero except when an earth fault occurs. This system therefore gives *E/L* protection only.

Magnetic Core Balance Protection

This system is used in cases where it is physically possible to pass all three conductors through a single ring type C/T as shown in figure 10.7.

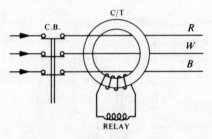

FIG. 10.7

The resultant m.m.f. in the ring is zero except when an earth fault occurs so that this system also gives E/L protection only.

Simple E/L Protection when Neutral is Available

In figure 10.8, there can be no current in the C/T except when an earth fault occurs.

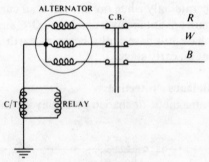

FIG. 10.8

Induction Overcurrent Relay

This relay consists of an aluminium disc suspended between two electromagnets as shown in figure 10.9.

The relay primary current I_P produces primary flux Φ_P which induces an e.m.f. $= e_s$ in the secondary winding on the top magnet. This winding supplies the bottom magnet winding with current I_S which lags e_s since the relay secondary circuit is partly inductive. I_S produces secondary flux Φ_S and bottom magnet flux Φ_B.

Due to the air gaps in the top magnet, there is a leakage flux Φ_L which is the phasor sum of Φ_P and Φ_S. Thus there are two fluxes which cut the disc, Φ_L from the top magnet and Φ_B from the lower magnet. Since these fluxes differ in phase by angle θ, the disc rotates against spiral hair springs to close a pair of relay contacts. Movement of the

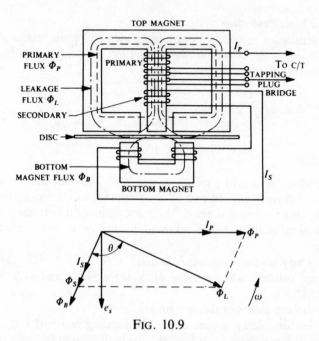

FIG. 10.9

disc is damped by eddy currents induced by a permanent magnet. The time taken to close the contacts is approximately inversely proportional to I_P and can be altered by adjusting the angle through which the moving contact has to turn before closure. For example, in figure 10.10, the contacts have been set further apart to obtain the upper curve.

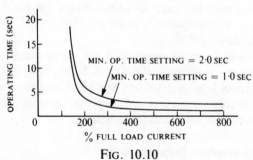

FIG. 10.10

Altering the number of relay primary turns by means of the tapping plug bridge alters the sensitivity of the relay. For example, if the number of primary turns is reduced, the effect is to move the curves in figure 10.10 to the right.

Graded Time Protection

Induction overcurrent relays having identical plug bridge setting but differing time settings are connected to C/T's and circuit breaker situated at *a*, *b*, and *c* in figure 10.11.

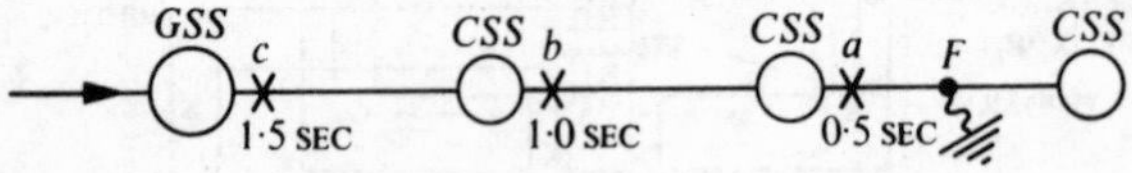

FIG. 10.11

GSS denotes a grid substation and CSS consumers' substations. The fault current should cause '*a*' to operate in 0·5 sec, leaving the circuits up to this point alive. Thus discrimination between through and section faults is being achieved by means of the graded time settings.

If, for any reason, the circuit breaker at '*a*' fails to clear the fault 'back-up' protection is provided at '*b*' 0·5 sec later and at '*c*' 0·5 sec later still.

The disadvantages of this system are:

(i) The time delay is greatest at the sending end where it should be least. When a short circuit occurs, the fault current is partly limited by the impedance of the distributor between the sending end and the fault. If, for example, a S/C occurs near the left-hand end of section *cb* the fault current will be much greater than for a S/C on a more distant section. Therefore faults on section *cb* should be cleared more quickly than faults on other sections.

(ii) Sensitivity is only good at the minimum operating times. At currents just above full load, the time delays are longer and more erratic. Therefore this system is more suitable for S/C than for over current protection.

(iii) Operation becomes unstable if the relays are set closer than about 0·4 sec to each other, or if the most distant relay has a minimum operating time of less than 0·4 sec. Since the maximum delay which can usually be tolerated is less than 2 sec, this system cannot be used to protect more than four sections in series.

Directional Overcurrent Induction Relay

This relay comprises two induction elements as shown in figure 10.12

The upper element has its bottom magnet winding connected in series with the contacts of the lower element. The lower element is both current and voltage actuated and is called a wattmeter element. The disc of this element will only rotate in the direction which closes its

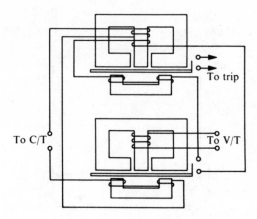

FIG. 10.12

ontacts for one of the two possible directions of power flow in the
protected section. In this way, the lower element makes the upper
element directional, so that it can be used for ring main protection.

A single element directional relay can be constructed by having a
single winding on the top magnet connected to a V/T and a tapped
lower magnet winding connected to a C/T. This constitutes a *reverse
power relay* whose operation is practically instantaneous. This type of
relay is not used for graded time protection of a ring main because the
inverse time characteristic of the induction overcurrent relay is
required.

Graded Time Protection of a Ring Main

Directional induction overcurrent relays having identical plug bridge
settings but differing time settings are connected to V/T's, C/T's and
circuit breakers situated at the points indicated in figure 10.13.

GSS denotes a grid substation and CSS consumers' substations.
The arrows indicate the direction of fault energy flow for which each
relay will trip its respective circuit breaker.

Suppose a fault occurs at *F*, then relay *D* operates before relays
A, *B*, and *C*, thus isolating the fault from CSS 3. Relay *E* does not
operate because the flow of fault energy at this point is opposite to the
operating direction.

Of the relays *P*, *Q*, *R*, *S*, and *T*, only *P* and *Q* tend to close. *Q* operates
before *P* thus isolating the fault from CSS 4.

Thus, for a fault on any one section only, none of the consumers'
substations loses its supply.

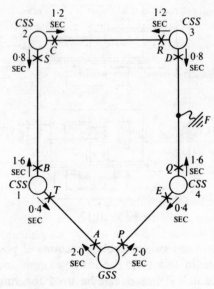

FIG. 10.13

Distance (or Impedance) Protection

An example of this type of protection is shown in figure 10.14.

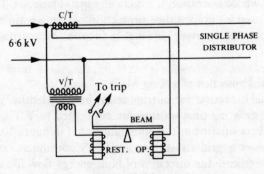

FIG. 10.14

In the balanced beam relay shown, the current is trying to operate the relay and the voltage is trying to restrain it. The relay may be biased mechanically by moving the pivot or electrically by altering the number of turns on one of the coils.

Most modern distance relays comprise an aluminium disc instead of the balanced beam and two shaded pole magnets replace the operating and restraining electromagnets. One shaded pole magnet turns the isc in the operating direction and the other in the restraining direction.

In both types of relay, the contacts close almost instantaneously
once the operating torque exceeds the restraining torque, that is when
V/I falls below a certain value. This value is usually set to be equal to
or slightly less than the impedance of the section being protected.

Consider the three-section, single-phase distributor shown in
figure 10.15.

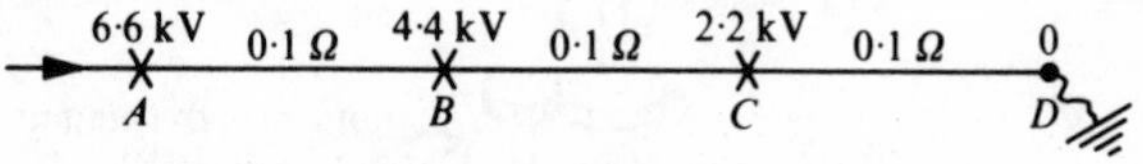

FIG. 10.15

An impedance relay is connected to a circuit breaker, a V/T and a
C/T at the feeding end of each section. Suppose a zero impedance
S/C occurs at *D*, then the fall of potential along the distributor will be
as shown. The S/C current is $6\cdot6/0\cdot3 = 22$ kA.

Let the impedance setting of each of the relays at *A*, *B*, and *C* be
$2\cdot2\,\text{kV}/22\,\text{kA} = 0\cdot1\,\Omega$. Then each relay will only operate when the voltage across the primary of its V/T falls to $2\cdot2$ kV or below, and when the
current through the primary of its C/T rises to 22 kA or above. Thus
the relays at *A* and *B* can never operate for a fault in section *CD*.
Discrimination between through and section faults is being achieved
by measuring the impedance or distance between each relay and the
fault. Now suppose the S/C fault had occurred half-way along section
CD. Then the S/C current is $6\cdot6/0\cdot25 = 26\cdot4$ kA and the p.d. at *C*
equals $6\cdot6/5 = 1\cdot32$ kV.

The impedance between the point *C* and the fault is now $1\cdot32/26\cdot4 =
0\cdot05\,\Omega$. Hence relay *C* again operates. The impedance between relay *A*
and the fault is now $0\cdot25\,\Omega$ and that between *B* and the fault $0\cdot15\,\Omega$,
so that neither of these relays operate.

Impedance (or Distance)/Time Protection

The relay comprises an overcurrent induction relay coupled by
means of a spring to a restraining voltage electromagnet as shown in
figure 10.16.

The current element rotates the disc to wind up the spring. When the
spring torque exceeds the restraining torque of the voltage element,
the relay operates. The combined characteristic of the spring and
restraining magnet is such that, for a given current, the time delay is
directly proportional to *V*. Also, since an induction overcurrent
element is used, the time delay is inversely proportional to *I*. Thus the
time delay is directly proportional to $V/I = Z$.

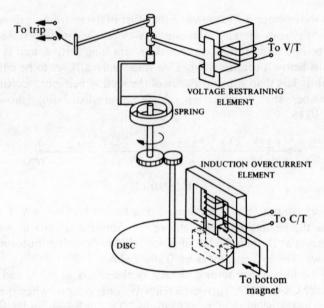

FIG. 10.16

In figure 10.17, impedance/time relays connected at the feeding end of each section give the operating characteristics shown. Note that each of the three relays 'sees' the same fault current, but relay one has the least restraint and therefore operates first. The discs of the other relays are winding up their springs but take longer to overcome the pull of their restraining magnets.

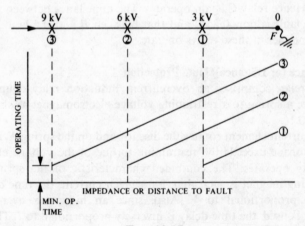

FIG. 10.17

The advantages of impedance/time protection are:

(i) Accurate discrimination is obtained on S/C faults without the use of pilots.

(ii) Extra series sections can be added easily since the relays all have the same impedance setting, that is, the same ratio of restraining turns to operating turns.

(iii) Back-up protection is provided.

(iv) Directional protection of ring mains can be achieved in the same way as with graded time protection (see figures 10.12 and 10.13).

(v) Faults near the feeding end of the system are cleared much more rapidly than with graded time protection.

The disadvantages of impedance/time protection are:

(i) It is only suitable for long lines. On a short line, the resistance of the arc at the fault may be comparable with the impedance of the line itself. The fault then seems to be further away from the relay than it actually is and faulty discrimination may result.

(ii) V/T's as well as C/T's are required.

(iii) Greater time delays occur in clearing a fault at the far end of a section. For such a fault, the voltage at the V/T will be higher than for a fault nearer the V/T and the restraint will therefore be greater.

(iv) Variations in system voltage affect operating times.

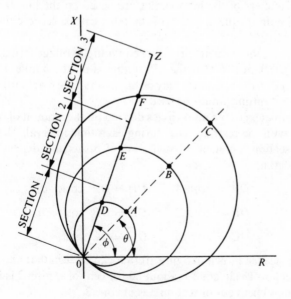

FIG. 10.18

Switched Distance (MHO) Protection (English Electric Co. Ltd)

A system suitable for the detection of interphase faults on a three-phase feeder fed from one end only will be described.

A three-phase V/T and three C/T's are required at the sending end of each section.

The C/T's are connected to instantaneous overcurrent relays called overcurrent starters. When an interphase fault occurs, the starters initiate the following sequence:

(i) The appropriate phases of the V/T are connected to the polarizing and restraint coils of a single admittance (mho) relay.

(ii) The appropriate C/T's are connected to the operating coil of the mho relay.

(iii) A timing relay is started which inserts additional resistance in series with the restraint coil of the mho relay at the end of two successive adjustable time intervals. In this way, the range or 'ohmic reach' of the mho relay is increased to give three zones of distance measurement. These are represented by the three mho circles of the impedance diagram shown in figure 10.18.

The line OZ represents the impedance of the feeder being protected

so that $\cos \phi = \dfrac{\text{resistance of feeder}}{\text{impedance of feeder}}$.

The diameters of the mho circles are based on the line $OABC$ and the maximum torque angle, θ, of the relay can be set to either 45° as shown or to 30°.

In general, the inductive reactance of a high voltage feeder is larger than its resistance so that the 45° setting is most suitable. For a low voltage feeder, the resistance may be higher than the reactance, in which case the 30° setting would be used.

The diameters of the mho circles depend on the amount of resistance in series with the restraint coil during each time interval. The portion of each section included in each zone of protection depends on the angle $\phi-\theta$ thus:

$$OA = \text{ZONE 1.} \qquad OD = OA \cdot \cos(\phi-\theta).$$

$$OB = \text{ZONE 2.} \qquad OE = OB \cdot \cos(\phi-\theta).$$

$$OC = \text{ZONE 3.} \qquad OF = OC \cdot \cos(\phi-\theta).$$

For the feeder shown in figure 10.18 it can be seen that about 80 per cent of section 1 is in zone 1, about 60 per cent of section 2 is in zone 2 and about 40 per cent of section 3 is in zone 3.

The stepped time/distance characteristic of the mho relay is shown in figure 10.19.

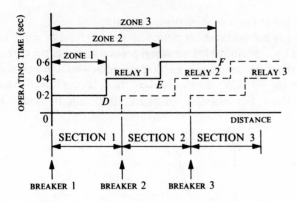

FIG. 10.19

The characteristic shown in full has been derived from the impedance diagram and is for a relay situated at the feeding end of section 1. The characteristics shown dotted are for relays with similar settings at the feeding ends of sections 2 and 3.

For a fault anywhere in zone 1, the voltage restraint on relay 1 is low enough to trip breaker 1 after 0·2 sec.

For a fault between *D* and *E*, the voltage restraint on relay 1 is too great to allow it to trip, until 0·2 sec has elapsed when the restraint is reduced by the timing relay. Relay 1 then trips breaker 1 0·2 sec after this reduction.

The voltage restraint on relay 1 is further reduced after 0·4 sec so that it will trip breaker 1 for a fault between *E* and *F* after 0·6 sec. Thus relay 1 backs up relay 2 for faults on section 2.

The advantages of mho protection are:

(i) Faults anywhere in zone 1 are cleared in the minimum operating time. (In an impedance/time system the operating times increase with distance. In a graded time system, faults near the feeding end take longest to clear.)

(ii) Directional mho is cheaper than directional impedance/time since C/T's, V/T, and relay are required at one end only in mho. (Directional graded time is cheaper than either because the relay is less complex.)

(iii) Resetting after a fault clearance is better on the mho scheme than on graded time and impedance/time. (This is due to the design of the overcurrent starter used in the mho scheme. On other systems, the discs of the relays near to the tripped relay may have acquired sufficient momentum to close their contacts, particularly if the fault current settings are near to system full-load current. Also, a second fault could occur before the discs have returned to their normal positions.)

The disadvantages of mho protection are:

(i) Mho is not suitable for detecting single-phase to earth faults on 11 and 33 kV lines mounted on wood poles without earth wires. This is because the high resistance earth path increases the resistive component of the impedance measured by the relay and may cause faulty discrimination. For example, in figure 10.20, a fault occurs at F on feeder OZ.

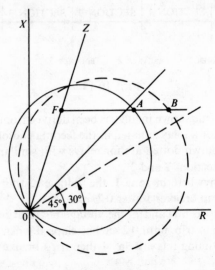

FIG. 10.20

Provided that the resistance of the fault itself does not exceed FA the fault will be detected by the mho relay with the 45° setting (shown in full). For values of fault resistance between FA and FB, the fault will only be detected if the relay is given a 30° setting (shown dotted). Note that the diameters of the two mho circles have been adjusted to protect the same portion of feeder OZ.

(ii) Discrimination may be faulty on high resistance phase-to-phase faults.

Simple Merz-Price Protection

(a) Balanced Voltages.

Identical C/T's are used at each end of the section to be protected as shown in figure 10.21.

Both for a healthy loaded line and on through fault conditions, the secondary induced e.m.f.'s are equal and opposite so that no current flows through the relay R.

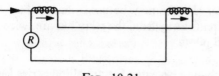

FIG. 10.21

When a section fault occurs, the secondary e.m.f.'s no longer cancel and their resultant drives current through the relay.

(b) Balanced Currents.

In this system, the identical C/T's at each end of the protected section are connected in series as shown in figure 10.22.

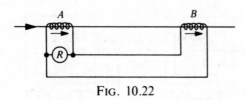

FIG. 10.22

Both for a healthy loaded line, and on through fault conditions, current circulates in both C/T secondaries but there is no current in the relay R.

When a section fault occurs the primary and secondary currents in C/T 'A' are much greater than those in C/T 'B'. The excess secondary current from C/T 'A' cannot flow through the secondary of 'B' because there are no counterbalancing ampere turns in the primary of 'B' to cancel the secondary flux. The secondary of 'B' therefore offers a high impedance to the excess current from 'A' and most of this current flows through the relay.

The disadvantages of the above simple systems are as follows:

(i) For stability (i.e., not operating on heavy through faults) with high sensitivity (i.e., quick operation on own section faults), the C/T's must be carefully magnetically matched so that their B/H curves are identical. Also distributed air gaps throughout the C/T cores are required to prevent magnetic saturation on through faults. Thus the C/T's required are expensive.

(ii) On long sections, the capacitance currents between the pilot wires may be high enough to operate the relay, causing instability. This is most likely on through faults when the secondary induced voltages will be high. Instability could be avoided by using a relay with a high minimum fault setting but the system would then be insensitive to own section faults. Alternatively, special pilot cables having conducting outer sheaths may be used. Such cables divert the pilot capacitance currents away from the relay but are twice as expensive as simple insulated pilots.

Translay Protection (Associated Electrical Industries Ltd)

This is essentially a voltage balance system and a simplified scheme of connections for the protection of a single-phase feeder is shown in figure 10.23.

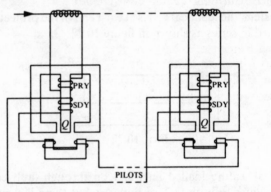

FIG. 10.23

The relays used are basically similar to the induction overcurrent relay and the discs and contacts have been omitted for clarity.

For a healthy loaded line, the relay secondary induced voltages are equal and opposing and there is no current circulating in the bottom magnet windings of the relays. Thus the aluminium discs do not rotate since there is only one flux cutting them.

On heavy through faults, there is still no series current circulating in the bottom magnet windings, but due to the high voltages induced in the relay secondaries, these windings carry pilot shunt capacitance currents. By suitable adjustment of the quadrature loops situated at the points Q, the manufacturer can obtain a value of α which causes Φ_P to lag Φ_B as shown in figure 10.24.

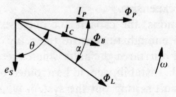

FIG. 10.24

Φ_P = primary flux in top magnet.

Φ_L = leakage flux from top magnet.

I_C = pilot capacitance current flowing in bottom magnet windings. This current leads e_s by angle θ which is less than 90° due to the resistance and inductance of the bottom magnet windings.

Φ_B = flux due to I_C flowing in bottom magnet windings.

For the above condition, the phase relationship between the two fluxes Φ_L and Φ_B cutting the discs is such as to tend to turn them in the opposite direction to that required for contact closure. In this way a restraining torque is exerted on the discs giving stability on through faults.

On section faults, the voltages induced in the relay secondaries are unequal and a lagging series current I_B flows in the lower magnet windings, whilst the pilot capacitance currents are negligible.

Φ_L now leads Φ_B as shown in figure 10.25.

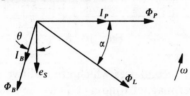

FIG. 10.25

Thus a forward operating torque is now exerted on the discs, causing the contacts to close to trip the circuit breaker.

The advantages of the Translay system over simple Merz-Price voltage balance are as follows:

(i) Ordinary C/T's without distributed air gaps or careful matching in pairs may be used. Each C/T is reasonably well matched against a manufacturer's standard and the current circulating in the bottom magnet windings of the relays due to imperfect matching is so small as to cause no forward movement of the discs.

(ii) Pilot capacitance currents are used to improve stability.

(iii) Less expensive pilots. Anti-capacitance screens are not necessary. Also the maximum p.d. between pilot wires is 130 V compared with 1,000 V for Merz-Price.

The Translay system may also be used to protect a three-phase section fed from both ends as shown in figure 10.26.

The principles of operation are basically the same as for the single-phase version.

Suppose a fault occurs at F between the R and W phases only. The currents that flow in sections 1 of the relay primary windings induce

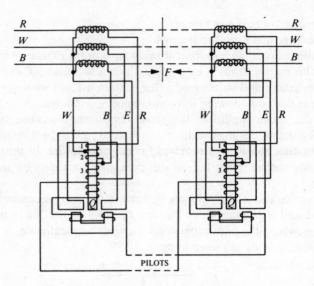

Fig. 10.26

e.m.f.'s in the relay secondaries which are additive and cause current to flow in the lower magnet windings. Thus the relays trip the circuit breakers at each end of the section.

For a fault between the *W* and *B* phases, sections 2 of the relay primaries are energized and for a fault between *R* and *B* sections 1 and 2. Thus the system is twice as sensitive to faults between the *R* and *B* phases. Similarly for an earth fault on phase *R* sections 1, 2, and 3 of the relay primaries are energized. For a fault on phase *W*, sections and 3 are energized. For a fault on phase *B* section 3 only is energized. The approximate relative sensitivities are then 1 for the *B* phase, 1·43 for *W*, and 1·82 for *R*.

Biased Differential Protection (McColl) (General Electric Co. Ltd)

This is essentially a current balance system. The relay used is basically similar to the aluminium disc type impedance relay in that it comprises two shaded pole elements, one giving restraint and the other operation.

When used to protect short sections, such as alternators and transformers, the restraint coil is split into two halves and connected as shown in figure 10.27.

On through faults, there is a heavy circulating current passing through both halves of the restraint coil but little or no current in the operating coil. Thus high stability is achieved.

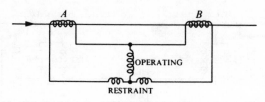

FIG. 10.27

On section faults, C/T '*B*' offers a high impedance to the flow of current from C/T '*A*' so that the majority of this current flows through the operating coil and the left-hand half of the restraint coil. The operating torque is then greater than the restraining torque and the relay trips.

When used to protect a single-phase feeder, the connections are as shown in figure 10.28.

In figure 10.28A, R_A and R_B are non-inductive adjustable resistors each set to equal the resistance of one pilot, that is, $R\,\Omega$.

The resistance of each operating coil equals the resistance of each restraint coil, $C\,\Omega$.

Hence the circuit may be simplified to that shown in figure 10.28B.

On healthy loaded line conditions, the secondary current from C/T *A* takes the following paths:

  (i) C/T *A*, op. *A*, R_A, C/T *A*.

  (ii) C/T *A*, rest. *A*, pilot *q*, rest. *B*, C/T *B*, pilot *p*, C/T *A*.

Hardly any current passes through op. *B* and R_B since C/T *B* secondary offers a low impedance to current from C/T *A* secondary. Ignoring the low impedance of the C/T secondaries, the total resistance of path (i) $= C + R$ and that of path (ii) $= 2C + 2R$. Therefore the current from C/T *A* divides as shown in figure 10.28B.

Similarly, the current from C/T *B* divides as shown in figure 10.28C.

These two sets of currents are superimposed in figure 10.28D. It can be seen that each operating and restraint coil carries the same current. Each relay is designed so that, for this condition, the restraining torque exceeds the operating torque and neither of the relays trip.

On through fault conditions, the current distribution is as in figure 10.28D except that all the currents are larger. Any pilot capacitance currents flow through the restraint coils only and therefore improve stability.

On section faults, C/T *B* secondary offers a high impedance to current from C/T *A*. This current therefore takes the following paths:

  (i) C/T *A*, op. *A*, R_A, C/T *A*.

  (ii) C/T *A*, rest. *A*, pilot *q*, rest. *B*, op. *B*, R_B, pilot *p*, C/T *A*.

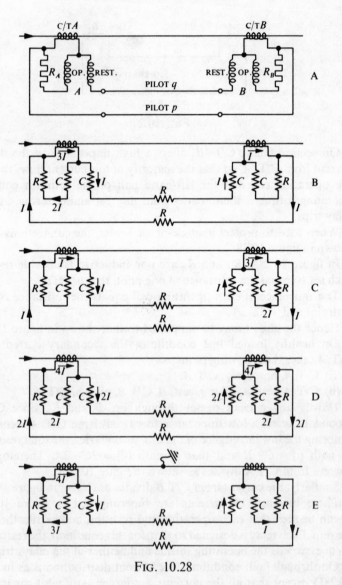

Fig. 10.28

The resistance of path (i) = $C + R$ and that of path (ii) = $3C + 3R$.
Therefore the current from C/T A divides as shown in figure 10.28E.
If the section is fed from end A only, there will be little or no current
in C/T B. The restraining torque is now exceeded by the operating
torque in relay A but not in relay B. Thus the circuit breaker at end A
is tripped.

Had the section been fed from end *B* only, relay *B* would operate for a section fault. For a section fed from both ends, the two C/T secondary induced voltages are in opposition when a section fault occurs so that both relays then trip their respective circuit breakers.

The advantages of biased differential protection over simple Merz-Price current balance are as follows:

(i) C/T's need not be matched in pairs nor have distributed air gaps.

(ii) Inexpensive low voltage pilots without anti-capacitance screens may be used.

Current balance systems also have an inherent advantage over voltage balance systems in that frequent testing of pilots is unnecessary in the former since a break causes both relays to operate.

Solkor-B Protection (A. Reyrolle & Co. Ltd)

This is essentially a voltage balance system employing ordinary C/T's connected to saturable summation transformers as shown in figure 10.29.

C—Tuning capacitor	*S*—Summation transformer
C/T—Current transformer	*SRU*—Solkor-B relay-unit
OC—Operating coil	*TC*—Trip coil
RC—Restraining coil	*TS*—Test sockets

The effect of the saturable summation transformers is to distort the pilot voltage waveform under heavy through fault conditions so that any difference between the secondary output voltages at either end is largely composed of higher harmonics (3rds etc.). The resulting out of balance current flowing in the pilot circuit is therefore also composed of higher harmonics and does not cause the relays to operate since they are tuned for 50 Hz. This tuning also makes the system immune from operation by high frequency transient surges in the feeder. The summation transformers also limit the pilot voltage to 160 V at 20 times full-load current so that the pilot capacitance currents are small.

There are other forms of Solkor protection, such as Solkor-R, which is based on current balance. This system has been specially designed for use with privately owned pilot cables having relatively little insulation and relatively high core resistance. This is a high speed system, the time from fault occurrence to energization of the circuit breaker trip coil being in the region of 60 milliseconds. There is also a system which has been designed mainly for use with telephone pilots which can be rented from the GPO.

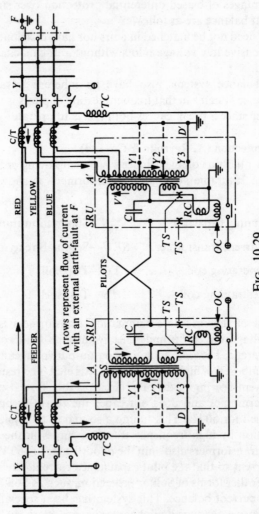

Arrows represent flow of current
with an external earth-fault at F

Fig. 10.29

Biased Differential Protection of an Alternator

Consider the various faults indicated in figure 10.30.

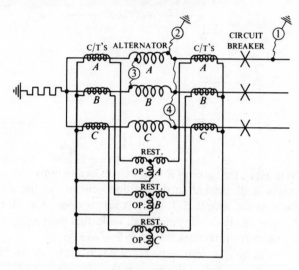

Fig. 10.30

Fault 1 is a through fault with respect to the alternator. Current circulates in both C/T A secondaries and in the A phase restraint coil. No relays trip.

Fault 2 is a section earth fault and current circulates in the left-hand C/T A secondary and in the left-hand half of rest. A and the whole of op. A. Thus relay A operates.

Fault 3 is a section phase-phase fault and current circulates in the left-hand C/T A and C/T B secondaries to trip relays A and B.

Fault 4 is a section three-phase fault and will cause all three relays to operate.

Effect of Earthing Resistor on Alternator Protection

Consider an 11-kV, 30-MVA, three-phase, star-connected alternator earthed through a non-inductive resistor of $4.03\,\Omega$ as shown in figure 10.31.

$$\text{Alternator full-load current} = \frac{30 \times 10^6}{\sqrt{3} \times 11 \times 10^3} = 1{,}575\,\text{A}.$$

When an earth fault occurs at A, fault current is

$$\frac{11{,}000}{\sqrt{3} \times 4.03} = 1{,}575\,\text{A}.$$

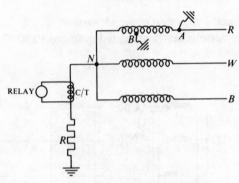

FIG. 10.31

Thus, as is usual, the value of R has been chosen to limit the maximum value of earth fault current to the full-load current of the alternator.

Suppose that the simple E/L relay is set to operate at 30 per cent F/L, then for a slowly developing earth fault, this relay operates when the earth fault current reaches $0.3 \times 1,575 = 473$ A.

Now suppose that a zero-impedance earth fault occurs at B, the point B being 30 per cent of the way up the winding from N.

Since only 30 per cent of the e.m.f. is available for circulating fault current, this is $0.3 \times \dfrac{11,000}{\sqrt{3}} \times \dfrac{1}{4.03} = 473$ A.

For an earth fault anywhere between N and B the fault current would be less than this and the relay would not operate. Thus 30 per cent of the winding is unprotected from zero-impedance earth faults and the whole of the winding is unprotected from slowly developing faults until the fault current reaches 473 A.

The relay could, of course, be given a more sensitive setting. For example, had the setting been 20 per cent, then only 20 per cent of the winding would be unprotected and the relay would operate when the fault current reaches 325 A.

Alternatively, the value of the earthing resistor could be reduced. This would reduce the percentage of the winding unprotected but would increase the earth fault currents.

Example 10-1. A 10-kV, three-phase, star-connected alternator is earthed through a non-inductive resistor of $10\,\Omega$. The alternator is protected by a circulating current system in which the relay operates when the out of balance current in the pilot wires reaches 1 A. These pilots are in the secondary circuit of 1,000/5-A ratio current transformers.

Calculate:

(a) the percentage of alternator winding protected against zero-impedance earth faults.

(b) the value of earthing resistor required to protect 90 per cent of the alternator winding.

(a) Earth fault current $= \dfrac{10{,}000}{\sqrt{3} \times 10} = 578\text{ A}$.

Relay is set to operate at $1 \times 200 = 200\text{ A}$ in the primary circuit. Therefore the percentage of alternator winding unprotected is

$\dfrac{200}{578} \times 100 = 34\!\cdot\!6\%$, and the percentage protected is $65\!\cdot\!4\%$.

(b) Let value of earthing resistor required be $R\ \Omega$. Then for a zero-impedance earth fault, earth fault current is

$$\frac{10{,}000}{\sqrt{3} \cdot R}.$$

Percentage of winding unprotected is 10 per cent.

Hence

$$\left[200 \middle/ \frac{10{,}000}{\sqrt{3} \cdot R} \right] \times 100 = 10,$$

from which $R = 2\!\cdot\!89\ \Omega$.

Protection of Three-phase Transformers

Consider the star-connected transformer shown in figure 10.32.

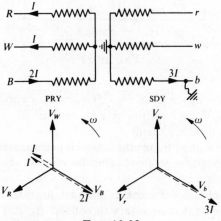

Fig. 10.32

When there is an earth fault current of $3I$ A on the blue phase of the secondary, the currents in the primary windings will be as shown, if a $1:1$ ratio is assumed. This current distribution can be seen to be correct by considering the phasor diagrams.

Neglecting losses, power output $= 3I \cdot V_b$ watts $=$ power input $= 2I \cdot V_B + I V_W \cdot \cos 60° + I V_R \cdot \cos 60° = 3I \cdot V_B$ W.

Suppose this transformer is to be protected by using six C/T's and three simple overcurrent relays connected as shown in figure 10.33.

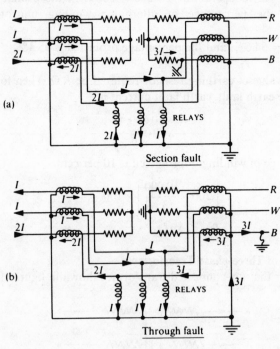

Fig. 10.33

Part (a) of this figure gives the C/T secondary current distribution for a section earth fault on the blue phase. Part (b) gives the current distribution for a through fault.

It can be seen that, although the system is twice as sensitive to section faults as to through faults, there is insufficient discrimination between the two.

In order to obtain sufficient discrimination, that is, operation on section faults only, it is necessary to connect the C/T secondaries in delta as shown in figure 10.34.

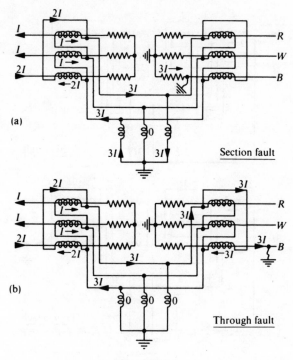

Fig. 10.34

If a delta-star connected transformer is to be protected, then the
C/T secondaries must be connected star-delta, as shown in figure 10.35.

Symmetrical Components

Any unbalanced three-phase system of current or voltage phasors
can be resolved into two balanced systems and one single phase system.

In figure 10.36, both diagrams represent balanced systems since there
is no resultant in either case. Only diagram (a) is symmetrical, however,
since all the phasors are equal in magnitude and equally spaced.

In order to resolve a system into symmetrical components, it is
necessary to use operator 'a'. 'a' is defined as an operator which
advances the position of a phasor anticlockwise through 120°.

For example, in figure 10.37,

$$\bar{E}_a = E_a\angle 0° = \bar{E}_a, \qquad \bar{E}_b = E_a\angle 240° = a^2 . \bar{E}_a$$

and $\qquad \bar{E}_c = E_a\angle 120° = a . \bar{E}_a.$

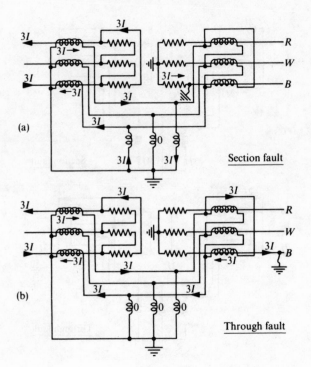

Section fault

Through fault

FIG. 10.35

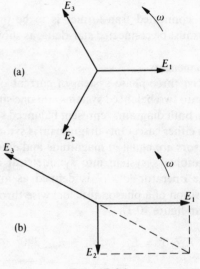

FIG. 10.36

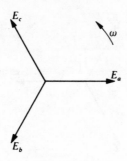

Fig. 10.37

Since these phasors form a symmetrical, balanced system.

$$\bar{E}_a + \bar{E}_b + \bar{E}_c = \bar{E}_a(1 + a + a^2) = 0. \qquad \text{Therefore} \qquad 1 + a + a^2 = 0.$$

Expressed in terms of j notation:

$$a^2 \cdot \bar{E}_a = (-0 \cdot 5 - j0 \cdot 866)\bar{E}_a$$

and $\qquad a \cdot \bar{E}_a = (-0 \cdot 5 + j0 \cdot 866)\bar{E}_a.$

Hence $\qquad a + a^2 = (-0 \cdot 5 + j0 \cdot 866) + (-0 \cdot 5 - j0 \cdot 866) = -1,$

and $\quad 1 + a + a^2 = 1 - 1 = 0$, as before.

Also, multiplying any phasor by a^3 is the same as multiplying by 1. In j notation, $a \times a^2 = (-0 \cdot 5 + j0 \cdot 866)(-0 \cdot 5 - j0 \cdot 866)$

$$= +0 \cdot 25 + 0 \cdot 75 = 1.$$

There are three systems of symmetrical arrangement of phasors:

(i) Positive phase sequence (p.p.s.).

This is defined as a system of three equal phasors, 120° apart, which rotates anticlockwise in the sequence $\bar{E}_a$, $\bar{E}_b$, $\bar{E}_c$, as shown in figure 10.37.

This sequence is the same as $\bar{E}_b$, $\bar{E}_c$, $\bar{E}_a$ and $\bar{E}_c$, $\bar{E}_a$, $\bar{E}_b$.

(ii) Negative phase sequence (n.p.s.).

This is defined as a system of three equal phasors, 120° apart, which rotates anticlockwise in the sequence $\bar{E}_a$, $\bar{E}_c$, $\bar{E}_b$, as shown in figure 10.38.

This sequence is the same as $\bar{E}_c$, $\bar{E}_b$, $\bar{E}_a$ and $\bar{E}_b$, $\bar{E}_a$, $\bar{E}_c$. Alternatively, a negative phase sequence may be considered as a system of three equal phasors, 120° apart, rotating in the opposite direction to that shown in figure 10.37.

This gives the same negative phase sequence, $\bar{E}_a$, $\bar{E}_c$, $\bar{E}_b$, as before.

(iii) Zero phase sequence (z.p.s.).

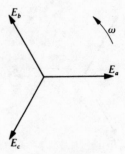

Fig. 10.38

This is defined as a system of three equal, coincident, rotating phasors as shown in figure 10.39.

Fig. 10.39

This is a symmetrical system since the phasors are equal in length and the same angle apart (0°). As there is a resultant, however, this system is unbalanced whilst the p.p.s. and n.p.s. systems are both symmetrical and balanced.

Resolution of a Three-phase, Unbalanced System of Phasors into its Symmetrical Components

The original system shown in figure 10.40A can be resolved into the three symmetrical component systems shown in figure 10.40B.

$$\text{Original system} = \text{z.p.s.} + \text{p.p.s.} + \text{n.p.s.}$$

$$\bar{I}_A = I_{a0} + I_{a+} + I_{a-} \tag{1}$$

$$\bar{I}_B = I_{b0} + I_{b+} + I_{b-} \tag{2}$$

$$\bar{I}_C = I_{c0} + I_{c+} + I_{c-} \tag{3}$$

Rewriting the above in terms of I_a only, using the 'a' operator, gives

$$\bar{I}_A = I_{a0} + I_{a+} + I_{a-} \tag{1}$$

$$\bar{I}_B = I_{a0} + a^2 I_{a+} + a I_{a-} \tag{4}$$

$$\bar{I}_C = I_{a0} + a I_{a+} + a^2 I_{a-} \tag{5}$$

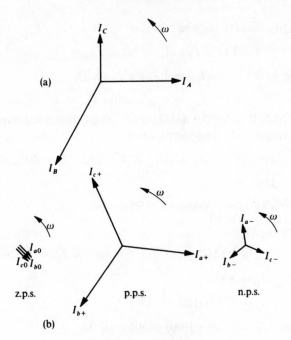

FIG. 10.40

Adding equations (1), (4), and (5) gives

$$\bar{I}_A + \bar{I}_B + \bar{I}_C = 3I_{a0},$$

so that

$$\boldsymbol{I_{a0} = \tfrac{1}{3}(\bar{I}_A + \bar{I}_B + \bar{I}_C) = I_{b0} = I_{c0}}.$$

Multiplying equation (4) by a and equation (5) by a^2 gives

$$a\bar{I}_B = aI_{a0} + I_{a+} + a^2 I_{a-} \tag{6}$$

$$a^2\bar{I}_C = a^2 I_{a0} + I_{a+} + a I_{a-} \tag{7}$$

Adding equations (1), (6), and (7) gives

$$\bar{I}_A + a\bar{I}_B + a^2\bar{I}_C = 3I_{a+},$$

from which

$$\boldsymbol{I_{a+} = \tfrac{1}{3}(\bar{I}_A + a\bar{I}_B + a^2\bar{I}_C)}.$$

Hence

$$I_{b+} = a^2 I_{a+} \quad \text{and} \quad I_{c+} = a I_{a+}$$

Multiplying equation (4) by a^2 and equation (5) by a we obtain

$$a^2\bar{I}_B = a^2 I_{a0} + a I_{a+} + I_{a-} \tag{8}$$

$$a\bar{I}_C = a I_{a0} + a^2 I_{a+} + I_{a-} \tag{9}$$

Adding equations (1), (8), and (9) gives

$$\bar{I}_A + a^2\bar{I}_B + a\bar{I}_C = 3I_{a-},$$

and hence $$I_{a-} = \tfrac{1}{3}(\bar{I}_A + a^2\bar{I}_B + a\bar{I}_C).$$

Thus $$I_{b-} = aI_{a-} \quad \text{and} \quad I_{c-} = a^2I_{a-}.$$

Example 10-2. Resolve the unbalanced system shown in figure 10.40A into its symmetrical components when

$$I_A = 346\angle 0°. \qquad I_B = 400\angle 240°, \quad \text{and} \quad I_C = 200\angle 90°.$$

$$\bar{I}_A = 346 + j0.$$

$$\bar{I}_B = 400(-0\cdot5 - j0\cdot866) = -200 - j346.$$

$$\bar{I}_C = +j200.$$

Hence $$I_{a0} = \tfrac{1}{3}(146 - j146) = 48\cdot7 - j48\cdot7 = I_{b0} = I_{c0}.$$

$$a\bar{I}_B = 400.$$

$$a^2\bar{I}_C = 173 - j100.$$

Therefore $$I_{a+} = \tfrac{1}{3}(919 - j100) = 306 - j33\cdot3.$$

$$a^2\bar{I}_B = -200 + j346.$$

$$a\bar{I}_C = -173 - j100.$$

Thus $$I_{a-} = \tfrac{1}{3}(-27 + j246) = -9 + j82.$$

$I_{b+}, I_{c+}, I_{b-},$ and I_{c-} can be calculated but it is easier to draw them in their appropriate positions shown in figure 10.40B with the aid of a protractor.

It can be seen from figure 10.41A that the symmetrical components of each phase sum to the original phasors. Figure 10.41B shows that the resultant of the original system is equal to the sum of the zero phase sequence components. This is true of any three-phase unbalanced system. A three-phase balanced asymmetrical system will resolve into p.p.s. and n.p.s. components only. A three-phase, symmetrical system will have p.p.s. components only, these being equal to the original phasors.

Significance of Symmetrical Components in Protective Systems

The currents in a balanced three-wire system with no earth fault present will resolve into p.p.s. components only.

The currents in a three-wire system with no earth fault but supplying an unbalanced load, will resolve into p.p.s. and n.p.s. components only.

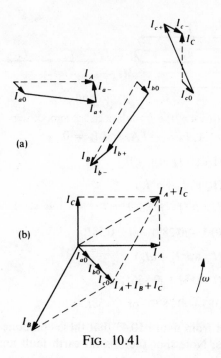

FIG. 10.41

The currents in a three-wire system with earthed star-point will resolve into p.p.s., n.p.s., and z.p.s. components when a single-phase to earth fault is present.

Thus the growth of an earth fault current will be indicated by an increase in the z.p.s. components. Methods of earth leakage protection like those shown in figures 10.6, 10.7, and 10.8 are therefore z.p.s. component detectors.

Similarly, growth of unbalanced load in a three-wire system will be indicated by an increase in the n.p.s. components. If these can be detected and measured separately from the other components, relays can be arranged to trip the appropriate circuit breakers when the degree of unbalance exceeds reasonable limits. Slight unbalance is normally caused by unequal phase loading but severe unbalance will be caused when a phase/phase fault occurs, as illustrated in the following example.

Example 10-3. Calculate the magnitude of the symmetrical components of the currents in a three-wire system which is short-circuited between the R and W lines, the fault current being I A.

This fault condition is indicated in figure 10.42.

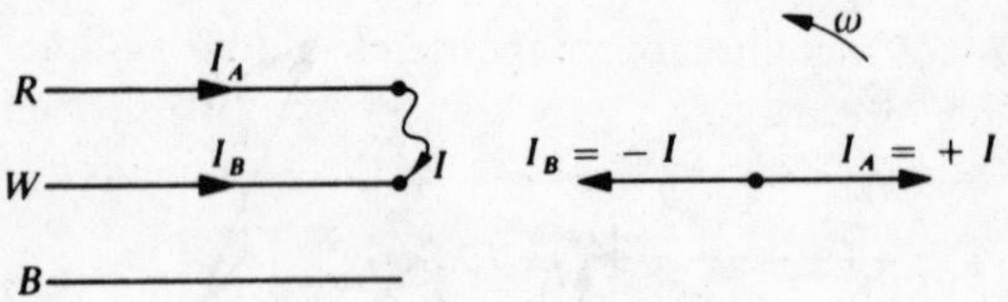

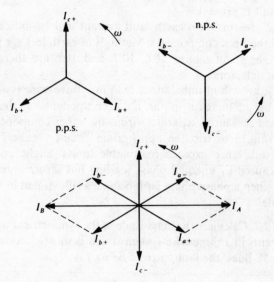

FIG. 10.42

When $I_A = +I$ A, $I_B = -I$ A, and $I_C = 0$.

$$I_{a0} = \tfrac{1}{3}(I + (-I) + 0) = 0.$$

$$I_{a+} = \tfrac{1}{3}(I_A + aI_B + a^2I_C)$$

$$= \tfrac{1}{3}(I + 0\cdot5I - j0\cdot866I)$$

$$= I(0\cdot5 - j0\cdot289) \quad \text{or} \quad 0\cdot58I.$$

$$I_{a-} = \tfrac{1}{3}(I_A + a^2I_B + aI_C)$$

$$= \tfrac{1}{3}(I + 0\cdot5I + j0\cdot866I)$$

$$= I(0\cdot5 + j0\cdot289) \quad \text{or} \quad 0\cdot58I.$$

It can be seen from figure 10.43 that these components sum to the original phasors. Note that there is no earth fault and therefore no z.p.s. components.

FIG. 10.43

Example 10-4. Calculate the magnitudes of the symmetrical components of the currents in a three-wire system with earthed star-point
in which there is an earth fault of I A on the R line only.

$$I_A = I \text{ A}, I_B = I_C = 0.$$

$$I_{a0} = \tfrac{1}{3}(I + 0 + 0) = 0.33I.$$

$$I_{a+} = \tfrac{1}{3}(I_A + aI_B + a^2I_C) = 0.33I.$$

$$I_{a-} = \tfrac{1}{3}(I_A + a^2I_B + aI_C) = 0.33I.$$

It can be seen from figure 10.44 that the 'a' components sum to I_A
whilst the 'b' and 'c' components sum to zero.

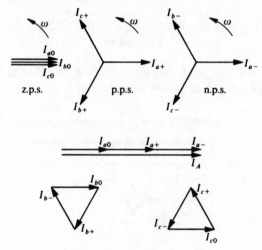

FIG. 10.44

Detection of p.p.s. and n.p.s. Components of Current

In the circuit shown in figure 10.45, the resistance and inductance
Z_1 are such that the current through this impedance lags the voltage

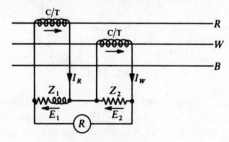

FIG. 10.45

across it by an angle of 60°. Z_2 is a pure resistance, the ohmic value of which is equal to that of Z_1.

From figure 10.46 it can be seen that the above circuit detects n.p.s. but not p.p.s. since the relay R measures the phasor sum $\bar{E}_1 + \bar{E}_2$.

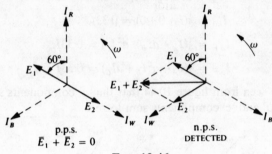

$$\underset{\bar{E}_1 + \bar{E}_2 = 0}{\text{p.p.s.}} \qquad \underset{\text{DETECTED}}{\text{n.p.s.}}$$

Fig. 10.46

In order to detect p.p.s. and not n.p.s., the impedances Z_1 and Z_2 must be interchanged, as shown in figure 10.47.

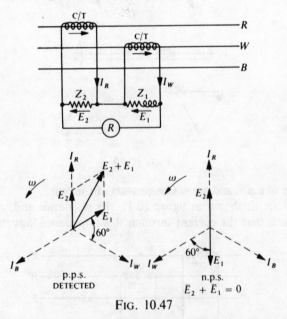

$$\underset{\text{DETECTED}}{\text{p.p.s.}} \qquad \underset{\bar{E}_2 + \bar{E}_1 = 0}{\text{n.p.s.}}$$

Fig. 10.47

The detection of p.p.s. can be used in overload protection and the detection of n.p.s. can be used to limit the degree of unbalance. The latter is particularly important with reference to the currents in the stator windings of a three-phase alternator.

First suppose that the stator currents consist of p.p.s. only. The magnetic field set up by these currents rotates at synchronous speed in the same direction as the rotor. Thus there is no relative motion between the stator field and the rotor.

Now suppose that the stator currents contain some n.p.s. The field due to the n.p.s. components only rotates at synchronous speed in the opposite direction to that of the stator since a negative phase sequence is equivalent to a symmetrical system of phasors rotating in a clockwise direction. Thus, in the case of a 50-Hz, two-pole alternator, the field due to n.p.s. cuts the rotor at 100 Hz or 6,000 r.p.m. If the n.p.s. field exceeds limits set by the design of the machine, extensive rotor damage may result from overheating caused mainly by eddy currents induced in the rotor iron.

In four-wire systems, the circuits shown in figures 10.45 and 10.47 will be disturbed by z.p.s. To exclude z.p.s. from the detecting relays, cross-connected C/T's are used as shown in figure 10.48.

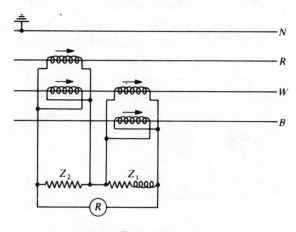

FIG. 10.48

Since the z.p.s. currents of each phase are coincident, each cross-connected C/T secondary provides a low impedance path which diverts practically all of the z.p.s. from the measuring circuit.

Detection of p.p.s. and n.p.s. Components of Voltage

In the circuits shown in figures 10.49 and 10.50, the resistance and inductance of Z_1 are such that the current through this impedance lags the voltage across it by an angle of 60°. Z_2 is a pure resistance, the ohmic value of which is equal to that of Z_1. The relay measures $\bar{I}_2 - \bar{I}_1$.

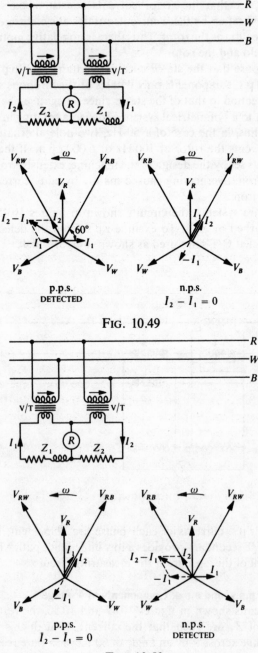

p.p.s.
DETECTED

n.p.s.
$I_2 - I_1 = 0$

FIG. 10.49

p.p.s.
$I_2 - I_1 = 0$

n.p.s.
DETECTED

FIG. 10.50

The circuit shown in figure 10.49 is arranged to detect p.p.s. only whilst that shown in figure 10.50 detects n.p.s. only.

EXAMPLES 10

1. Draw connection diagrams of the current transformers and relays for the following forms of automatic protection for a three-phase system:

(a) simple overcurrent and earth leakage;
(b) overcurrent with separate earth leakage;
(c) core balance.

Briefly outline the principle underlying each form and draw a sketch of a suitable relay.

Why is it desirable to have separate earth leakage and overcurrent protection for large machines and feeders?

2. Briefly outline, with the aid of diagrams, the fundamental principles of Merz-Price balanced voltage and balanced current protective systems. Show, by a description of one modern balanced system, how the defects of the above simple systems have been overcome.

3. Draw a connection diagram of one form of modern balanced system suitable for the protection of a three-phase feeder. Explain the principle of operation and give details of the relays used.

4. Describe briefly, with the aid of a sketch, the construction and action of a single-magnet, shaded-pole type, overcurrent relay. Indicate the means of adjusting the sensitivity and operating times.

Draw circuit diagrams to show how current transformers and simple overcurrent relays may be used to protect (a) star-star, and (b) delta-star connected power transformers with earthed secondary neutrals against faults only within their windings.

For (a) and (b) assume the power transformers have 1:1 ratios and that there is an earth fault of $3I$ A on the blue phase in each case. Indicate the direction and magnitude of current in each part of the primary, secondary and protection circuits when the transformers are on no-load.

Draw two additional diagrams to show why the system of protection chosen is not responsive to earth faults outside the transformers.

5. (a) Draw a fully labelled sketch of an induction-type overcurrent relay indicating the essential parts and the method of construction. Explain the action of this relay with the aid of a fully labelled phasor diagram.

(b) Draw an additional connection diagram to show how the above type of relay may be made suitable for use in directional graded time protection.

(c) Show by means of a fully labelled sketch, how directional induction-type overcurrent relays may be used to give directional graded time protection of a ring main consisting of four consumers' sub-stations fed from a single grid sub-station. Assume a fault on one section of this ring and explain how the faulty section only is isolated.

6. Describe the essential features of (a) impedance/time, and (b) switched (mho) distance protection of a three-phase, three-section feeder fed from one end only.

For (a) include a simple sketch of the type of relay used and briefly describe the principles of operation.

For (b) include an impedance diagram showing the zones of protection and also the stepped time/distance characteristic of the mho relay.

Give the advantages and limitations' of the mho scheme.

7. Outline the principles of operation of (a) definite impedance (distance), and (b) impedance/time protection. Illustrate the difference between the two by simple sketches of the relay used for each.

Explain, with the aid of a graph, how back up protection is afforded with (b).

State, with reasons, the circumstances under which distance protection is most suitable and give its limitations.

8. Explain, with the aid of a diagram of connections, the principle of operation of a system of biased differential protection suitable for a three-phase alternator.

9. An 11-kV, 10-MVA, three-phase, star-connected alternator is earthed through a non-inductive resistor of $5\,\Omega$. An earth leakage relay connected to a current transformer in the earthing connection is set to operate when the current reaches 30 per cent of full load.

Estimate the percentage of the alternator winding remaining unprotected against zero impedance earth faults.
(Answer **12·2%**.)

10. Why is the detection of n.p.s. currents particularly important in the protection of a three-phase alternator?

Explain, with the aid of circuit and phasor diagrams, (a) how n.p.s. currents may be detected in a three-phase system, and (b) how z.p.s. currents, if present, may be eliminated from the detecting network.

Show graphically, that in a three-wire system carrying balanced currents, there are no z.p.s. or n.p.s. components.

11. Resolve the following three-phase system of currents into its symmetrical components:

$$I_A = 40\underline{/0°}, \qquad I_B = 30\underline{/-150°}, \qquad I_C = 60\underline{/120°}.$$

Sketch the phasor diagrams representing the symmetrical component systems and hence show, by drawing a phasor diagram for each phase, that the symmetrical components of each phase sum to the original phasors.

(Answers $I_{a0} = -5 \cdot 33 + j12 \cdot 33$, $I_{a+} = 42 - j5$ and $I_{a-} = 3 \cdot 33 - j7 \cdot 33$.)

12. Resolve the following three-phase system of currents into its symmetrical components:

$$I_A = 50 \angle 0°, \qquad I_B = 25 \angle -120°, \qquad I_C = 43 \cdot 3 \angle 150°.$$

Explain the significance of the value of the z.p.s. components. Sketch the phasor diagrams representing the symmetrical component systems.

(Answers $I_{a0} = 0$, $I_{a+} = 37 \cdot 5 + j7 \cdot 2$, and $I_{a-} = 12 \cdot 5 - j7 \cdot 2$.)

Index